THE PENGUIN CLASSICS

EDITED BY E. V. RIEU

L 66

LUCAN

PHARSALIA

DRAMATIC EPISODES OF THE
CIVIL WARS

*

TRANSLATED
BY ROBERT GRAVES

PENGUIN BOOKS

Penguin Books Ltd, Harmondsworth, Middlesex
U.S.A..: Penguin Books Inc., 3300 Clipper Mill Road, Baltimore 11 Md
CANADA: Penguin Books (Canada) Ltd, 178 Norseman Street,
Toronto 18, Ontario
AUSTRALIA: Penguin Books Pty Ltd, 762 Whitehorse Road,
Mitcham, Victoria
SOUTH AFRICA: Penguin Books (S.A.) Pty Ltd, Gibraltar House,
Regent Road, Sea Point, Cape Town

—

Published in Penguin Books 1956

Made and printed in Great Britain
by Hunt, Barnard & Co, Ltd,
Aylesbury

CONTENTS

*

INTRODUCTION   7

PHARSALIA   25

INTRODUCTION

SUETONIUS'S *Life of Lucan* begins:

Marcus Annaeus Lucanus of Cordoba made his first public appearance as a poet at the Neronia, a literary and musical contest held every five years. Later he gave a public reading of his epic poem about the Civil War between Pompey and Caesar; and compared himself, in a prologue, with Virgil as he had been at the same age. Here he was bold enough to ask:

> And tell me now, am I still at
> The stage when Virgil wrote his *Gnat*?

While still a boy he heard that his father was living deep in the country because he had made an unhappy marriage...

Here some sentences are missing. From the *Life* written by Vacca four centuries later, and from references in Statius's *Silvae*, Tacitus, the *Eusebian Chronicle*, and Sidonius Apollinaris, a few more facts can be added to Suetonius's account. Lucan was born on November 3rd, A.D. 39, in the third year of Caligula's reign, and taken from Cordoba to Rome at the age of seven months. His father, Marcus Annaeus Mella, was a Spanish provincial of equestrian rank who had grown immensely rich as Comptroller of the Revenue; but did not seek advancement in literature or politics like his brothers Lucius Annaeus Seneca and Junius Gallio. The 'unhappy marriage' may have followed the divorce of Lucan's mother Acilia. At Rome Lucan received the best education then available, the emphasis being on literature and rhetoric, and was something of an infant prodigy. He studied Stoic philosophy under Cornutius, with the poet Persius as a fellow-pupil. Lucan's uncle Seneca, another professed Stoic and the most famous writer of the day, had been appointed tutor to the young Emperor Nero; he used his position to amass a fortune of some £4,000,000 in gold, by most questionable means; and became Consul in A.D. 56. Lucan was two years older than Nero, by whom he was for awhile greatly admired. His earliest poems, which no longer exist, concerned the recovery of Hector's dead body by Priam; the descent of Orpheus to the Underworld in pursuit of Eurydice; and a letter to his wife Polla Argentaria, whom he loved dearly and who had youth, beauty, wealth, virtue, and intellect to commend her. Other early short poems appear to have been worked into his *Civil War*: Hercules's wrestling match with Antaeus in Book IV, Perseus's killing of Medusa in Book IX, the account of the Nile in Book X. From Rome he went to study Greek literature at Athens.

Nero recalled Lucan from Athens and made him one of his intimates, besides bestowing a quaestorship on him; but this favour did not last long. Nero interrupted a reading of Lucan's poetry by suddenly summoning a meeting of the Senate, and going out himself, with the sole object of ruining the performance. The hostility that Lucan thereafter showed him, in word and deed, is still notorious. Once, after relieving himself explosively in a public convenience, he declaimed a half-line of Nero's:

'... and it sounded like underground thunder – '

which made a number of men who had been easing themselves beside him take to their heels and run. He also satirized Nero, and his own influential friends as well, in a most bitter and damaging poem. Finally he became, so to speak, the standard-bearer of Piso's ill-fated conspiracy, ranting publicly about how glorious it was to murder a tyrant, and even offering to present his friends with Nero's head. When the conspiracy came to light, however, he lost his cocksureness and was easily compelled to make a confession; after which he resorted to the most abject pleas for pardon, going so far as to accuse his own innocent mother of being one of the conspirators. Apparently he thought that, since Nero was a matricide, he would appreciate this lack of decent devotion. Nero did indeed allow him to choose the manner of his death. Lucan took advantage of the respite by writing his father a letter which contained amendments to some of his verses; then ate a huge dinner, and told a physician to cut the arteries in his wrists.

I remember that his poems were published by all sorts of editors, reputable and disreputable, and even lectured on by professors of rhetoric.

*

Lucan's quaestorship, during which he staged some gladiatorial shows, was a great mark of Imperial favour, since he had not yet reached the age at which a man could legally hold public office. Nero also appointed him to the exclusive College of Augurs. According to one account the cause of Lucan's animosity was that Nero, who had reserved the Latin Verse Prize at the Neronia for himself, grew jealous when the audience in the theatre applauded Lucan's *Orpheus and Eurydice* somewhat too enthusiastically, and forbade him to give poetry recitals even in private. Lucan died on April 30th, 65 A.D., at the age of twenty-five; declaiming some lines of his own about how a Macedonian soldier bled to death. He still had two and a half books of the *Civil*

Wars to write, and seven to revise. His reckless and inept behaviour during the conspiracy forced his father and both his uncles to commit suicide as well. Polla Argentaria buried him in the garden, and continued to celebrate his birthday for many years; there were no children of the marriage. Nero acknowledged Lucan's talents, briefly but adequately, in a memorial tablet:

> MARCO ANNAEO LUCANO CORDUBENSI POETAE,
> BENEFICIO NERONIS, FAMA SERVATA.

*

The eloquent Quintilian, Lucan's contemporary and fellow-Spaniard, wrote of the *Civil Wars*: 'This poem is full of fire and energy and famous for its epigrammatic wit; but in my opinion affords a safer model to the rhetorician than to the poet.' Agreed; yet except for Ennius and Lucretius, both of whom had something urgent to say, and Catullus, whose Celtiberian passion marked him off from his stolid or frivolous fellows, very few Latin writers recognized the distinction between poetry and verse-rhetoric; nor did the educational system countenance it.

Rhetoric and poetry were both imported to Rome from Greek cities in Italy. When the Republic, enlarged by hard and ruthless fighting, needed diplomats to consolidate her gains by cleverly playing off one enemy against another, the traditional virtue of blunt and laconic speech could be questioned. In ancient days, a Roman envoy might draw a circle around some enemy king with the ferrule of his staff, saying: 'We offer you peace at the price of a million gold pieces, payable before the moon wanes. Leave this circle without accepting our terms, and you will live to rue it.' Not every king, however, could be overawed so simply; and it began to be realized from certain hard bargains driven by eloquent foreign embassies that Rome had often involved herself in unnecessary fighting by a simple lack of suppleness and tact. A few far-sighted senators resolved to educate their sons as diplomats; very much as they had once resolved to challenge the Carthaginians at sea, though wholly ignorant of ship-building or naval tactics. This inspired decision was taken only after much heart-searching; for in 161 B.C., the Senate ordered the Praetor Marcus Pomponius to prevent rhetoricians – who seem to have been Italian-Greeks – from settling at Rome; and as late as 92 B.C. the Censors Gnaeus Domitius Ahenobarbus and Lucius Licinius Crassus published an edict against rhetorical schools as nurseries of idleness. Yet Suetonius records: 'Little by little, rhetoric came to seem useful and honourable, and many addicted themselves to it as a defence and for glory' – in fact, the diplomatic corps, by following the principle 'Divide and conquer', were worth many legions to the military establishment.

It became fashionable to study at Athens, the centre of Greek culture. There the Roman student discovered that he could hope to graduate as a diplomat only after taking a master's degree in rhetoric; and that rhetoric, the art of persuading an opponent by flattery, threats, or fraud to accept one's own proposition, however unsound, would help him to win magistratial elections and plead public causes with confidence, besides being a valuable adjunct to warfare. Yet before being allowed to rhetorize in the schools, he must take the prescribed course in Homeric study and learn as much as possible of the *Iliad* and *Odyssey* by heart. This was a *sine qua non*, because the Sons of Homer, the original disseminators of polite culture at early Greek courts, had won such Scriptural authority whenever disputes arose on history, geography, genealogy, religion, science, or morals, that an apt quotation from 'the poet' (as he was simply called) clinched every argument, unless the opposing orator could contrive to cap it. A civilized attitude to poetry is said to have first been adopted at Rome, which so far had known only ballads and rough military marching songs, as the result of a typically Roman street-accident: Crates the Milesian, sent as ambassador by King Attalus of Pergamus in 167 B.C., broke his leg by falling into an uncovered sewer, and spent his convalescence giving lectures on poetry – meaning, of course, Homer. Thus the quantitative hexameter, though awkward in Latin, an accentual language, became the main literary metre at Rome, displacing the native Saturnian; and Ennius, the father of Latin poetry, adopted archaisms and invented novelties to make the change possible.

Because the rhetorician's art, securely based on the *Iliad* and *Odyssey*, was to persuade his hearers, regardless of truth, Roman students understood that Homer must have been a consummate diplomat; from which it followed that, since one could not always establish what special pleading had prompted the poet's lines, his art in concealing art should be all the more admired. Literary education branched from Homer into prose-rhetoric and verse-rhetoric. In the prose direction lay history, philosophy, law, literary criticism, scientific theory; in the other, epics, drama, satires, didactic pieces, pastorals, odes, and so forth. The student worked industriously to rid himself of a natural preference for simple, practical language, and to outdo his professors in a passionate slipperiness of expression.

When at last Latin literature could challenge Greek in all departments of prose-rhetoric, and all departments of verse-rhetoric except the Homeric corpus, the Romans began to ask why they should perpetually yield the epic palm to crabbed old Homer. Could they not find and build up a Homer of their own? They could. Inevitably the choice fell on Virgil, who had shown such exquisite craftsmanship that the rhetorical object in his *Aeneid*, namely glorification of the divinely-descended Caesars as destined rulers of the world, was pervasive without being patently offensive. The Court lent Virgil such strong support that he had scarcely set about his task before Sextus Propertius wrote an epigram proclaiming it 'greater than the *Iliad*'; and a loyal Senate supplied much the same hearty glow of enthusiasm as leads patriotic Scots to rank Robert Burns above William Shakespeare. Suetonius in his *Lives of the Roman Poets* dutifully remarks that 'Virgil never lacked for detractors; which is not strange, because neither did Homer.' These detractors listed his pilferings and historical errors, but they envied his talents no less than his financial success; and only the independent-minded admiral, Marcus Vipsanius Agrippa, made a really brutal comment. 'Virgil,' he said, 'is a suppositious child of Maecenas, and has invented a new type of rhetoric which steers a careful course between bombast and baldness of expression, concealing its artificiality by the use of every-day phrases.' Virgil's shyness, his literary perfectionism, his temperance, his idealism, his valetudinarianism, his avoidance of bawdy society, and his notorious passion for beautiful boys – which in those days could be gratified without loss of reputation – combine to make a recognizable picture. How exquisite the interior decorations of his house on the Esquiline (a gift from Augustus) must have been: especially the gilded bedrooms where sleep kissed the eyelids of Alexander and Cebes, his poetical boy-slaves! This Alexander, the 'Alexis' of the *Bucolics*, had been a present from Asinius Pollio, the most enlightened man of his age.

Virgil became a school classic overnight; and though Lucan – born two generations later and brought up on *Arma virumque cano* – seems to have felt jealously resentful, he knew that it would be foolish to challenge Virgil in his own field. I suspect that he also disguised his jealousy by decrying Virgil as an effeminate old toady. He decided to stop writing mythological fables in the approved Augustan style and launch a modernist movement which would confine the *Aeneid* to the school-room, where it was obviously due to last as long as the Latin language itself.

A sophisticated reaction against Virgil had begun some twenty years before, when the Emperor Caligula nearly carried out his plan of suppressing Virgil's 'dull and uneducated' works; but an Augustan revival under Claudius gave them a reprieve. Lucan's Neronian modernism was well calculated: he had chosen a historical rather than a legendary theme for his neo-epic, and in Book IX gives a drily realistic account of how Caesar visited Troy, by then a run-down tourist centre. So far from being divinely welcomed by Venus in person (as he would have been in the *Aeneid*), Caesar is taken by a garrulous guide to see the sights, including the grove where the Goddess had first seduced his ancestor Anchises. Nor does Lucan send the heroic Cato to consult his ancestral ghosts in Virgilian style, but lets a horror-comic witch called Erichtho resuscitate a dead Pompeian soldier with grisly spells and then threaten him with eternal punishment unless he prophesies the future. This modernism is equally anti-Virgilian in its deliberate neglect of craftsmanship; the rhythms are monotonous; often words are clumsily iterated before the memory of their first use has faded from the reader's ear; the argument is broken by impudent philosophical, geographical or historical asides. Lucan lacks religious conviction; dwells lovingly on the macabre; hates his times; and allows his readers to assume that he is as self-centred, degenerate, cruel, and cowardly as the next man. His hyperboles are patently ridiculous: the Thracian cranes, for instance, delay their winter migration in order to gorge on Roman corpses at Pharsalus – though Pharsalus was not fought until the Spring, and cranes are non-carnivorous. Yet his occasional polished epigrams make highly serviceable quotations:

Victrix causa deis placuit, sed victa Catoni
'The conquering cause pleased the Gods; the conquered pleased Cato.'

Nulla fides unquam miseros elegit amicos
'Nobody ever chooses the already unfortunate as objects of his loyal friendship.'

Nescit plebes ieiuna timere
'Starve the mob, and it grows restless.'

Metiri sua regna decet, vires-que fateri
'It is best to take stock of the resources at your command, and admit their inadequacy.'

Lucan may be called the father of yellow journalism, for his love of sensational detail, his unprincipled reportage, and his disregard of continuity between to-day's and yesterday's rhetoric. Thus the Roman Senate who disgrace themselves by a panic-stricken rush from Rome, because of wild rumours that Caesar intends to sack the City, become, two books later, the courageous, dignified, truly Roman Senate who reassemble in Epirus, and appoint Pompey dictator. Again, Pompey calmly leaves the field of Pharsalus when the battle is going against him, hoping that this unselfish action will limit Roman bloodshed; but in the next book spurs his jaded horse towards Tempe with a panic-stricken heart; and presently sends his ally Deiotarus to arrange for a merciless Parthian invasion of Italy – yet still remains Rome's most devoted son. Caesar is more consistently maligned as a ferocious and treacherous ogre; feels disappointed to meet so little opposition during his march on Rome; picnics heartily on the battlefield of Pharsalus, delighting in the already stinking mounds of corpses; and sheds crocodile tears when presented with Pompey's head. His remarkable clemency is denounced as a diabolical trick to humiliate and enslave Rome; his treacherous assassins win rapturous applause; Pompey's own breaches of the Constitution are glossed over. Lucan claimed that posterity, reading his epic, would be sure to take Pompey's side; which was to hope that Caesar's own unrhetorical and obviously truthful commentaries on the war would no longer be extant. Yet posterity has recognized that, for Lucan, Caesar's crime lay principally in his name, which Nero had inherited; and Nero's not in absolutism and cruelty, but in having offended Lucan by thwarting his poetic career. The case is given away when Lucan forgets his brief for awhile, and mentions the totally false picture of Caesar the Monster which hatred and fear conjured up at Rome, after the crossing of the Rubicon, among men who should have known better.

Lucan may also be called the father of the costume-film. If lopped of all digressive rhodomontade, the *Civil Wars* is a script which could be put almost straight on the floor. It consists of carefully chosen, cunningly varied, brutally sensational scenes, linked by a tenuous thread of historical probability; and alternated with soft interludes in which deathless courage, supreme self-sacrifice, memorable piety, Stoic virtue, and wifely devotion are expected to win favour from the great sentimental box-office public. He used his own beautiful, high-spirited wife Polla Argentaria – said to have helped in the revision of his manuscripts – as a model for Pompey's Cornelia; and so strong was the Roman taboo on any display of uxoriousness, that Pompey's low spirits when he sends Cornelia away to safety in Lesbos must have seemed an indecently modern touch. Yet if Lucan was sincere in his most commendable plea for closer ties between husband and wife, how sincere can he have been in eulogizing Pompey's supporter Cato? Cato treated his wife Marcia as though she were a brood-mare, allowing himself no sensual pleasure during the act of procreation, and selling her, while pregnant of a fourth child, to a noble friend who wished to have his empty cradles filled with good stock.

Lucan must, I think, have been so single-minded a rhetorician that all his values were melodramatic ones. Unless a situation yielded a surprising paradox – the cruelty of Caesar's clemency, the loyal comradeship that the Oderzo Gauls showed by mutual murder, or the unkindness of the Roman refugee who gave Pompey's body decent burial – it did not interest him. Was the grand paradox, then, that neither his wife, his mother, his father, nor his own moral reputation meant anything at all to Lucan, compared with poetic ambition – which he based on an outstanding command of rhetoric? Was his account of Caesar's attempt to cross the Adriatic in a two-oared dinghy, though waves rose two or three thousand feet high, symbolic of his own insane self-assurance? He seems, however, to have had twinges of doubt. Valerius Probus, in his life of Lucan's friend, the poet Persius, 'who was gentle, virginally modest, handsome, good and pure, and showed an exemplary devotion to his mother, sister and aunt,' records Lucan's immense admiration for him. 'When Persius read his poems aloud, Lucan could hardly wait until he had finished before crying out that this was true poetry; and his own, mere fooling.' Yet all Persius's virtue did not make him much of a poet, at that.

*

Christopher Marlow first attempted the formidable task of translating Lucan into English. Perhaps it should here be explained that the Fathers of the Christian Church had experienced much the same difficulty in consolidating their empire as had the Fathers of the Republican Senate. How were they to combat the clever arguments of

pagan sophists? Faith in timely inspiration by the Holy Ghost was not
reckoned enough; and Paul's tactical success when he caused a division
between Sadducees and Pharisees in the Sanhedrin offered so hopeful
a precedent that they allowed their deacons to study under professors
of rhetoric. The Classical curriculum, with certain necessary changes,
became the basis of clerkly education throughout Christendom –
though Virgil and Cicero ousted Homer and Demosthenes – and
Virgil was actually credited with divine inspiration. In Marlow's
London, Classical rhetoric still flourished as vigorously as in Lucan's
Rome; and it was claimed that Elizabethan English could take an even
higher polish than Latin.

Now, these are the opening lines of the *Civil Wars*:

> *Bella per Emathios plus quam ciuilia campos*
> *iusque datum sceleri canimus, populumque potentem*
> *in sua uictrici conuersum uiscera dextra*
> *cognatasque acies, et rupto foedere regni*
> *certatum totis concussi uiribus orbis*
> *in commune nefas, infestisque obuia signis*
> *signa, pares aquilas et pila minantia pilis.*
>   *quis furor, o ciues, quae tanta licentia ferri?*
> *gentibus inuisis Latium praebere cruorem*
> *cumque superba foret Babylon spolianda tropaeis*
> *Ausoniis umbraque erraret Crassus inulta*
> *bella geri placuit nullos habitura triumphos?*

Marlow rendered them magnificently:

> Wars worse than ciuill on Thessalian playnes,
> And outrage strangling law & people strong,
> We sing, whose conquering swords their own breasts launcht,
> Armies allied, the kingdoms league vprooted,
> Th' affrighted worlds force bent on publique spoile,
> Trumpets, and drums like deadly threatning other,
> Eagles alike displaide, darts answering darts.
> Romans, what madnes, what huge lust of warre
> Hath made Barbarians drunke with Latin bloud?
> Now Babilon, (proud through our spoile) should stoop,
> While slaughtred Crassus ghost walks vnreueng'd,
> Will ye wadge war, for which you shall not triumph?

However, he never got beyond the first book; this was perhaps a
reconnaissance, rather than a serious attempt to turn the whole 48,000
lines into English. Nobody else in those pre-Commonwealth days

proved capable of continuing in the same strain, though both Sir F. Gorges and Thomas May tried. By 1718, when Nicholas Rowe made the translation which Dr Johnson subsequently pronounced 'one of the greatest productions of English poetry', the language had lost its exuberance.

> Emathian plains with slaughter cover'd o'er,
> And rage unknown to civil wars before,
> Establish'd violence, and lawless might,
> Avow'd and hallow'd by the name of right;
> A race renown'd, the world's victorious lords,
> Turn'd on themselves with their own hostile swords;
> Piles against piles oppos'd in impious fight,
> And eagles against eagles bending flight;
> Of blood by friends, by kindred, parent, spilt,
> One common horrour and promiscuous guilt;
> A shatter'd world in wild disorder tost,
> Leagues, laws, and empire, in confusion lost;
> Of all the woes which civil discords bring,
> And Rome o'ercome by Roman arms, I sing.
>
> What blind, detested madness could afford
> Such horrid licence to the murdering sword?
> Say, Romans, whence so dire a fury rose,
> To glut with Latian blood your barbarous foes?
> Could you in wars like these provoke your fate?
> Wars, where no triumphs on the victor wait!
> While Babylon's proud spires yet rise so high,
> And rich in Roman spoils invade the sky;
> While yet no vengeance is to Crassus paid,
> But unatton'd repines the wandering shade . . .

It may be argued that Marlow's poetic fire honours Lucan above his deserts; and that the monotony of Rowe's eighteenth-century rhymed couplets matches Lucan's use of the hexameter more exactly. Rowe's translation went into several editions and can be bought second-hand without trouble. But, though readers capable of facing a verse epic are rare nowadays, and though it may seem easy enough to convey Lucan's sense in simple English prose, anyone who tries will soon find Latin rearing its ugly head and winding its absurd coils about him. In 1890, H. T. Riley provided a literal version, with valuable notes, for *Bohn's Library*. This is how he began:

Wars more than civil upon the Emathian plains, and licence conceded to lawlessness, I sing; and a powerful people turning with victorious right-hand against its own vitals, and kindred armies engaged; and, the compact of rule rent asunder, a contest waged with all the might of the shaken earth for the universal woe, and standards meeting with hostile standards, the eagles alike, and darts threatening darts.

What madness, this, O citizens! what lawlessness so great of the sword, while nations are your hate, for you to shed the Latian blood? And, while proud Babylon was to be spoiled of the Ausonian trophies, and the shade of Crassus was wandering unavenged, has it pleased you that wars, doomed to produce no triumphs, should be waged?

It is a valuable crib to the Latin original; but the more literal the rendering the less comprehensible to readers ignorant of Latin. A closer approximation to English was made by J. D. Duff for *Loeb* (1928):

Of war I sing, war worse than civil, waged over the plains of Emathia, and on legality conferred on crime; I tell how an imperial people turned their victorious right hands against their own vitals; how kindred fought against kindred; how, when the compact of tyranny was shattered, all the forces of the shaken world contended to make mankind guilty; how standards confronted hostile standards, eagles were matched against each other, and pilum threatened pilum.

What madness was this, my countrymen, what fierce orgy of slaughter? While the ghost of Crassus still wandered unavenged, and it was your duty to rob proud Babylon of her trophies over Italy, did you choose to give to hated nations the spectacle of Roman bloodshed, and to wage wars that could win no triumphs?

Yet just how much can the general reader understand of this? Where is Emathia? What is worse than civil war? What Ausonian trophies were laid up in Babylon?

Only Marlow, of all these translations, changed Emathia to 'Thessaly'; aware that Lucan had been using thoroughly off-target geographical terms. Emathia was part of Macedonia and lay not far from Thessaly; so, because *Thessalios* would not scan after *Bella per*, Lucan wrote *Emathios*, with the excuse that Thessaly had at one time formed part of the Macedonian Empire. *Ausoniis*, again, is a nicely scanning word, like *Emathios*; it originally referred to the Oscan city of Ausona. When the Ausonians revolted (Livy: ix. 25), the Romans of the early Republic massacred them to a man. But since the Alexandrian Greeks used *Ausonia* as a handy poetic term for the whole Italian peninsula, and Virgil adopted this convention in the *Aeneid*, Lucan makes it mean 'Rome'. Even Marlow retains 'Babylon', which Lucan uses as a more manageable word than 'Seleuceia', the name of the Parthian capital since Hellenistic times, though Babylon had lost its importance long before the Civil Wars. To say that the Ausonian trophies – meaning the Roman eagles captured from Marcus Licinius Crassus by the Parthian king in 53 B.C. – had been laid up at Babylon, was rather like saying that Pictish trophies had been laid up at Winchester – meaning that Scottish standards captured at Flodden in 1513 were brought to London, which had now succeeded Winchester as capital of England. The war was 'worse than civil' because Caesar and Pompey had been related by marriage; but since the general reader cannot be expected to know this, or the meanings of 'Emathia', 'Ausonia', and 'Babylon', I have decided to bring up into the text what most translators either leave to the reader's historical apprehension, or supply in footnote form.

I give this version:

The theme of my poem is the Civil War which was decided on the plains of Pharsalus in Thessaly; yet 'Civil War' is an understatement, since Pompey and Caesar, the opposing leaders, were not only fellow-citizens but relatives: the whole struggle was indeed no better than one of licensed fratricide. I shall here describe how, after the breakdown of the First Triumvirate, Rome turned the imperial sword against her own breast: how kinsman faced kinsman on the field of battle, each line of legionaries armed with identical javelins and carrying the same familiar eagle-standards as its opponents; and how the civilized world reeled under this contest of iniquity.

What made our forefathers embark on such an orgy of self-destruction? And why were their hated enemies permitted to enjoy the spectacle? Why was proud Parthia not first obliged to disgorge the Eagles taken from Crassus, whose ghost still wandered unavenged over her plains?

Latin poetry, as established by Ennius, had its own special vocabulary, devised to assist versification. A number of common Latin words were excluded by their scansion from the hexameter: for instance, Nero's family name, Domitius Ahenobarbus. 'Domitius' contains too many short syllables in a row, and 'Ahenobarbus' has a short syllable hopelessly imprisoned between two long ones. So if one wished to write the hexameter: 'And Domitius Ahenobarbus also came,' the only way out would be to address him in the vocative, which is a manageable anapaest; and use the historical present for 'came'; and explain 'Ahenobarbus' as meaning 'Brazen Beard':

> *Tu-que venis, Domiti, quem signat ahenea barba*
> 'And thou comest also, Domitius, whom a brazen beard distinguishes.'

Naturally, circumlocution of this sort need not, and should not, be reproduced in English prose – who would translate the French *'Qu'est ce que c'est que ça?'* as anything but 'What's that?' The morbidities of this Latin poetical convention have been summarized in the well-known Victorian *Gradus ad Parnassum* ('Steps to Parnassus'); but even this distressing handbook withholds a full description of the disease.

One remarkable symptom was the poet's readiness to perpetuate any foolish mistake made by a reputable predecessor; thus, since Ovid in a moment of aberrancy had recorded Procne's transformation into a nightingale and Philomela's into a swallow (not contrariwise), 'Procne' was thereafter legitimized as a synonym for 'nightingale', whenever 'Philomela' would not fit the line. And when Virgil assumed that the decisive Battle of Philippi fought between Augustus and Brutus in 44 B.C., had taken place on the same field as the equally decisive one between Caesar and Pompey in 48 B.C. – having heard the name 'Philippi' mentioned in both connexions – he was followed by Ovid, Manilius, Florus, Petronius, and Lucan. These poets were highly educated, and must have known that the large Thracian Philippi lay 150 miles or so north-east from the small Thessalian Philippi; yet they all continued to descant on this strange poetical coincidence. Horace alone failed to follow suit; he doubtless had clear memories of Philippi, where he had fought on the wrong side and, not very gloriously, cast away his shield.

In another context, Lucan writes:

> *Invidus annoso qui fama derogat aevo,*
> *Qui vates ad vera vocat.*

'It would be churlish to challenge the authority of legend and expect poets to be truthful.'

and the Romans held that lies are necessary to poetry. Practical anatomic experience told them, for example, that Centaurs could not exist, because they were popularly depicted with two more limbs and one more stomach than any mammal was known to possess. However, since Homer had mentioned them in the *Iliad* and *Odyssey*, and Pindar had described their monstrous origin, Centaurs formed a necessary part of poetry – along with the one-eyed Cyclops, the winged horse Pegasus, and the fire-breathing Chimaera. Since no one troubled to discover the original poetic meaning of these anomalous concepts, disciplined students took the view: 'If our professor of rhetoric tells us to employ absurd mythical figures, it is our duty not only to obey but to convince our verse-audience that we believe in their practical reality.'

Lucan liked to pretend that poetic artifice had not been forced on him merely by metrical requirement and a study of the best models, but that he honoured Apollo by deliberately making verses as dark as some of the Delphic oracles; and therefore strained sense almost, though not quite, to breaking point. Thus:

> *Mitis Atax Latias gaudet non ferre carinas*
> *finis et Hesperiae, promoto limite, Varus;*
> *quaque sub Herculeo sacratus nomine portus*
> *urguet rupe caua pelagus: non Corus in illum*
> *ius habet aut Zephyrus, solus sua litora turbat*
> *Circius et tuta prohibet statione Monoeci . . .*

which appears in the *Bohn* translation as:

. . . the placid Atax rejoices at no longer bearing the Latian keels; the Varus, too, the limit of Hesperia, her boundaries now extended; where, too, beneath the divine authority of Hercules, the consecrated harbour adjoins the sea with its hollowed rocks; no Corus holds sway over it, nor yet the Zephyr; alone does Circius disturb the shores his own, and withholds the ships from the safe harbour of Monoecus.

and which Marlow versified as follows:

> Mild Atax glad it beares no Roman boats,
> And frontier Varus that the campe is farre,
> Sent aide; so did Alcides port, whose seas
> Eate hollow rocks, and where the north-west wind
> Nor Zephir rules not, but the north alone .
> Turmoiles the coast, and enterance forbids . . .

but which, when reduced to simple English, means:

Caesar's galleys no longer patrolled either the slow-flowing Aude, or the Var which now formed the frontier of Greater Italy. Moreover, his flotilla had been withdrawn from the rocky cove of Monaco, sacred to Hercules who touched there during his Tenth Labour – it offers safe anchorage when the wind blows from the north-west, but no protection against the dreaded Sirocco.

And here is another puzzle:

> . . . *excepta quis morte potest? secreta tenebis*
> *litoris Euboici memorando condite busto,*
> *qua maris angustat fauces saxosa Carystos*
> *et, tumidis infesta colit quae numina, Rhamnus,*
> *artatus rapido feruet qua gurgite pontus*
> *Euripusque trahit, cursum mutantibus undis,*
> *Chalcidicas puppes ad iniquam classibus Aulin.*

which has been translated in *Bohn*:

The secret recesses of the Euboean shore thou shalt possess, buried in a memorable tomb, where rocky Carystos straitens the outlets of the sea, and where Rhamnus worships the Deity hostile to the proud; where the sea boils, enclosed in its rapid tide, and the Euripus hurries along, with waves that change their course, the ships of Chalcis to Aulis, hostile to fleets.

The person concerned is Appius Claudius who had been told by the Pythoness, when he consulted the Delphic Oracle, that he could escape the Civil War by 'taking his solitary ease in Euboea, that heaven of refuge.'

The sense is:

'Appius, you are fated to take your solitary ease in Euboea: by being buried in a sequestered but famous tomb near the quarries of Carystos. It will face across the narrow sea towards the town of Rhamnos in Attica, sacred to Nemesis, the goddess who punishes human ambition. In between lie the so-called Hollows of Euboea, where the sea is disturbed by the rapid, constantly-shifting current from the Straits of Euripus: a current which sets the ships of Calchis adrift and swings them across to Aulis in Boeotia – that fatal shore where long ago Agamemnon's ships assembled before sailing to Troy.'

Since this is what these passages mean, surely they should be so rendered? I see no point in letting them remain obscure, just because a few Latinists can nod appreciatively at the concealed references to Hercules's Tenth Labour, and Agamemnon's expedition to Troy, and the Goddess Nemesis's temple at Rhamnus, and the asbestos quarries of Carystus; or can recognize *Portus Menoecus* as the present Principality of Monaco, and *Atax* as the River Aude. Granted, I have denied Lucan credit for his *Gradus ad Parnassum* dexterity, letting him read more like Herodotus or Pausanias; but the lover of rhetoric may always, if he prefers, consult Rowe's version, which here adds mis-translation to Lucan's obscurity.

Convinced that it would be 'churlish to demand truth from poets', Lucan reaches the pitch of grotesqueness in his Ninth Book. Cato's was a bold and exhausting march along the eastern coast of the Gulf of Sirte, and took six days; the men carried their own rations and at night camped by scanty water-holes. Lucan, however, sends him on a two-months' march for thousands of miles in a wide semi-circle through the waterless Sahara; meanwhile the troops battle day and night, appar-ently without any food but sand, against fantastically unzoological serpents. Sir John Mandeville pales beside Lucan:

. . . An unlucky soldier named Sabellus felt the barbed fangs of a tiny seps fixed in his leg. He pulled it off and pinned it to the ground with the point of his javelin. This seps is the most destructive of all snakes, despite its smallness. The skin next to the bite began to break and the flesh to melt away until the white thigh-bone showed; then, as the wound widened farther, the body swam in corruption and slowly disappeared, starting with the calves, knees, and thighs. Black matter dripped from the thighs, the muscles which held the belly in place snapped and the in-testines slid out. Sabellus, in fact, slowly trickled into the ground, and there was unexpectedly little of him left, because the seps' venom reduces the limbs by a chemical process to a puddle of filth. His anatomy was for awhile revealed with painful clearness: ligaments, sinews, the structure of the lungs, the bones of the chest, and all the inner organs. Slowly the strong shoulders and arms and neck and head liquified, as it were snow when the warm South Wind blows, or wax exposed to the Sun. It is not much to record that the flesh was eaten away – that happens whenever corpses are cremated – but no pyre reduces bones to nothing as this venom did . . .

Nasidius, once a Marsian farmer, died in a very different manner: by expansion, not liquefaction. When a fiery prester struck at him, his face turned red as a glowing coal and began to swell until the features could no longer be recognized. Then the virus spread and puffed him out to the gigantic proportions of ship's canvas in a storm. The man himself was buried deep inside this bloated mass, and the breastplate flew off like the lid of a fiercely steaming cauldron. Soon Nasidius became a great moun-tain of flesh in which limbs were indistinguishable from trunk; no vultures or wild beasts could have ventured to feast on him, and even his comrades dared not consign him to a pyre. They fled in horror, and as they glanced back the body was still swelling in every direction.

In 1927, A. E. Housman, better known as the author of *A Shropshire*

Lad, stabilized the text of the *Civil Wars*. Prevented by the self-denying ordinance to which textual critics subscribe from expressing any poetic judgement, he merely allows himself a few dry comments, in an appendix, on Lucan's astronomical ignorance. But the savagery of his attack on former editors suggests that he is using them as whipping-boys for Lucan; did not Lucan himself use Caesar as a whipping-boy for Nero? After charging Cortius with egotism and tediousness; Burman with diffuseness and triviality; Bentley with senile ill-temper; Weise with ludicrous ignorance; 'passing over C. F. Weber's perfectly useless edition'; and saying hard words about Hosius, Housman writes:

An elaborate edition with apparatus criticus and commentary was produced in 1896 and 1897 by C. M. Francken. Hardly a page of it can be read without anger and disgust. Francken was a born blunderer, marked cross from the womb and perverse; and he had not the shrewdness or modesty to suspect that others saw clearer than he did nor the prudence and decency to acquaint himself with what he might have learned from those whom he preferred to contradict. For stupidity of plan and slovenliness of execution his apparatus criticus is worse than Breiter's apparatus of Manilius; and I never saw another of which that could be said.

*

Why has Lucan's reputation flared up so high, every now and then, and always at the expense of Virgil, to whom as a verse technician at least, he could not hold a candle? One may equally ask why the modernist movement in Anglo-American poetry which Ezra Pound, T. S. Eliot, T. E. Hulme, and others started over forty years ago, by way of revolt against the Virgilian tradition of Tennyson, Longfellow, William Morris and others, has enjoyed such success. The truth is that at the close of the First World War much the same moral and aesthetic gap separated neo-Georgian from Victorian London, as had separated Neronian from Augustan Rome. Standards had changed radically and the smooth, languid, pellucid verse – *splendidior vitro* – hitherto demanded by critics could no longer adequately express the consequent malaise. To poets whom loss of faith in their own national institutions, ethics, religion, and even in themselves, sends marching and countermarching through the Waste Land, Lucan can be as much a 'standard-bearer' as he was for Piso's ill-considered conspiracy. His un-Virgilian rhetoric, and all the modernist traits mentioned above – impatience with craftsmanship, digressive irrelevances, emphasis on the macabre, lack of religious conviction, turgid hyperbole, inconsistency, appeal to violence, and occasional flashes of real brilliance – have been redis-covered by this new disagreeable world. Accounts of the extravagant and tyrannical behaviour to which ordinary Romans were ready to submit under Nero do not now read so fantastically as they did before the rise of totalitarianism in Europe; and many people who to-day pass as Stoics are hardly more able to stand the test of violent moral suasion than was Lucan.

Shelley has been taken to task for preferring Lucan to Virgil, but he too lived in a cranky age and showed extreme emotional instability; the melodramatic sublime of his *Cenci* often spills over into the bathetic ridiculous, like Lucan's account of Cato's heroic struggle with the Libyan serpents. It is only to be expected, similarly, that Pound (the most Lucan-like of modernists) should please the young and dis-orientated better than Tennyson. Yet surely there are poetic alterna-tives to the soft-voiced skilful rhetorician, 'wielder of the stateliest measure ever moulded by the lips of man' (Tennyson on Virgil), who prides himself on his *ars est celare artem* technique, and the brassy-voiced intemperate rhetorician, for whom *ars est in arte praeconari* (art lies in advertising, rather than concealing, artistry)? The Romans, for ex-ample, could choose the unrhetorical Catullus who was tender without being soft, and manly without being strident: a true poet. But although the two-thousand-year-old tradition of rhetorical education has at last lapsed at the Universities, its effects are still apparent in popular literary taste. The verse-reading public has always preferred sound to sense; and since the rhetorician disguised as a poet is no longer challenged to justify his tropes logically, he can get away (so to speak) with rape, arson, and murder.

Why then, if I dislike Lucan so much (as Dr E. V. Rieu, the Editor of these *Penguin Classics*, very pertinently asks) have I chosen to spend six months in translating *The Civil Wars*? Because the book is a historical phenomenon that cannot be argued away, and because like other prodigiously vital writers with hysterical tendencies – Rudyard Kipling is a convenient instance – Lucan exerts a strange fascination on even the reluctant reader; and because, as I have tried to show, he antici-pated so many of the literary *genres* dominant to-day that it would be unfair not to put him in modern dress for the admiration of the great majority whose tastes differ from mine.

Deyá, Marjorca, Spain   R.G.

BOOK ONE

THE theme of my poem is the Civil War which was decided on the plains of Pharsalus in Thessaly; yet 'Civil War' is an understatement, since Pompey and Caesar, the opposing leaders, were not only fellow-citizens but relatives: the whole struggle was indeed no better than one of licensed fratricide. I shall here describe how, after the breakdown of the First Triumvirate, Rome turned the imperial sword against her own breast: how kinsman faced kinsman on the field of battle, each line of legionaries armed with identical javelins and carrying the same familiar eagle-standards as its opponents; and how the civilized world reeled under this contest in iniquity.

What made our forefathers embark on such an orgy of self-destruction? And why were their hated enemies permitted to enjoy the spectacle? Why was proud Parthia not first obliged to disgorge the Eagles taken from Crassus,[1] whose ghost still wandered unavenged over her plains? That should have been Rome's immediate duty. It is bitter indeed to reflect how much of the earth's surface – from the lands of sunrise to those of sunset, from the burning Equator to the perpetually frozen seas of northernmost Scythia – could have been bought for Rome with the lives so fruitlessly squandered. We might well have brought the Chinese under our yoke, and the wild men of the Araxes, and whatever human creatures live at the sources of the Nile. Granted that Romans have an insatiable craving for war, why could we not have waited at least until all foreign nations had become subject to our laws before entering upon this criminal career? It is not as though Rome ever lacked enemies. If now, in Italian cities, even some of the most venerable, the walls of empty houses still bulge outwards under broken roofs; if the streets are littered with huge stones; if no porters stand at the doorways and only a rare inhabitant wanders

---

1. Defeated by the Parthians in 53 B.C.

among the ruins; if the fields lie fallow year after year, bristling with
thorns and pleading in vain for the plough – who, pray, is to blame?
Not Pyrrhus, not Hannibal! Neither of those proud antagonists succeeded in wounding Rome so deeply as she wounded herself. Only
when brothers fall out is the sword driven home.

However, if the Fates could not prepare for Nero's advent by any
other means – if eternal empire may not be bought except at a heavy
price, as when of old a War of the Giants was needed to secure Juppiter's throne – then I naturally abstain from further complaints:[1] the
end may here be offered as sufficient justification of the means – including all the crimes committed during the troubles. What if merciless
fighting at Pharsalus[2] heaped the plain with corpses, if at Thapsus[3]
rivers of blood glutted the thirst of Hannibal's revengeful shade, and
if the final battle at Munda[4] proved no less costly in life? And what if
we must add to these horrific annals the famine at Perusia,[5] the ghastly
struggle at Mutina,[6] the seafight[7] near the rocky island of Leucas, the
defeat of Sextus Pompey's slave-manned fleet within view of burning
Etna?[8] Even so, it is arguable that Rome has greatly profited from her
Civil Wars: were they not fought, Caesar, that you might reign
to-day?

And O, great Prince, when your watch among men ends, and you
finally rise skywards, the celestial palace of your choice will receive
you amid the loud acclamations of Heaven. I cannot venture to pro-
phesy whether you will assume Juppiter's sceptre, or prefer to mount
Apollo's fiery chariot and survey the earth from it as you drive along –

1. The whole passage is heavily satirical.

2. Where Caesar defeated Pompey in Thessaly, 48 B.C.

3. Where Caesar defeated King Juba of Mauretania, who had sided with
Scipio's Pompeians; 46 B.C.

4. Where Caesar defeated Pompey's sons, near Malaga, with the loss of
30,000 men; 45 B.C.

5. Where Mark Antony's brother Lucius was besieged, in Tuscany, by
Caesar's heir, Octavianus (Augustus); 41 B.C.

6. Where Mark Antony besieged Decimus Brutus Albinus, one of Caesar's
murderers; 44 B.C. The Consuls Hirtius and Pansa tried to raise the siege but were
killed in action near by.

7. The battle of Actium, where Octavianus defeated Mark Antony and
Cleopatra's fleets in 31 B.C.

8. Agrippa defeated him off Mylae and Naulochus in 36 B.C.

an earth quite untroubled by the change of divine charioteers.[1] But this much is certain: every deity will shrink humbly back, while Mother Nature waits for you to decide which god to be, and where to establish your seat of power. As for that, I beseech you not to choose the Arctic Circle, or the torrid southern skies, from either of which your light would beam only squintingly[2] on Rome. And, if you put too much weight on any single portion of the limitless aether, you will endanger its balance;[3] it would be best to take up your stance in the very centre of Heaven and thus preserve universal equipoise. May that region remain serene and cloudless, affording us an uninterrupted view of our Emperor![4]

One further wish: may mankind ground arms and consult its own welfare in an epoch of international love: may Peace, sent flying about the world, keep the iron gates of Janus's Temple[5] tight shut. For my part, I have already come to regard you as a god; and if your divine afflatus[6] enters my breast and provokes me to verse, I shall not ask to be visited by either Apollo of Delphi or Bacchus of Mount Nysa. You are sufficient inspiration for any Roman poet.

I must now provide the historical background of these tremendous events. It is indeed a formidable task to explain how it came about that our nation ran so frantically to arms and drove Peace from the world. The fact is that long-lasting national supremacy soon attracts the resentment of Fate; and Rome, top-heavy with her own greatness, had grown ripe for a spectacular collapse. Call it, if you will, a foretaste of what must happen when the framework of the world buckles and its long cycles suddenly end; when chaos supervenes; when the constellations collide and dash themselves in pieces; when Earth heaves up her shores and shakes off the stream of Ocean; when the Moon in her two-horse gig usurps the daylight course of her brother's four-horse

1. Nero fancied himself as a charioteer but, when competing at Olympia, took a bad toss and failed to stay the course. Lucan hints that he would not have much greater success in driving the Sun's chariot than the foolish Phaëthon in the myth.

2. Nero had a noticeable squint.

3. Nero was grossly fat.

4. Nero was ashamed of his premature baldness, which he tried to conceal.

5. In Rome the iron gates of Janus's Temple were never closed while a war was in progress.

6. Nero's musical and poetic talents were a by-word at Rome.

chariot; and when the mechanism of the Universe gets thrown out of gear, to the utter annulment of all natural law.

As great edifices collapse of their own weight, so Heaven sets a similar limit to the growth of prosperous states. In this case, however, no foreign nation acted as the instrument of divine Nemesis: it was the Romans, now supreme on land and sea, who foolishly brought doom on themselves when they consented to be governed by a trium-virate. They should have known that supreme sovereignty had never been divided among so many as three men except with bloody results. Alas, in this case too, the partners, all disastrously pledged to the same purpose but each blinded by his own ambitions, joined hands in com-mon mischief. Never so long as earth supports sea, or air supports earth, or the Sun makes his perennial journey through the signs of the Zodiac, or night follows day – never will loyalty be found among fellow-despots! It is a law of Nature that every great man inevitably resents a partner in greatness. And why quote foreign history to prove my thesis? Romulus bathed the rising walls of Rome with the blood of his brother Remus, and was not even rewarded for this madness by an empire stretching over land and sea. He gained the mere chieftain-ship of a small community recruited from runaway slaves and criminals who had taken sanctuary in a near-by grove.

For awhile an unnatural harmony reigned in the Triumvirate: Crassus's mediation somehow kept his pugnacious colleagues from flying at each other's throats. One may liken Crassus to the narrow Isthmus of Corinth which barely prevents a head-on collision between the Ionian and Aegean Seas; if it disappeared, what a welter of water would result![1] So when Crassus disappeared, falling miserably at Carrhae – where the Syrian soil was dyed with the blood of our legions – his colleagues at once felt free to impose their madness on the world. The Arsacid dynasty of Parthia had, in fact, gained far more at Carrhae than they realized then: civil war had been let loose on the enemy, by severing the bond which united the three tyrants. It soon became apparent that even a powerful Empire, spread across the whole civil-ized earth, did not provide enough elbow-room for both of them!

The unfortunate death of Caesar's daughter Julia had been ominous of the coming breach; the same bridal torches which welcomed her in bridal array to Pompey's house presently lighted her corpse to the

1. Nero planned, but did not carry out, a Corinth Canal project.

pyre. And with Julia went the last ties that bound these two great men together. Had it been her destiny to live a few years longer, she and she alone might have prevented the quarrel. Julia could have forced her husband and her father to fling away the swords they had drawn against each other – as the kidnapped Sabine women did long ago when their kinsmen marched against Rome. But, as it chanced, Julia's death dissolved the league of friendship sealed by this union: the ambitious rivals now felt at liberty to embark on their struggle for power.

Pompey feared that Caesar's recent conquest of Gaul might put into the shade his own famous suppression of the Cilician pirates.[1] Caesar, for his part, was encouraged to prosecute the military career in which he had now won valuable experience and the favours of Fortune. He disdained to accept a subordinate position at Rome. In a word, Pompey could allow no man to be his equal, and Caesar no man to be his superior. Who am I to judge which of the two had more right on his side? Each could claim the support of a high authority: for the winning cause pleased the Gods, but the losing cause pleased Cato.[2]

Pompey and Caesar met on unequal terms. Pompey, now past middle age, had not taken the field for some years.[3] His main preoccupation was to keep his fame alive by courting the favour of the common people; he distributed largesse, provided costly spectacles, and exulted in the applause that greeted him when he entered the great theatre which he had himself built.[4] Resting on his well-earned laurels, he made no attempt to win fresh ones, but basked in the glory of his surname, 'the Great', which had been officially bestowed on him by the Senate. It was as when an oak towering above a lush meadow – the repository of votive offerings and enemy spoils hung on its branches by bygone tribal chieftains – ceases to derive any support from the roots, but relies merely on its bulk to keep it upright. Leafless boughs

1. Pompey's fleet of five hundred vessels had finally routed the pirates at Corocaesium in 67 B.C.

2. Supposedly the noblest-hearted Roman of those times, and the hero of *Book IX*.

3. Not since his triumph over King Mithridates of Pontus, in 62 B.C., fourteen years previously.

4. It was the first stone theatre built in Rome and seated forty thousand spectators. At its opening, five hundred lions and eighteen elephants were hunted, numerous gladiatorial fights took place, and Rome enjoyed its first view of a live rhinoceros.

protrude into the sky, it throws no more than a skeletal shadow and totters in the breeze: the first north-easter will send it crashing down. How strange that though many near-by trees are still green and firmly rooted, this hollow oak alone is an object of veneration!

Caesar, on the other hand, had not only won the reputation of a successful general, but was burned with so restless a desire for conquest that he felt disgraced by inactivity. Headstrong, fierce, and never hesitating to flesh his sword, he stood prepared to lead his troops wherever hope of glory or personal resentment offered a battlefield. Confident in Fortune's continued favours, he would follow up each advantage gained; thrusting aside all obstacles that barred his march to supreme power, and rejoicing in the havoc he occasioned. Caesar may, indeed, be justly compared to lightning. Discharged by the winds from a pack of clouds, it darts out jaggedly with a crash that splits the daylight skies, dazzling every eye, striking terror into every heart, and blasting its own airy seats. Nothing may stand against it, either during that furious progress through the clouds, or when it bursts against the earth and at once recomposes its scattered fires.

So much for the opposing leaders; but the people too had a secret propensity for war, characteristic of every sovereign race. The Romans had become masters of the world and were endowed by Fortune with such an excess of wealth that it had corrupted their public morality. Spoils won in war tempted them to extravagance; they all felt entitled to possess as much money and as many houses as they pleased and to despise dishes that once tempted their palate. Men adopted a luxurious style of dress unsuitable even for married women; and because the poverty which had once bred a virile stock now seemed odious, they rifled every foreign land of whatever product had most contributed to its downfall. Great estates were formed; and employers entrusted the very soil once laboriously ploughed by Marcus Furius Camillus,[1] or dug by Marius Curius Dentatus,[2] to labourers whose very names they never troubled to learn. No such nation could be satisfied to hang up its arms and grow fat in the free enjoyment of peace and tranquillity. Frequent breaches of the peace resulted, as did also vile crimes prompted by the unequal distribution of wealth. To be above the laws of one's own country became a distinction worth

1. Died 365 B.C. He was taken from the plough to become Dictator.
2. Died 270 B.C. He withstood Pyrrhus, and triumphed over the Samnites.

winning; and might was right. Hence the unconstitutional measures which both Consuls and Tribunes of the People enacted. Hence the bribes offered by candidates for high office; and the disgraceful yearly scene on the Campus Martius, where the Commons sold their votes to the highest bidder. Hence also usury with its avaricious counting of the days until payment became due; one result of which was the destruction of credit and a ready recourse to arms for the settlement of debts.

Caesar had crossed the icy Alps before he began to consider the disastrous and far-reaching effects of this war; but on his arrival at the Rubicon, a small river which divides the pastures of Gaul from the cornfields of Italy, he was granted a night vision of Rome, his own distressed motherland. She stood bare-armed, her features expressing profound sorrow and her white hairs streaming dishevelled from underneath a mural crown. 'Where are you bound, soldiers?' she asked, sighing deeply. 'Where are you carrying my standards? If you are honest, law-abiding men, you will halt at this stream!'[1] Caesar trembled, his scalp crawled with horror and his feet dragged; yet he edged nearer to the bank and prayed aloud to Juppiter: 'O Thunderer, as you gaze down at the great walls of Rome from your temple beside the Tarpeian Rock; and you, Household-gods of the Julian clan, whose images my ancestor Aeneas saved from burning Troy; and you, Romulus, our founder, mysteriously elevated to Heaven as the God Quirinius; and you, Latin Juppiter, in your shrine on the Alban Mount; and you, Vesta, whose sacred fire our virgins tend; and you, too, Goddess of Rome, whose power equals that of any major deity – favour my enterprise! Ah, Rome, I wage no frantic war against you! I am Caesar, the soldier who won great victories for you on land and sea, and who will continue to be your champion while you consent. If any blood is destined to flow, let it fall on the head of the villain who has falsely represented me as your enemy!'

With these words, Caesar unleashed war by hurrying his standards over the rushing stream. It was as when a lion crouches in the parched fields of Libya, uncertain whether or not to spring on the enemy whom he has sighted. He rouses himself to fury by lashing his cruel tail and

1. According to Suetonius, a being of superhuman size and beauty was playing on a reed as Caesar reached the Rubicon. It was a male deity, and he snatched a trumpet from one of Caesar's men, blew a loud blast and crossed the stream.

uttering a loud, cavernous roar. The nimble Moor may then contrive to wound him with an assegai, but what of that? Even if a hunting-spear should pierce the beast's broad chest, he will continue to attack, driving the weapon yet deeper into his own body.

The rust-coloured Rubicon issues from an insignificant spring, and when it crawls along its valley-bed in hot summer, the stream is scanty enough. On this occasion, however, not only was it swollen by three nights and days of winter rain following a change of moon, but damp, warm winds had melted the Alpine snows and greatly increased the force of the current. Caesar therefore made the cavalry form up slant-wise across the stream, which the rest of the army then forded without difficulty under the protection of this improvised breakwater. Finally Caesar himself crossed, and made a speech from the forbidden Italian bank.

'Men, I am here leaving peace behind me, and defying the Roman Constitution. Henceforth let the Goddess Fortune be my guide. Enough of solemn covenants; I have observed them too carefully by far. Only war can now decide between Pompey and myself.'

He brusquely signalled the advance, and his army moved forward through the night, swift as a bolt from a Balearic sling or a Parthian horse-archer's parting arrow. They swooped down on Rimini at dawn, when only the morning-star still shone in the sky, and caused panic in the town. The weather on this first day of conflict was appro-priately gloomy – perhaps the gods themselves had ordered the South Wind to drive up those murky clouds. Caesar's men[1] occupied the local Forum without opposition and halted to plant their standards. Blaring trumpets and bugles, and braying horns, sounded the alarm of Civil War and roused the drowsy inhabitants from sleep. The men snatched down the arms hanging in their household shrines: tattered shields, javelins with bent or broken points, swords blunted by old rust – mute witnesses of a long-unbroken peace. But when they saw the shining Roman Eagles and lesser standards, and recognized Caesar seated on a charger at the head of his troops, they stood motionless in cold terror. Every man thought: 'This was an unlucky site to choose for a town, so close to Gaul! Profound peace reigns throughout the rest of the world, yet we are the victims of a mad uprising: ours is the

1. According to Caesar's own account, they were men of the Thirteenth Legion.

first place to be occupied by the rebels. If only we lived somewhere else – in the Far East, say, or in the icy north, or among the nomads of the Steppes – anywhere else but here, at the gateway to Italy. First it was the Sennonian Gauls, next it was Hannibal's Carthaginians, and then came the furious Teutons and Cimbrians;[1] whenever Rome is threatened, the invader always chooses this route.' Yet not a man among them dared do more than groan inaudibly, however great his anxiety or sorrow. The consequent silence recalled that of the country-side when winter strikes all singing birds dumb; or of the high seas during a calm.

It was broad daylight, and if Caesar still wavered in his resolution, or felt tempted to compromise, the Goddess Fortune gave him a new incentive to battle. She had decided on providing occasions which would clearly justify the revolt. Now, when Caesar offered to resign his command on reaching Rome, if Pompey would do the same, two Tribunes of the People had hotly supported his proposal; but the Consuls, in violation of the law which made the Tribunes' persons sacrosanct, threatened them with the fate of the Gracchi[2] unless they kept silent. The Tribunes thereupon fled from Rome to the protection of Caesar's army in Gaul, but found him already across the frontier. With them came bold Caius Scribonius Curio, the man whose elo-quence was reputedly on public sale; a spokesman of the people and a champion of their liberties, he had dared reduce armed dignitaries to the level of private citizens.[3] Realizing now that Caesar was still in two minds about which course to follow, he said: 'Caesar, while I could continue to defend your party, despite our opponents in the Senate, I did so, and even persuaded the wavering to vote a five years' extension of your command in Gaul. But the Constitution has since been suspended, on the ground that civil war threatens, and these two Tribunes and I find ourselves driven from Rome. We are, however, prepared to endure exile until your victory restores our rights as citizens. The City is in a turmoil, and it would be folly to let your enemies consolidate their power; procrastination is always dangerous

---

1. 390 B.C.; 218 B.C.; 101 B.C.

2. Tiberius and Gaius Gracchus were well known for their support of the Plebeians against the Patricians; both met with violent deaths in consequence.

3. Curio had been a supporter of Pompey, but deserted him in the confidence that Caesar would pay off his heavy debts.

once a man is ready to act. You have campaigned ten years in Gaul to win only an insignificant part of this earth's surface; to-day it will cost you little more exertion or anxiety to gain vastly greater rewards. Fight two or three extra battles, and Rome will be found to have conquered the world for your sake alone. Here lies your only hope of being rewarded with a triumph when you reach the City, and wearing consecrated laurels in a procession to the Capitol. Envy gnaws at your son-in-law's heart and he has decided to cheat you of the honours that you have long been owed; in fact, you will be lucky to escape being punished for your conquests. Very well: since he withholds your half-share of the world, why not claim his in addition to yours?'

Caesar was already eager to let the sword decide between himself and Pompey, but Curio's words added new fuel to his anger. He resembled a race-horse at Olympia, straining at the closed wooden gates of the barrier, and trying to work the bolts loose with its head; the shouting of the spectators excites it still more. At once he rallied his infantry around the standards and, with set face and raised arm, soon quieted their bustle. This is what he told them: 'Men, you have faced the enemy with me a thousand times, and in the last ten years we have never known defeat. But what will your reward be for the blood you shed on Northern battlefields, and for the cold winters you spent beyond the Alps? Such frantic military preparations are in progress at Rome to-day that this might be Hannibal's army, not mine. Every battalion there is being brought up to strength with picked recruits, forests are being felled to build ships, and orders have gone out that I am to be harried ashore and afloat. I wonder what would have happened if we had lost the war and were being pursued by a victorious Gallic army? It is only because Fortune has proved kind, and the Gods have summoned us to the high places of this earth, that our enemies are offering this challenge. Well, we are ready to accept it. Their leader, Pompey, once arranged a triumph for himself before he had reached legal age,[1] but long years of peace have made him flabby. Let him by all means lead his hastily raised troops against us – and such unwarlike hangers-on as Marcellus the Talker, and fellows like Cato who have nothing to boast about but their names. Do you think it right that Pompey should once more be allowed to renew his despotic

1. The legal age was thirty. Pompey had triumphed over King Hiarbas of Numidia when he was only twenty-five.

34

power – awarded him over and over again without a break by the dregs of the people whose votes he has bought? Should he never be forced to disgorge the dignities which he has usurped? And is it nothing that he has now assumed control of the world's corn supplies and can make famine a political instrument? Or that his troops have illegally broken into the Courts of Justice – you remember Milo's trial?[1] – and terrorized juries with their glittering standards and swords?

'Once again Pompey is preparing for civil war; he hopes, no doubt, to postpone his inglorious return to private life. He learned this wicked lesson from Sulla, and is now bent on outdoing his master. The man reminds me of a savage tiger reared by his dam in the Hyrcanian jungle and taught to lap the blood of slaughtered cattle. Pompey used once to lick the blood off Sulla's sword blade, and has never since lost the craving for it. But a diet of human blood turns a man into a savage; so why should we suppose that he will ever lay down his badges of office and end this long history of crime? There was one honourable lesson at least that Sulla might have taught the wretch: the duty of eventual abdication.[2] Yes, I am aware of his successes against the elusive Cilicians, and against King Mithridates of Pontus who, though exhausted by forty years of war with Rome, had at last to be removed ingloriously enough, by poison, not force of arms. But shall Pompey crown his career with a triumph over Caesar – Caesar, who has had the audacity to insist on his constitutional right of entering Rome at the head of these victorious legions? Very well, let me be defrauded of my hard-earned triumph; but I shall never allow you veterans to be denied yours. You shall march in, I swear, under some commander or other, never mind whom. And what of my re-enlisted men? What settlement will be made for those brave veterans when they retire? Can they expect awards of public land and a fortified town to shelter them in their old age? Or will Pompey grant them less even than his defeated pirates won? You will remember that he settled them all over

1. Titus Annius Papianus, when accused of murdering Clodius, briefed Cicero as his defending counsel. The truth seems to be that Pompey did not exactly terrorize the jury into condemning Milo, but took emergency measures for preventing mob violence during the trial.

2. Sulla the Dictator, Pompey's former father-in-law and commander-in-chief during the civil war against Marius, retired to private life in the town of Puteoli (79 B.C.) at the age of sixty, and died soon after.

the Empire, not only in their native Cilicia, but in Achaea, and in Italy itself!

'Lift high those victorious standards, men! We must make good use of the strength we have built up; for the proverb runs: "Deny a strong man his due, and he will take all he can get." And you may count on divine favour; since my object is neither plunder nor power, but only to rid Rome of the tyrant who dominates her.'

Caesar's speech was not, however, greeted with immediate applause. On the contrary, a doubtful whispering spread through the ranks. Though fierce-hearted, and proud of their battle record, the soldiers were too patriotic not to hesitate awhile before supporting Caesar's cause. Yet a passion for fighting, combined with the fear of offending him, soon tipped the balance. Laelius, a leading centurion, winner of an oak-leaf badge for saving a comrade's life in battle, raised his voice.

'My lord Caesar,' he shouted, 'may I be given leave to speak? To be frank, our complaint is that you have been far too patient and held back too long. Knowing you for the finest general in the army, we could suppose only that our loyalty had ceased to inspire your confidence. For how could you fail to call on us while we still had blood in our veins, and strength to hurl the javelin? We asked ourselves: "Will he submit to the tyranny of the Senate and disgrace himself by tamely putting on a toga? Is victory in a civil war, after all, so fearful a fate?" My lord, we have always been ready to follow wherever you lead: even against the Scythian hordes, or around the inhospitable Gulf of Sirte, or across the thirsty midsummer deserts of Libya. You led us forward through conquered Gaul, and we consolidated our gains as we went; we took ship and rowed over the Ocean Stream to Britain; we navigated the turbulent mouth of the Rhine. If I may speak of myself for a moment, loyal performance of the tasks you impose has become second nature to me. Command the trumpets to blow the assault against whatever General you please, and I will deny that he is my fellow-countryman. And I swear by these standards, victorious in ten campaigns, and by your future triumphs – it is no business of mine over what enemy they are gained – that this sword-arm will continue to obey your orders even where they may happen to conflict with my rooted inclinations. Tell me to plunge a sword into my brother's breast, my father's throat, or the belly of my wife, now great with child, and I will not fail you. Or to plunder the temples of the gods and set them on fire; I will gladly break up the sacred images and melt them into coin for your war-chest. Instruct me to encamp my men beside the Tiber; I will unhesitatingly mark out the tent-lines across the familiar fields of home. Whenever you wish to level a city wall, call upon me; I will help to swing the battering-ram and send huge stones crashing down – though they be the walls of Rome herself!'

Impressed by this speech, every man present raised his right hand, swearing to follow wherever Caesar led, and a great shout arose; it recalled the roar of pine-trees on the cliffs of Mount Ossa, when the North-easter from Thrace bursts upon them, bending their tops to the ground, and when they spring upright again during flaws in the gale.

These fortunate circumstances – the Tribunes' arrival and the bellicose spirit shown by his troops – decided Caesar not to pause for a moment, but to recall every Roman garrison from Gaul and rally all available troops for his march on Rome.

Some detachments came from far distant camps: from Lake Leman; from the Vosges mountains, where the pugnacious Lingones with their enamelled weapons needed careful watching; and from the fords of the Isère, a tributary of the famous Rhône. The fair-haired Ruthenians were also temporarily relieved of Roman occupation; and galleys no longer patrolled either the slow-flowing Aude, or the Var, which now formed the frontier of Greater Italy. Moreover, Caesar's flotilla had abandoned the rocky cove of Monaco, sacred to Hercules who touched there during his Tenth Labour – it offers safe anchorage when the wind blows from the north-west, but no protection against the dreaded Sirocco. Further troops were recalled from the flat coast of the Lowlands, which is sometimes above water, sometimes awash, according to the tides of the great Ocean. (What causes these tides, I must leave the natural philosophers to decide. One theory is that they occur when the winds have driven masses of water forward from beyond the horizon; another, that the movements of the Moon affect them, and that they vary with her phases; still another is that the Sun quenches its thirst by sucking up the waves of the sea. I am not interested in such cosmological questions, being content to let them remain a perpetual mystery – as the Gods wish them to be.)

Caesar's Spier garrison too moved off, so did that of Lacq, where the Tarbellians occupy both banks of the meandering Adour, a river which rises in the Pyrenees. The people of Saintes and Bourges were delighted at the Roman evacuation; so were those of Soissons, dexterous fighters with the long spear; and the famous javelin-throwers of Toul and Rheims; and the horsemen of the Seine, whose squadrons wheel about in such remarkable unison. And the Belgians, expert in driving the war-chariot, though it is an importation from Britain; and the people of Auvergne, who falsely claim Trojan descent and therefore kinship with the Romans; and the rebel Nervians of the Ardennes, disgraced by their treacherous murder of Caesar's general Quintus Aurunculeius Cotta; and the people of Worms, who wear long pantaloons in Sarmatian style; and the fierce Batavians, who rouse themselves to battle fury by harsh blasts of brazen war-horns.

The Spaniards of the Cinca bend were equally pleased; and the Gauls at the junction of the rapid Rhône and the Saône; as were also the mountaineers of the rocky, snow-capped Cevennes; and the people of Trèves; and the Ligurians, who have taken to cropping their heads, though once they had boasted longer and more beautiful hair, tumbling over their necks, than any of their neighbours; and those Gauls who propitiate with human sacrifices the merciless gods Teutas, Esus and Taranis[1] – at whose altars the visitant shudders because they are as awe-inspiring as those of Scythian Diana. The Gallic bards, who compose elegies for heroes fallen in battle, and transmit these to posterity, were once more free to declaim their verses. The Druids, too, took advantage of the armistice to resume the barbarous rites of their wicked religion. (These men live deep in the forests, and claim – perhaps idly, perhaps not – that they alone understand the secrets of divinity and astrology. They hold that the soul of a dead man does not descend to the silent, sunless land of Hades, but becomes reincarnate elsewhere; if they are right, death is merely a point of change in perpetual existence. These Northerners are most fortunate to believe in a doctrine which frees them from that besetting terror of mankind: fear of extinction. The soldier advances eagerly to meet his enemy, faces death with courage, and despises as a coward whoever hesitates to lay down his life which he will soon enjoy again.)

Finally, the garrisons detailed to protect Northern Gaul against the long-haired Chaucians, quitted the unfriendly banks of the Rhine and

1. The Romans identified these respectively with Mercury, Mars and Juppiter.

marched back towards Rome. In effect, Caesar had denuded his frontiers of troops, leaving them wholly unprotected. So large were the forces thus assembled that he was strong enough to occupy all the neighbouring towns of Northern Italy. Then, of course, as always happens when war threatens, idle rumours increased the very reasonable anxiety felt by the civilian population. Countless tongues wagged with presentiments of imminent disaster. A report reached Rome that Caesar's barbarian cavalry had occupied Mevania in Umbria, where the famous white oxen are bred, and were boldly sweeping towards the junction of the Nar and the Tiber; and that Caesar himself was grimly following with legion after legion, each swelled by a crowd of irregulars. Terror conjured up a novel portrait of him. He was no longer the Caesar they knew, but a monster more inhuman than any of the tribes whom he had subjugated. They were even willing to believe that he had uprooted every German tribe from its home between Rhine and Elbe, and compelled the fighting men to form up in his rear; and that these savages had been promised the pleasure of sacking Rome while he looked on.

Such rumours, despite their total lack of confirmation, increased in terror with each retelling; and it was not the common people alone who deceived themselves. Panic spread to the Senate House, where the Senators sprang from their seats, hastily voted that the two Consuls should be given plenary powers for conducting the war – an odious act[1] – and fled. That was a mad rush! None of them knew where danger threatened or where a refuge offered; they pelted after the mob of flying citizens and resigned themselves to the general terror. Massed columns of fugitives rushed pell-mell down the City streets, as though impious hands had fired the houses, or an earthquake were making them nod and totter. Nobody knew where he was bound, though a general obsession prevailed that the one hope of safety lay in precipitate flight beyond the City walls. It was as when the stormy South Wind, driving up huge waves from the Gulf of Sirte, catches a ship under full canvas and dismasts her with a crash; helmsman and crew at once leap overboard, instead of waiting for the hull to be shattered by the seas, so that each (as it were) assures his own ship-

---

1. Caesar, in his own account of the war, complains that such a decree had hitherto been resorted to only when fire threatened to burn Rome down, or public safety was otherwise endangered in equal degree.

wreck. Rome was similarly abandoned by her citizens, but in a flight which necessarily precipitated war. No decrepit father could restrain his son from flight; no wife, her husband. Every man darted across the threshold without waiting even long enough to offer the household-gods a prayer for protection, or bestowing so much as a lingering glance at the well-loved scene that he might never again set eyes upon. The stampede was, in a word, irresistible.

Although ready at times to grant supremacy to a particular nation, the Gods are equally ready to withhold it. Rome, a city thronged with her own native population and with slaves drawn from countless conquered nations, had walls extensive enough, if necessary, to contain the entire human race; yet the same Rome lay now deserted, abandoned in rank cowardice for Caesar to plunder at his leisure. What a paradox! When fighting abroad, the Roman was then, and still is, renowned for his defensive tenacity: hemmed in behind a flimsy stockade, he will limit the dangers of a night attack by extemporizing entrenchments, and as soon as he is relieved of his watch go calmly off to sleep in a tent. Yet at Rome the mere whisper of war now provoked a panic-stricken exodus; and her massive walls were no longer considered adequate shelter for a single night!

The chief excuse for panic was that Pompey himself had left in a hurry;[1] but menacing portents of disaster in earth, sky and sea also persuaded everyone that the future must be yet blacker than had been feared. Unknown stars and lights and showers of meteors gilded the night sky; and a long-tailed comet appeared, of the kind that portends the death of princes. No clouds hung overhead, but lightning flickered incessantly on the murky horizon, like long javelins of flame, or like torches scattering sparks. And presently a thunderbolt, armed with fire from the far North – not, as usually happens, from the South – hurtled down from the clear sky without so much as a warning rumble and struck Alba Longa, the ancient capital of the Latin League. Then the Earth's shadow passed across the full moon and caused an eclipse. And, as if this were not enough, the sun suffered a similar eclipse next day in mid-course, and such thick darkness prevailed that terrified mankind began to despair of daylight;[2] much the same thing had once

1. According to Caesar, he had gone to reassure himself that the legions wintering in Apulia were still loyal to his cause.
2. These phenomena are unhistorical.

happened at Mycenae – when the Sun-god observed the horrible sight of Thyestes dining ignorantly on the flesh of his own sons, he turned his chariot about and brought night back.

Furthermore, Mount Etna went into eruption and the volcanic fires, instead of rising vertically, squirted sideways, towards Italy.

Nor were these the only manifestations. In the Straits of Messina, the whirlpool of Charybdis churned up bloody water; and from the rocks of Scylla a dismal sound arose, like the barking of dogs. The fire on Vesta's altar was mysteriously extinguished, and the blaze of the bonfire which always concludes the Latin Festival, divided – a portent recalling a similar occurrence at Thebes long ago, when the inveterate animosity of the brothers Eteocles and Polyneices, who had killed each other, prevented the flames of their common funeral pyre from uniting. Earth shuddered on her axis, which caused the Alpine range to hurl down avalanches of ancient snow; while an enormous tidal wave struck the rock of Gibraltar and drenched the heights of Ceuta.[1] There is also a tradition that the tears of the native deities,[2] and sweat pouring from the brows of the household-gods, attested to Rome's misery; that *ex voto* offerings tumbled from temple walls, that ill-omened night-birds appeared in broad daylight, and that wild beasts emerged from the midnight woods and boldly made their lairs in the very heart of Rome. Animals, too, spoke with human voices,[3] women gave birth to many-limbed monsters which frightened them out of their wits, and a calamitous prophecy attributed to the Sibyl of Cumae passed from mouth to mouth.[4]

The priests of Bellona, who danced their boisterous dance that spring, howling and hacking at their own limbs, babbled of divine wrath; and the Galli, Cybele's eunuch priests, tossed their blood-stained tresses in a similar ecstasy and prophesied widespread disaster. Funereal

---

1. This, rather than 'the top of Mount Atlas', seems to be the sense of *Atlantem summum*.

2. Janus, Faunus, Picus, Latinus, Quirinius, Virbius, etc.

3. According to one of the scholiasts on Lucan, an ass spoke (its words are not quoted) and a plough-ox asked its master: 'Why goad me on, when the customers for your crops will all have died by harvest-time?'

4. According to another scholiast it ran: R,R,R – P,P,P,P – F,F,F; which meant *Romanum Ruit Regnum* (the Roman State is ruined); *Pompeius, Pater Patriae, Pellitur* (Pompey, Father of the country, is driven out); *Ferro, Flamma, Fame* (by steel, flame and famine).

urns, filled with the calcined bones of the dead, were heard to groan aloud. From the depths of pathless forests sounded the clash of arms, the shouts of fighting men, and the confused roar of spectral armies coming to grips. Labourers tilling the fields on the outskirts of Rome fled in all directions, terrified by a huge Fury, with serpents for hair, who went coursing around the walls. Her torch was a blazing pine-tree which she shook, top downwards, in token of mourning. Such a Fury had once maddened Agave when, at the head of the Theban women, she tore her son King Pentheus in pieces; or King Lycurgus of Thrace, when he killed his wife and child and hewed off his own legs, mistaking them for vinestocks; or Hercules, when Megaera, chief of the Furies, came at the orders of cruel Hera, to madden him – though he had already dared to harrow Hell.[1] The tranquillity of a moonless, windless night was torn by the braying of trumpets and the roar of embattled armies. Sulla's ghost rose from his sepulchre in the middle of the Campus Martius, and uttered gloomy forebodings; and farmers beside the Anio fled when they saw the ghost of Marius raise his head from the tomb which Sulla had vengefully violated, and flit towards the cold river.

Recourse was therefore had to certain soothsayers of Etruria, as was the custom in such crises. In the otherwise deserted town of Luca lived their dean, Arruns, an expert on presages drawn from lightning, the inspection of smoking entrails, and the flight of birds. He gave the following orders: 'Those accursed monsters which Nature, revolting against her own laws, has formed in the womb without due process of impregnation, must be burned on a fire of ill-omened logs – either saved from a funeral pyre or cut from a lightning-blasted tree. All citizens must then circumambulate Rome in procession, keeping outside its ancient limits. At their head must march the priests whose duty it is to sprinkle purifying water on the walls. Their assistants must follow behind, with togas tightly knotted around the belly and shrouding the brow in Gabinian fashion.[2] The High Priestess of Vesta, who alone may set eyes on the Trojan Palladium, must bind a woollen fillet about her head and lead along the Vestal Virgins.

----

1. Lucan errs. It was because Hercules had been induced to kill his wife and children in a fit of madness, that Juppiter ordered him to perform his twelve penitential Labours, the last of which would be the harrowing of Hell.

2. Household-gods were represented as so dressed.

'Next must come the Fifteen, to whose care the Sibylline Books are consigned, and who are annually obliged to bathe Cybele's image in the Almo and conduct it safely back to her shrine. Then the Augurs whose specialty is observing the flight of birds on the unlucky left hand; then the Seven Feasters, who dine in honour of Juppiter and the other Gods; then the Titian Guild of Sabine Augurs; then the Leaping Priests of Mars, who dance exultingly with the sacred shields hung from their necks; lastly, the nobly-born Chief Pontiff himself, wearing his tall sheepskin cap-of-office.'

While this procession duly assembled and moved off, Arruns collected the scattered relics of the thunderbolt which had struck Alba Longa and buried them with a doleful grumbling; then he proclaimed the place sacred,[1] and led a carefully chosen bull to the sacrificial altar. Holding his knife point downwards, he began to pour wine and sprinkle spelt-flour, mixed with salt, between the victim's horns. The bull struggled vigorously – a bad sign – until the aproned attendants bore down on its dangerous horns, forcing it to kneel and offer its neck to the knife stroke. But then, instead of the usual spurt of red blood, a disgusting slime oozed from the wound. Arruns, blanching at this loathsome sight, picked up the entrails to discover whether Heaven was as furious as he feared. Their very colour scared him: they were sickly-looking and flecked with dark, malignant patches of congealed blood. The liver stank of corruption, and in the half which traditionally refers to the enemy, ominous streaks appeared. He could not see the root of the still-quivering lung, and only a thin membrane separated the vital organs. The heart lay flat, the foul entrails were torn, disclosing the caul. Finally he noticed something truly horrible, something that had never failed to portend disaster; a secondary lobe growing from the main lobe of the liver – the first drooping and flaccid, the other throbbing vigorously and still pumping blood through the veins.[2] On realizing the full significance of this sight, Arruns exclaimed: 'I hardly dare disclose the trouble in store for us. Great Juppiter has, it appears, rejected my sacrifice and let the Infernal Gods take possession of this carcase. Unspeakable disasters threaten,

1. It was customary to fence off the place where lightning had struck, or the fragments of a meteorite had been buried. The Romans imagined that every flash of lightning contained some solid missile.

2. The first, presumably, represented Pompey; the second, Caesar.

worse than the most pessimistic imagination could conceive. I pray
that there may be a brighter side to these omens, that the signs are mis-
leading, or even that Tages, the founder of our divinatory art, may
prove to have been an impostor!' Arruns then concealed in tortuous
and ambiguous language the presages which he had deduced.

Nigidius Figulus, the astrologer, likewise prophesied. His patient
observation of the heavenly bodies, and the scientific calculations he
made were unsurpassed even at Egyptian Memphis. He said: 'Unless
the Universe is in a state of random flux, with the stars moving about
erratically, Fate has clearly planned the immediate destruction of Rome
and of the entire human race. I cannot foresee in what form this will
come: whether the earth will gape and engulf whole cities, or whether
our temperate climate will be ruined by a fearful heat-wave, or whether
the soil will deceive us by going barren, or whether all the water will
turn poisonous. The Gods are consumed by anger; but how will they
show it? Horoscopes that I have drawn indicate that many thousands
of men are destined to die at the same time. It is not as though this were
the Watercarrier's month, and the cold and malicious planet Saturn
had lighted his dusky fires aloft, thereby raising a truly Deucalionian
Flood to overwhelm these lands; or as though the Sun were in the
Lion, and setting the upper air on fire, for the flames to scorch the
surface of Earth. Neither Saturn nor the Sun is, indeed, particularly
active at the moment. But look at the planet Mars! What mischief has
he in mind? Why is he firing the tail and claws of the dreadful Scorpion; at a time when the propitious planet Jupîter has sunk far below
the western horizon, and health-giving Venus has dimmed, and Mercury's swift course is retarded? Now Mars dominates the Heavens.[1]

'Why, again, have all the constellations, save only Orion with his
sworded thigh, strayed from their courses to move unseen through the
skies; and why does Orion blaze brighter than usual?[2] The truth is

1. Dr P. H. Cowell, Superintendent of the Nautical Almanac Office, has calculated the aspect of the heavens on 28 November 50 B.C., when Nigidius
made his alleged prognostications. Lucan is proved utterly wrong: all the planets
were visible and in full or normal lustre, except Saturn, which lay rather near the
Sun. Mars was not in the Scorpion (this would have increased his potency), but
wandering somewhere between the Watercarrier and the Fishes.
2. Astrology does not, however, take stock of atmospheric conditions which
make constellations appear unusually dim or bright.

that we are threatened by the madness of war, when every sword becomes a law to itself and wickedness is called heroism. For many years this madness will continue, and it would be vain to implore Heaven for a respite: peace will bring nothing but tyranny in its train. Rome would be wise to endure her sufferings without complaint, since a prolongation of Civil War can alone keep her free.'

Though the report of these presages naturally terrified all Romans, worse followed. A respectable matron[1] was seized by much the same spirit of prophecy as seizes the Edonian Bacchantes and sends them hurtling down the slopes of Mount Pindus: but Apollo, not Theban Bacchus, inspired her. She caused fearful consternation as she rushed through the City and screamed: 'Apollo, Averter of Evils, you have snatched me off through the air. Where will I touch land again? I see Mount Pangaeum's snowy ridges, and the city of Philippi lying in the shadow of the Haemus Range.[2] Tell me, Phoebus Apollo, what madness is this? Why do two Roman armies clash in battle? How can there be a war without a foreign enemy? Oh, and now you are hurrying me on again, but where? Eastward, it seems; yonder the Ptolemaic Nile debouches and discolours the sea. Ha, I recognize that mutilated corpse on the sands.[3] Look, the grim Fury named Enyo has embarked the remnants of the army defeated at Pharsalus. Off they sail across the sea, to the treacherous quicksands of Sirte, and the burning deserts of Libya[4] lying behind. These, too, I see. Now I am rapt over the cloud-capped Alps and the giddy Pyrenean peaks.[5] So back to Rome, my native city, where this impious war must end in the very heart of the

---

1. Named Sulpicia.
2. Did Sulpicia, Apollo, or Lucan himself blunder? There were two Philippi's, both called after Philip of Macedon: an obscure one, near Pharsalus, in the centre of Thessaly, where Pompey was defeated by Caesar in 48 B.C.; and a larger one in Thrace, some 150 miles away to the north-east, where in 44 B.C. Octavianus (later Augustus) defeated Caesar's murderer Brutus. Lucan's lines about Mount Pangaeum and the Haemus Range refer to the latter Philippi, since Mount Pangaeum rises close by, in Eastern Macedonia, and extends across Northern Thrace. The mistake originated, it seems, in Virgil's *First Georgic* (line 490), where the two Philippi's are carelessly identified, and had become a poetical convention through its successive adoption by Ovid, Manilius, Florus, and Petronius.
3. Pompey's.
4. Where they were defeated at Thapsus in 46 B.C.
5. To watch Caesar's war against Pompey's sons in 45 B.C.

Senate House.[1] But once more armed factions arise,[2] and once more I must set off to tour the world. But I beseech you, Great Apollo, to vary the scene of these battles; I have already seen Philippi once![3]'

With these words, she sank exhausted to the ground.

1. Where Caesar was murdered by Brutus and Cassius in 44 B.C.
2. The civil wars fought between Augustus and Mark Antony against Brutus and Cassius.
3. Again the confusion of the two Philippi's.

BOOK TWO

THE wrath of the Gods had now been manifested in the heavens by unmistakable portents of war; and that it would be civil war – a repudiation of all such natural bonds as bind man to man – was made equally clear on earth with a crop of monstrous and unnatural births. Yet why should it have pleased Olympian Juppiter to plague his anxious subjects by thus advertising the disasters in store for them? It may be that when the primal element of fire receded and the Creatrix first brought order out of Chaos, she established certain universal rules, which she bound herself to observe, and which would guide the world in its passage through the destined cycles of time. Or it may be that no such hard and fast laws have ever been enacted, that every train of events is motivated by the caprices of Fortune, and that mankind must consequently be regarded as the slave of accident. Though I can venture no opinion on the subject, I do heartily wish that Juppiter would not disclose his purpose with warning signs; if doom must come, let it come suddenly, and let us never lose hope!

On this occasion, the certainty of the approaching catastrophe which Heaven had decided to visit on the City put an end to all judicial business: the Consuls forbore to wear their official purple and dismissed their attendant lictors. As for the people, they were too downcast even to vent their grief in tears. A numbed silence prevailed, as in a house where a beloved son has just breathed his last, and the mother still presses her lips to the cold features of his stiffening corpse. She has not laid it out, nor shut the staring eyes, far less dishevelled her own hair and ordered the servant girls to beat their breasts and wail for the departed. Though anxiety has faded with the realization of death, she feels no grief as yet, but continues to bend over the bed in witless dismay at this calamity.

The matrons of Rome put on mourning dress and crowded into the temples. Some wept and bathed the images with their tears, some flung themselves on the marble floors, others distractedly pulled out their hair, scattering it on the sacred threshold, and shrieked at the Gods instead of praying to them. Nor did they all crowd into the temple of Capitoline Juppiter, but divided their forces, thus no altar throughout the whole City lacked women to cry shame on its presiding deity. One matron, who had scratched her cheeks until the blood streamed down, and pummelled her shoulders until they were black and blue, screamed: 'Come, you poor mothers, now is the time to beat your breasts and tear your hair! Why leave lamentation until the day of final disaster? While the conflict between these two rivals remains undecided nobody can prevent you from weeping; but once it is over, you will have to rejoice, whoever wins.' Their grief was catching and gathered intensity as it spread.

The men, too, marching out to war on one side or the other, complained to the cruel Gods with equal justice: 'Pity us! And do not think that we are asking for peace in a cowardly spirit. By all means inspire aliens and barbarians with hostility towards us. Let the entire world run to arms: let the Parthians from Susa and hordes of blond unconquered Swabians from the mouths of Rhine and Elbe come sweeping down on us. At the same time, if needs must, let the Dacians and Goths take us on the flanks! We will face them all fearlessly. Only preserve us from civil war, for if that is our lot, we should far prefer to have been among those whom Hannibal slaughtered at Cannae and the River Trebia.[1] O merciful ruler of the Universe – why not send Caesar against the Spaniards, and Pompey against the Parthian bowmen? Every Roman would gladly draw a sword in that kind of war. But if you have already decided to ruin our nation, then by all means shower flaming thunderbolts upon us. Destroy the rivals and their armies too, at a single blow, before they commit the crime of mutual murder. Why should a dispute over sovereignty be settled in so wicked a fashion? Even if neither achieves his ambition, civil war will surely have been too high a price to pay for the moral lesson thus conveyed?'

But this noble spirit of patriotism was soon to become outmoded.

A more personal sorrow distressed those parents who, having already known civil war, had hoped to spend their old age in peace. Recalling the fateful days of his youth one of them said: 'This is as bad as when Marius, fresh from his triumphs over the Germans and the Numidians,

1. 218 and 216 B.C.

was expelled from Rome and obliged to hide among the reeds of the Minturnaean marshes,[1] where his pursuers were temporarily baffled by the bog-holes and spongy soil. Later, as you know, the old man languished awhile in prison, with his limbs fettered. Yet destiny ruled that after doing this penance for having ruined Rome, he should once more enjoy prosperity, and be elected Consul. Here was a man from whom Death himself had often retreated; and when a Cimbrian soldier who hated Marius had the opportunity of taking his life, he nevertheless let the sword slip from his palsied hand. A great light illumined the darkness of the dungeon,[2] showing him certain waiting Furies, and a vision of the Marius who was yet to be. A fearful voice cried: "Do not strike off that head, Cimbrian! Marius is destined to ruin a great many more men before he dies himself; let him be! Ay, if you wish to be avenged on the old man who massacred your people, spare his life! Divine providence, guided by wrath rather than loving-kindness, has preserved this savage as the instrument for Rome's destruction."

'Marius presently crossed the sea to a hostile Africa, where he was hunted through the deserted villages of Jugurtha's former kingdom – it was here that he had formerly fought and triumphed – and at last went to ground in the ruins of Carthage. Carthage and he were now quits;[3] each drew consolation from the other's plight and offered no protests to Heaven.

'In Africa Marius nursed a truly African hatred. At the first sign that Fortune was again with him, he freed a large number of prisoners,[4] who at once forged their fetters into swords; and he reserved the honour of carrying his standards for hardened criminals, who had not abandoned their evil ways on joining him. What a terrible and disgraceful day when Marius seized Rome![5] How swiftly Death stalked

1. After his defeat by Sulla, 88 B.C.
2. He was confined in the house of one Fannia, supposedly his enemy, but really his friend. When a Cimbrian soldier came to kill him, Marius shouted: 'Fellow, do you dare lay hands on Caius Marius?' The soldier fled. Later, Marius escaped to Africa in a small boat.
3. Marius had triumphed over Numidia in 104 B.C., leading Jugurtha in chains.
4. After sailing to Etruria.
5. With Lucius Cornelius Cinna, the Consul who had been driven from Rome by Gnaeus Octavius.

these streets, cutting off the nobility and the commons alike, without quarter! Pools of blood stood in the temples, and everywhere the pavements grew red and slippery. Nor did the victors even spare the aged, but cut short their declining years at a stroke. They murdered children too! How could an infant deserve to be killed for any crime whatsoever? Yet the wretches considered it sufficient evidence of guilt that a child had a life to lose. Their violence was such that whoever paused to ask whether a man might be innocent would have been considered half-hearted in Marius's cause. Some victims died merely to make up a round number; and many a blood-stained murderer, ashamed to go about empty-handed, would dock the first stranger he met of his head. Marius had a thousand swords at his service; and the nobility's sole hope of safety lay in seeking him out and kissing that polluted hand. Several men did so, although to earn even a long span of life by such disgraceful conduct, much less a brief respite lasting only until Sulla's vengeful return, would have been unbecoming in a man of principle.

'Who can spare a tear to-day for the countless victims of that massacre? For Marcus Baebius,[1] disembowelled and mangled by the Marian faction; or for Marcus Antonius who had foretold these disasters in the Senate – an officer took up his severed head by its ragged white hair and placed it, face forward, on the table where Marius sat carousing; or for Publius Crassus and his son of the same name, when Fimbria cut them in pieces; or for the Tribunes whose heads were carried aloft on pikes? Or for Scaevola, the Chief Pontiff, whose throat the Goddess Vesta allowed to be slit in her own inviolable temple, and before her very altar where the perpetual fire continued to burn; what little blood the old man had in him did not suffice to quench the flames?

'Then came Marius's seventh Consulship and his death;[2] having experienced the extremes of both good and evil fortune, he had measured the full extent of human destiny. Yet peace did not immediately follow. Terrible slaughter took place at Sacriportus,[3] and again

1. Terence, the comic dramatist, purchased his own life by disclosing Baebius's whereabouts.

2. Eighteen days later, in 82 B.C., at the age of seventy-one.

3. Here Sulla, on his return from the East, where he had been fighting Mithridates, defeated the younger Marius with great slaughter.

outside the Collinian Gate[1] of Rome – during that anxious time when Pontius Telesinus, having made common cause with the Marians, threatened to level the City walls and transfer the centre of world empire to Samnium – which would have been an even greater injury than that inflicted by his ancestors on our nation at the Caudine Forks.[2]

'Sulla's vengeance added to the already excessive slaughter. What few noblemen remained to be killed, he killed and while using the knife to amputate gangrened limbs, as it were, infringed the ethics of surgery by letting his hand run away with him. Those whom he executed had, of course, been guilty of yielding to Marius; otherwise they would never have survived his massacre.

'The assassins had leave to take whatever vengeance they pleased on personal enemies – not necessarily personal enemies of Sulla's. No questions would be asked, since every kind of crime had been legalized by a comprehensive decree. Slaves might freely plunge their swords into a master's bowels; sons, bespattered by their father's blood, might quarrel for the privilege of beheading him; brother might murder brother for money. Flocks of fugitives now took refuge among the entombed dead, or in the dens of wild beasts. To cheat the blood-stained victor, some hanged themselves, some leaped from a height, crashing on the stony pavement; one man stacked up the oaken logs of his own pyre, set it a-fire, then stabbed himself and yielded his dying body to the flames.

'The heads of Marian leaders were stuck on pikes, paraded through the horror-stricken City, and finally heaped up in the Forum. Every known crime was perpetrated. Never were so many grisly relics seen, even in Thrace when King Diomedes the Bistonian nailed the heads of strangers to his stable doors; or in Africa when the giant Antaeus beheaded those whom he had overcome at wrestling; or at Pisa, where King Oenomaus adorned the palace with the skulls of his daughter's suitors and sent all Greece into mourning. Bereaved Roman parents, having identified their sons' heads, waited until they decayed and became unrecognizable; then stealthily removed them. I remember

1. Here Sulla overtook and defeated the Samnites and Lucanians who were marching to sack Rome; fifty thousand men fell in this battle.

2. 321 B.C. The Samnites trapped a whole Roman army and made it pass under the yoke.

well the trouble I had myself, going from one to another of the corpses left lying unburied after Sulla's so-called pacification, trying to find a severed neck that would fit the ghastly object I carried with me! It was the mouldering head of my murdered brother for whom Sulla had forbidden funeral rites, but which I would none the less place secretly on a pyre.

'And oh, that bloody human sacrifice offered to placate Catulus's ghost! An adopted member of the Marian family, one Gratidianus, was the victim; he suffered unspeakable tortures at the tomb, tortures such as would have disgusted Catulus himself. We saw his mutilated body, with a wound in every limb and gashes everywhere, though none mortal; what a refinement of cruelty, to deny death to the dying! His hands were twisted off at the wrists and flung on the ground; his tongue had been cut out but continued to quiver noiselessly where it lay; they trimmed him of his ears and the nostrils of his aquiline nose. Yet his eyes were not torn from their sockets until they had witnessed all these cruelties. We found it difficult to believe any Roman capable of so foul an atrocity,[1] or Gratidianus of taking so much punishment. His body was no less mangled than if it had been caught in the collapse of a large building; and as unrecognizable as the corpse of a man drowned far out at sea and washed ashore after many days. I thought this ineptly done: if the murderers wished to earn Sulla's thanks by convincing him of Gratidianus's death, they should clearly not have obliterated his features.

'At Praeneste,[2] famous for its Temple of Fortune, all citizens were put to the sword simultaneously; and in "The Sheepfolds", the voting pens on the Campus Martius, Sulla massacred the whole fighting population of Latium, the best stock in Italy. Though history records numerous occasions on which many men have lost their lives together, as the result of famines, or storms at sea, or sudden earthquakes that send cities crashing down, or plagues on earth, or infections of the atmosphere, or hard-fought battles, such a mass-execution has never been witnessed before or since. So thick was the crowd of prisoners, with fear of death written in every face, that Sulla's butchers scarcely

1. The notorious Catiline presided at this scene.
2. The younger Marius (who had cut the Chief Pontiff's throat as described above) held Praeneste against Sulla until forced to capitulate; whereupon he committed suicide.

found room to swing their swords. Even when a prisoner had been killed, he often swayed and tottered on his legs without room enough to fall; and at times the dead took a hand in the massacre by tumbling on those still alive and smothering them. Sulla, watching from his high seat, betrayed not the least emotion; he thought it nothing to have passed sentence of death on so many thousands of poor fellows.

'The corpses were thrown into the Tiber, striking the water at first, but then their own mounting pile. Presently boats in passage down-stream ran against the obstacle and could go no farther, though the river below this point continued to flow on towards Ostia. The pent-up bloody waters rose higher and higher yet until they escaped from the river-bed, flooding the plain, so that some corpses drifted to land again; at last, however, the red flow broke the barrier and struggled through, to stain the blue expanse of Tuscan sea.

'Was it for deeds like these that Sulla was saluted as "Saviour of the People", winning the title of "Felicitous" and the right to erect his own tomb in the very middle of the Campus Martius? And must we now relive equally lamentable scenes, such days of blood as any civil war inevitably brings in its train? This time, I am afraid, even worse horrors will accrue, to the greater damage of humankind. Marius and his fellow-exiles aimed merely at the recapture of Rome; Sulla, merely at the extinction of his hated political opponents. But Caesar and Pompey, both of whom have enjoyed supreme power, are each relying on Fortune for an altogether different end to the struggle. If either were content to be a Sulla, this civil war would never have begun!'

The old man continued his lamentations, with bitter memories of the past, and anxious fears for the future.

Marcus Junius Brutus alone remained unaffected by the popular emotion: no terror of the approaching storm tempted him to join the crowds of mourners. But at dead of night, while the City slept and the seven stars of the Wain were tilted askew in the sky, he went to knock at the modest door of his kinsman Marcus Porcius Cato, and found him awake, brooding over the political situation and its possible outcome — though, indeed, anxious only for the fate of mankind, not for his own safety.

'Cato,' said Brutus, 'though Virtue has long been exiled from every land, she still finds a secure lodging in your heart, from which no trick of Fortune will evict her; which is why I have come to be guided and fortified by you. Others may side with Pompey or with Caesar; for my part, I acknowledge no leader but Cato. Confess: are you treading resolutely in the path of peace, while all the rest of us hesitate and doubt? Or have you decided to absolve these arch-criminals and their mad partisans of guilt, by assisting in the slaughter yourself? Everyone else seems to be justifying his participation on personal grounds: either he fears that if the peace is kept he will be punished for some domestic crime, or else he hopes to win wealth and settle his debts by the sword while the world topples in ruin. Nobody is fighting with warlike passion, but the prospect of making one's fortune is a seductive one. If you have chosen war for its own sake, you must be alone in doing so; yet, in that case, why did you trouble for so many years to remain unsullied by the corruptions of this age? The fee for your persistent practice of virtue will be that, whereas others go to war because they are already criminals, you will not be a criminal until you do go. May the Gods preserve you from taking active part in this fatal conflict! For your javelin will never fly in any blind volley; but lest such virtue should be wasted, you will be singled out as a focal point in battle. Every Roman, who has been mortally wounded by another's sword, will stagger towards you, hoping to receive his death-stroke from your hand and thereby make you no less guilty than himself.

'A life of peace, tranquillity and solitude becomes you best; as the untroubled constellations move persistently onward in their courses. The lower air is set afire by thunderbolts, and the flatter regions of earth are harassed by hurricanes and quick stabs of lightning; only Olympus rears his head above the clouds. Heaven has decreed, indeed, that while all lower things are plagued by discord, the loftiest alone shall enjoy peace.[1]

'How gratified Caesar will be to hear that so great a Roman as yourself has declared for war! He will hardly trouble to regret your having preferred his rival's camp, but will argue: "If Cato approves of civil war, he approves of me; because I started it." Moreover, he has taken it as a personal challenge that a majority of the Senate, led by the Consuls and other ministers of state, have consented to serve under a

1. The notion that the gods inhabited the summit of Olympus was due to its frequent appearance, from far out at sea, as if floating on a thick and continuous bank of clouds.

general who holds no office at all. If Cato also agrees to obey Pompey, Caesar will be the only free man left anywhere.

'However, should you decide, simply, to take arms in defence of our constitutional liberties, I am at your side. Though no enemy to-day of either Caesar or Pompey, I shall wait until the fighting is done and then declare against whichever emerges victorious.'

Cato replied oracularly from the depths of his heart. 'I agree, Brutus: nothing can be more evil than civil war; yet the virtuous man will obey his destiny without fear. If I, too, must incur the common guilt, let the Gods themselves be responsible for having fastened it on me. Who could witness the collapse of Heaven's starry arch and sit unperturbed, with folded hands, while the earth shudders beneath the shock of a universal catastrophe? And what if the kings of strange nations overseas should catch the madness raging among our Roman armies? Must I be the only man who refuses to fight? The Gods forbid that I could ever be indifferent to the fall of Rome, an event shocking enough to move the hearts even of Scythians and Goths! When death robs a father of his sons, he is compelled by grief to head the long procession of mourners; and he does not shrink from the smoky torch, but boldly thrusts it into the heap of kindling which sets the tall pyre ablaze. Likewise, no man will ever prevent me from embracing for the last time the cold corpse of Rome, whose other name was Freedom, and following it to the graveside. What must be, must be! Let Rome make full atonement to her ruthless Gods, and grudge no life where war requires.

'Ah, if only the supernal and infernal powers would jointly sentence me to be a national sin-offering! Decius[1] sacrificed his life for the army, rushing into the thickest of the fray until overborne by weight of numbers. How I wish that I might die in the same manner, but pierced through and through by the javelins of both armies; that Caesar's barbarous allies from Rheims[2] might make me their target; that I

1. Publius Decius Mus learned in a vision that, as commander of the Roman army against the Latins he had been devoted to the gods of the dead, and so had the enemy commander. He therefore put on sacrificial dress and allowed himself to be killed. His example was imitated by his son of the same name in the Battle of Sentinum, when the Gauls were defeated.

2. I read *Rhemi*, 'Rhemians', for *Rheni*, 'Rhinelanders'. The Rhemians were Caesar's most loyal allies in Gaul; and Lucan mentions them as skilled javelin-fighters in Book I (line 424). Cato would not have expected Caesar to bring German barbarians with him.

might intercept each and every blow struck in this war. Thus my blood would redeem all the nations in our empire of the guilt incurred by this civil war; and if they are willing to accept a tyrannous monarchy, why need they die? Let them strike at none but myself, one who fights vainly in defence of the just laws which they despise; so be it only that my sacrificial blood may redeem all Italians. Once I am gone, the intruding tyrant will find it no longer necessary to make war.

'And why may I not declare for Pompey, if the Senate and people of Rome elect him their leader, even though I knew well that he too hopes, with Fortune's help, to make himself master of the whole world? What prevents me from following Pompey to victory, and denying him the illusion that he has gained the day for himself alone?'

This speech of Cato's roused the hot-blooded younger man to a passionate and unbecoming eagerness for civil war.

Dawn had meanwhile broken, and a knock sounded at the door: the noble Marcia burst in, with grief-stricken face, having just returned from the funeral of Quintus Hortensius. Cato had taken her as his wife while she was yet a virgin; but after reaping the rewards of marriage by the birth of three children, Marcia was sent away, pregnant of a fourth, to fill an empty cradle in the house of Cato's friend Hortensius, and thus unite the two families. However, Cato was the better man, and when she had placed Hortensius's ashes in a funerary urn, she hurried back to him, pulling out handfuls of her disordered hair as she went and repeatedly beating her breasts. She was still dusty from the pyre, and tears coursed freely down her cheeks, yet she knew that her one hope of finding favour in his eyes lay in thus presenting herself.

'Cato,' she cried, 'while I had strength to undergo confinement after confinement, I did as you ordered. I even served as wife to another husband and prosecuted my task of childbearing. But now that I am no longer capable of continuing so, I return my worn-out body to you and will not consent to have it disposed of elsewhere. Let us be re-united – grant me at least the courtesy title of wife, so that I may be described on my tomb as "Cato's Marcia". Do not allow posterity to speculate whether I ran away from you, or whether you repudiated me, or whether you merely ceded me to a childless friend. I do not expect to profit by your good fortune; for these are unhappy days. On the contrary, I am here to share your troubles and anxieties. Let me take the field with you. Why should I be left to enjoy a sheltered life any more than Pompey's wife Cornelia?'

Marcia's words pleased Cato, and though this was no time for marrying, because Fate summoned him to war, yet the thought of a simple wedding devoid of all idle display attracted him; the Gods[1] alone would be invoked to witness the ceremony. There would be neither wreaths nor garlands hanging from the lintels, nor white fillets twined about the door posts, nor torches of hawthorn, nor a high couch, spread with a golden counterpane, into which the bride climbs by ivory steps – after she has entered the house, wearing a turreted crown and taking care not to touch the threshold as she crosses it. Indeed, Marcia remained downcast and even forbore to change her widow's weeds. She put on no saffron veil of the sort intended to screen a bride's modest blushes, no clinging bridal gown, no jewelled girdle, no beautiful necklace, no wisp of scarf tied across the bare shoulders. Solemnly she embraced her husband, very much as she would have embraced a son, and when she bent over him, her woollen mourning-robe covered and concealed his senatorial purple. No guests were present to taunt this gloomy bridegroom with the usual ceremonial ribaldries; he summoned no kinsmen nor members of his immediate family to act as witnesses. The hands of the bridal pair were joined in silence, and they felt it sufficient to be married under Brutus's auspices. Cato did not even shave, and his stern features remained utterly devoid of joy; ever since the outbreak of war he had left his grey hair and beard untrimmed. He alone, who felt neither love nor hatred towards either faction, had troubled to go into mourning for mankind; and now even abstained from sexual relations with his remarried wife. What a heart of oak – imagine a man resisting the legitimate joys of wedlock! But Cato's austere and inflexible character had led him to observe moderation in all things, adhere doggedly to principle, follow the dictates of Nature, devote his life to Rome, and believe that he had been born to serve humanity rather than his own selfish predilections. He thought it banquet enough if he could satisfy the pangs of hunger; and a princely life if he had a roof to shelter him from hard weather; and luxury if he could wear the rough woollen gown which is our Roman peace-time dress. In his view the sole purpose of love was the procreation of children. He regarded Rome as a daughter or a bride;

1. Juppiter, Venus, Suada, and Diana.

was a stickler for justice, and meticulous in all his dealings; always kept the interests of the community in mind; and throughout his life performed no single act that could be ascribed to self-indulgence.

Pompey, meanwhile, had marched hurriedly off and occupied Capua in Campania – a city said to have been founded by Capys the Trojan. This he made his general headquarters and principal base for a defensive campaign against Caesar's forces, intending to deny him passage through the wooded Appennines, the highest mountains of Italy. These stretch between the Adriatic and the Tyrrhenian seas, commanding the beaches of Pisa on the latter and the port of Ancona on the former, and are the source and watershed of many great rivers. Eastward run the swift Metaro, the Crustumium, the Savio which joins the La Foglia, the La Nevola, the Ofanto, and the Po which drains a great area of Northern Italy – as mighty a river as any that waters the surface of the globe, capable of sweeping away entire forests. Legend has it that this was the first river ever to be lined with poplars, and that when Phaëthon borrowed his father Apollo's sun-chariot and drove it below its appointed course – thus setting the air on fire, sucking streams dry and scorching the earth – the Po alone resisted this ordeal. It is as big a river as the Nile, though the Nile floods a wide extent of the flat soil in Lower Egypt; and as big as the Danube, except that the Danube in its progress through the world acquires tributaries, which might have fallen as rivers into any sea, had some other exit offered, so that on debouching into the Black Sea it no longer remains itself. On the other side of the Appennines flow the Tiber; the Roya in its deep bed; the rapid Volturno; the Sarno with its mephitic mists; the Garigliano which runs from Vestine territory past the shady grove of the Latin nymph Marica; the Silaro skirting the rugged region of Salerno; finally the Magra which is too shallow for shipping and discharges its waters into the Ligurian Sea near Luna.

The range extends even farther to the north, rising to a great height from which the fields of Gaul and the foothills of the Alps can clearly be seen. To the south they provide grain for the Umbrians, Marsians, and Samnites. Every Italian native race has, indeed, sheltered among the pine-clad rocks of this range, which continues down the entire length of Italy as far as Scylla on the Straits of Messina, and the promontory of Lacinia crowned with its temple of Juno. Yet the Appennines once extended beyond what is now Italy; I am speaking of the days before pressure of water broke the isthmus which linked the Italian peninsula with Sicily and converted the butt end of the range into Mount Pelorus.

Caesar, in his martial ardour, rejoiced to discover that he could not advance across the fields of Italy without bloodshed, and that his progress was being rewarded by a sequence of battles. He would far rather have broken down a city gate than find it tamely opened to admit his forces; or laid the cornland waste with fire and sword, than meet no farmers who dared defy him; he scorned to march along an undefended road like any peaceful citizen. The townsfolk of Italy, though wavering in their allegiance to this side or that, and prepared to surrender at the first hint of action, nevertheless strengthened their walls with earthworks and deep fosses; also collecting round stones and other missiles to discharge from the towers. For the most part, they favoured Pompey, but their loyalty would not stand the test of danger.

It was as when the roaring Sirocco takes possession of the sea and drives the waves before it; even if Aeolus, Guardian of the winds, thrusts his trident into the Lipara hillside and lets out an easterly gale, the sea continues for awhile unmoved by this change of weather. The sky may be darkened by rain-clouds, but the waves remain true to the Sirocco. However, the threat offered by Caesar's advance could not long be disregarded, and his successes soon affected the defenders' dubious attachment to Pompey.

Scribonius Libo, the Pompeian general who commanded in Tuscany, fled panic-stricken, leaving the district undefended; and the Praetor Thermus similarly withdrew from Umbria. Nor did young Faustus Cornelius Sulla distinguish himself in this civil war so brilliantly as his father had done in the former, but turned tail. And when Caesar's cavalry patrols swooped on Osimo, Publius Attius Varus escaped from the still uninvested southern gate and took refuge among the rocks and woods that lay beyond. Moreover, Publius Lentulus, the Consul, was driven from the strongly fortified town of Asculum; and Caesar, pressing hard on the rout, headed him off. Lentulus got clear away with his eagles, but lost his army. Lucius Scipio, likewise, abandoned the fortress of Nuceria without attempting to defend it, though he commanded a fine body of troops; namely the two legions which had been withdrawn from Gaul as a strategic reserve to meet the Parthian menace. One of these was the legion which Pompey himself lent Caesar, to make good his battle casualties; the condition being that they should be returned as soon as they were needed for service against the Parthians.

Lucius Domitius Ahenobarbus, however, showed fight. He held the strong walls of Corfinium and commanded the troops who, as recruits, had been posted around the Law Courts to prevent the criminal Milo from evading his just sentence. When Domitius saw a great cloud of dust moving towards him across the plain, and weapons glittering in the sun, he shouted: 'Forward, men, to the river bank! We must destroy that bridge; the river can be trusted to exert its strength against the alder timbers and carry them downstream. This is where Caesar's rapid advance must be checked. If we can hold him here and keep him cooling his heels on the farther bank, victory will be ours.'

However, Domitius's prompt and active leadership failed to achieve results. Caesar realized that the river would be used to deny him a passage, and cried angrily: 'Not content with skulking behind those walls, they want to bar my advance over the plain by harnessing that river to serve their cowardly ends. But having once put the Rubicon behind me, I am destined never again to be baulked by any stream, even though it were the Ganges in flood. Forward the cavalry, with the infantry in close support! Seize the bridge before it collapses.' At once the light horse charged ahead at full gallop, and javelins hurtled in showers at Domitius's men, who retreated to the safety of the town walls. Caesar then had no difficulty in occupying the farther bank; he gave orders for the erection of towers to mount siege-catapults, and soon his men were creeping close to the walls under the protection of mantlets. Suddenly a shameful sight greeted him: the town gates opened and out came a body of soldiers dragging along Domitius, with his arms pinioned. In the presence of his proud antagonist, Domitius stood scowling defiance; holding his head erect and loftily demanding to die there and then by the sword. Nevertheless Caesar, convinced that Domitius would prefer death to pardon, told him: 'You must live on, and bask in the sun of my mercy, however distasteful you may find it. I want your friends to realize that, when I have defeated them, all will not yet be lost. This act of clemency is unconditional: you may take up arms again if you please, and I do not even stipulate that, should I be defeated, you must repay me for having spared your life.'

Domitius was released. Yet how much kinder a fate, had he been

killed on the spot and spared the shame of being cruelly pardoned for
his crime – of patriotically serving in an army which the Senate had
unanimously placed under Pompey's command! Choking back his
indignation, but still undaunted, Domitius asked himself: 'After this
disgrace, can I return to a quiet life at Rome? Never! To show my
scorn of Caesar's generosity I will seek the forefront of the battle, and
die as quickly as possible.'

Meanwhile Pompey, unaware that Domitius had been captured,
encouraged his men by busy military preparations and, on the day
before he should have taken the field, tested their courage by addressing
them in a voice that compelled their respectful silence.

'Romans! The Senate has chosen you to defend your country. You
are marshalled behind the national standards, with orders to take
vengeance on the criminals who have raised this rebellion. Caesar is
wantonly ravaging and burning the fields of Italy: furious hordes from
Gaul are pouring after him over the wintry Alps, his swords have
already been defiled with Roman blood. Thanks be to Heaven, we are
the victims, not the aggressors; and now the Roman armies under my
leadership must call the rebels to account and punish them as they
deserve. The battles which face us will not be battles in the ordinary
sense, but a patriotic and angry chastisement of violence. Do not speak
of war: this is no more war than was Catiline's conspiracy, when he
and his wicked partners Lentulus Sura and that frantic fellow Caius
Cornelius Cethegus (who, like the rest of his family, wore no tunic
beneath his gown) decided to burn down Rome. Does this madness of
Caesar not deserve our pity? Though Fortune was prepared to enrol
his name beside those of the great Camillus who freed Rome from
subjection to the Gauls, or of Metellus who defended her against the
Carthaginians, he prefers to be remembered as another Marius or
Cinna! Now he cannot escape defeat, any more than did the Marian
leaders – the rebel Lepidus who marched on Rome from Tuscany but
met his match in Catulus; or Carbo who was captured on the island of
Gozo and brought to me at Lilybaeum in Sicily, where I beheaded and
cremated him; or Sertorius who fled to Spain and there led a native
revolt.

'Yet, upon my word, I am sorry to mention Caesar in the same
breath as these wretches, and deeply regret that Rome has entrusted
me with the task of bringing him to reason. If only Crassus had come

safe home from the campaigns in Parthia and Scythia, and were at hand to dispose of Caesar as faithfully as his ancestor Marcus Licinius Crassus disposed of the rebel Spartacus ... But, please Heaven, I shall increase my fame by conquering Caesar too. My heart glows fiercely with the hope of teaching him that men who can settle down to private life will not necessarily prove cowards when war breaks out again. So I am feeble and exhausted, am I? Nonsense! Look at this arm of mine, still strong enough to hurl a javelin; and that I am older than Caesar makes no odds when my soldiers are younger than his.

'Romans, you have raised me to as high a position as a free people can raise any fellow-citizen – only a little higher, and I should be a tyrant; so that whoever plans to rise above me must needs wish to become exactly that. Both Consuls are supporting me; and I have an army composed of magnificent fighting men, any one of whom would be fit to serve as a general if called upon. Can Caesar defeat the Senate? Certainly not! Is the Goddess Fortune so utterly blind and shameless as to allow that to happen? Then what gives him such confidence? Is it his successes in Gaul, though he has campaigned there for ten years and failed to subdue the inhabitants – which would be the undertaking of a lifetime? Is it because, fearing to cross the chilly waters of the Rhine and try conclusions with the Germans, he marched north to what he calls the Ocean – tidal mudflats is a better name for it – made a futile raid on the Britons, and retreated in disorder? Or is he boasting and threatening because reports of his lunacy have forced us to take arms and march out of our native city, which happens also to be his? The poor madman! He thinks that everyone is fleeing from him, rather than flocking to join me.

'When I commanded the fleet against the Cilician pirates, two months had not passed before they were driven from every sea and forced to plead for some narrow plot of land where they might settle down as farmers. Again, when the indomitable Mithridates blocked the march of our Empire, I pursued him into the isthmus which separates the Black Sea from the Caspian and there brought about his death; a feat which even Sulla the Felicitous had failed to perform. Have I not fought and raised trophies of victory all over the world? I campaigned beside the icy Rion which rises in the Caucasus; and at Syene, a frontier town of Upper Egypt where the midsummer sun casts no shadow at noon; and my name is feared throughout Spain where the most westerly river in existence, the Guadalquivir, struggles against the Atlantic tides. I have subdued the Arabians, and the fierce Heniochians of Colchis, whence Jason stole the famous Golden Fleece. The Cappodocians have learned to fear my name; and so have the Jews, who worship a mysterious god; and the effeminate men of Sophene. I have conquered the Armenians, the savage Cilicians, and the mountaineers of the Taurus range. What war have I left for my father-in-law to fight, except a civil war?'

The army listened respectfully; but when Pompey's address was over and he awaited a shrill demand to be led against the enemy, none came. His men were afraid. Realizing that their spirit had been broken by the news of Caesar's advance, he decided to abandon his campaign rather than risk a decisive battle. Pompey resembled a bull, worsted in a fight for the leadership of his herd, who retires alone to the woods and waste lands. There he keeps himself in fighting trim by butting the trees, and remains exiled until his neck-muscles have strengthened again. Then he seeks out his rival, defeats him and, with the young bulls at his back, leads the recovered herd to whatever pasture he pleases – whether the cattlemen may like it or not. Thus Pompey surrendered western Italy to his more powerful colleague, and retreated through the fields of Apulia, until he reached safety in the fortress of Brindisi.

Brindisi was originally colonized by certain Cretan exiles who came in the Athenian ships that had taken Theseus to Cnossos for his fight with the Minotaur – but the black sails of which he forgot to change on his triumphant return to Athens, so that he was supposed to have been defeated. The town stands on the Adriatic coast, at the narrowest part of the Italian peninsula; where a harbour is formed by a curving promontory and an island that acts as breakwater to the heavy seas driving down from the north-west. Brindisi is further sheltered from sea and weather by tall cliffs on either side of the harbour, which allow vessels to ride securely at anchor. A wide look-out can be kept from here: ships may even be seen coasting along the opposite shore between Corfu and Dyrrhachium. Moreover, this is a general port of refuge when the Adriatic is at its stormiest: when the Acroceraunian mountains of Epirus are shrouded in mist, and white seas beat on the Illyrian[1] island of Sasseno.

1. Lucan calls it 'Calabrian': perhaps meaning that Calabrian pirates used it as a base.

Pompey knew that by abandoning Rome he had forfeited her allegiance; and he could no longer make Spain his battle-ground, because the Alps intervened. He therefore summoned Gnaeus Pompey, the elder of his two fine sons, and gave him the following instructions: 'You are to visit every oriental city from the Nile to the Euphrates and beyond – wherever my victories have made the Roman army famous. Persuade the Cilicians to leave their farms and return to the sea. Rouse King Ptolemy and Queen Cleopatra of Egypt, and my ally Tigranes the Parthian; win over Mithridates's son, Pharnaus King of the Bosphorus; also the inhabitants of the two Armenias, and the fierce fighters of Pontus, and the Scythians of the western Urals, and those who drive their wagons across the frozen sea of Azov. In short: you are to raise my standard everywhere throughout the East, especially in countries which I have conquered, and rally all their armies to it.'

Then he turned to Lentulus and Marcellus, and said: 'You two should be well enough known, if only because every calendar year is distinguished from its predecessors by the names of its two Consuls. Your orders are to sail across to Epirus as soon as the wind blows from the north; then to raise levies for my army in Greece and Macedonia. Since campaigning is impossible until the Spring, you are not pressed for time in the execution of this task.'

Young Pompey and the two Consuls did as they were told, sailing away at the first opportunity.

Meanwhile Caesar, who always grew impatient when he had no war on hand, feared that the situation might worsen if he remained inactive, and trod hard on his enemy's heels. Any other general would have paused to consolidate his position after capturing so many garrison cities at the first rush and seeing Rome itself, the capital of the world and the greatest prize that any army could hope to win, fall into his lap like a ripe fruit. But Caesar was so energetic that he thought nothing done while anything still remained to be done. Though all Italy was now his, except for a strip of Eastern coast, he grudged Pompey even that small share of the country, and decided to deny him the command of the Adriatic by occupying the narrow mouth of the port and blocking it with a mole. However, this attempt failed. The sea swallowed up the countless rocks he threw into it and merely rolled them along its sandy bottom. He might just as well have tried to plant Mount Eryx in mid-Aegean, or Mount Gaurus in the unfathomable

lake of Avernus which lies at its foot; no more of either would have
shown above the surface of the water. But, though failing to build a
stable foundation for his mole, he had a great number of trees felled
and chained securely together to block the harbour's mouth. It will be
remembered that proud Xerxes, King of Persia, once flung a pontoon-
bridge across the rapid Hellespont from Sestos to Abydos, and passed
dry-shod from Asia to Europe; careless whether the wind blew from
the east or west, because he had also sent his engineers ahead to dig a
canal through the Athos peninsula. Caesar cut Pompey off from the sea
with a similar bridge, on which he heaped a mound of earth and
planted high wooden turrets, swaying to the swell.

Pompey grew anxious at the sight of what looked like a new spit of
land blocking the harbour mouth, and was puzzled how to recover
access to the open sea. Again and again he sent merchant ships – the
south wind swelling their sails and straining their cordage – to break
the boom at either flank and so afford him egress; siege engines were
mounted on their decks, which flung volleys of fire-brands, with split
ends, into the wooden turrets.

The captains finally succeeded in their task, and having chosen a day
for the secret evacuation of the port, Pompey forbade his crews to
raise any alarm ashore by shouting, piping the watches, or calling the
sailors or soldiers aboard by conch signal – because all had already been
warned for duty. The operation began just after midnight when the
last stars of the Virgin had appeared, soon to be followed by the Scales
– the House in which the Sun rose at that time of year. Anchors were
weighed in perfect silence, and the skippers watched anxiously while
the yards were being bent and the tall masts stepped. Sailors swarmed
up and unfurled the sails without so much as letting the wind whistle
through the thick shrouds. Pompey offered a prayer to the Goddess
Fortune, begging her at least to grant him a safe escape from Italy,
since she would not permit him to stay there. Reluctantly the Goddess
granted his plea; but the sea was rough, the ships were crowded close
together, and huge waves churned up by their hulls struck the shore
with a sullen roar.

The people of Brindisi forgot their loyalty to Pompey as soon as they
saw his back, and opened the city gates to admit the Caesareans. In
they poured, but only to set off at top speed along the quays on either
side of the harbour, cursing when they found the fleet gone; though

they should not have grudged Pompey this small success. The Pompeian fleet had little sea-room, less even than the Euboean Straits would have afforded at their narrowest. Two ships fouled the mole, and the Caesareans secured them with grappling-irons kept ready for that purpose. The crews struggled ashore and there continued the fight; this was the first blood shed in a naval engagement since the Civil War had begun.

The remainder of the fleet got clear away. It was as when the *Argo* on her voyage from Thessaly to the Rion had to pass between the famous Blue Rocks, which floated upon the water and had a habit of clashing together; just as the *Argo* escaped with the loss of her stern ornament – and by a decree of Fate the rocks thereafter remained fixed, one on each side of the straits – so Pompey's fleet escaped with the loss of only its two rear ships.

Now the eastern sky grew rosy with dawn, and the nearest stars turned pale; the Pleiads too, and Boötes, and his Wain, successively faded from the serene morning sky; last of all, the Morning Star itself fled from the warmth of the sun. By then Pompey was well clear of the land, but less of a favourite with Fortune than in the old days when he had scoured the sea for pirates. She had grown weary of his triumphs and in the end forsaken him; exiling him with his wife and children and household-gods. However, he was still a formidable figure, and great nations were ready to follow him into battle. His passing would, certainly, be inglorious; but if the Gods chose to deny him a tomb at home, and let him die on the faraway Egyptian sands, this was mercifully intended: they were hiding the horrid deed in a distant land and keeping the soil of Italy unstained by the blood of her favourite son, Pompey the Great.

BOOK THREE

THE wind blew briskly from the south and carried the fleet far out across the Ionic Gulf. Every eye looked straight forward, except Pompey's. He stood gazing aft at the retreating coast of Italy until the harbours could no longer be distinguished, and presently even the cloud-capped hills and mountains faded. He then went below and slept the sleep of exhaustion, but was troubled by a dreadful dream: the vengeful ghost of his wife Julia floated up from a chasm in the earth to the crest of her own funeral pyre, and there menaced him.

'Pompey,' she cried, 'this civil war has driven me from the Elysian Fields: I am now banished to the Stygian shadows where ghosts of the guilty are confined. There stand the avenging Furies; I have myself seen them threatening you with torches. What is more, Charon the ferryman has built a new fleet of boats to convey your armies across fiery Acheron; and the punishment-ground of Tartarus is being enlarged to accommodate them. Also, each of the Three Fates is now busily snapping the threads of life;[1] and they find the work almost too much for them. While I was your wife you were constantly heading triumphal processions, but what a difference your second marriage has made! Before the ashes of this pyre had time to cool you let Cornelia supplant me in your bed. Believe me, that woman not only hounded young Crassus to his death at Carrhae: she is fated to ruin her second husband too. By all means let her follow your standard over land and sea; so long as you do not expect much leisure for love. My father will plague your days, and I will do the same for your nights. Even after drinking the waters of Lethe I cannot forget how evilly you have treated me and am now authorized by the Rulers of the Dead to haunt you. My spectre will stalk in the thick of your battles to remind you whose daughter was once your wife. Why trouble to take a sword and

1. Normally only the third Fate, Atropos, did so; her sisters Clotho and Lachesis merely spun and measured the threads.

cut your family ties with Caesar? Civil war cannot but serve to make you everlastingly mine again.'

He clutched at her in terror, but she slipped from his arms and was gone.

Though he expected nothing less than disaster as a result of these menacing messages from the tomb, Pompey faced the war more resolutely than ever. He argued with himself: 'Why be alarmed? Either the dead forfeit the use of their senses, in which case the dream was absurd; or else they keep them, in which case death need have no terror for me.'

It was now late afternoon and the Sun had begun to plunge into the waves; when about as much of him remained as may be seen of the Moon's orb, just before or just after her middle phase, the fleet came within hailing distance of the friendly Greek mainland. The sailors at once unreeved the stays, unstepped the masts, and rowed ashore.

Pompey's abandonment of Italy gave Caesar little satisfaction; merely complaining that his enemy had fled overseas like a coward, he was so eager to finish the war that he took no pleasure in the enormous success he had already won. Yet for the moment he deliberately shelved all military problems, and set himself the peacetime task of conciliating the common people: he knew that whether he was loved or hated would depend wholly on the national food supplies. Revolutions are caused only by hunger, and a government prepared to feed the easy-going masses can count on their loyalty; starve the mob, and it grows reckless.

He sent Curio across the Straits of Messina to secure the Sicilian harvest. As I observe above, these straits were once dry land, but either a sudden subsidence took place or else the sea gradually washed the isthmus away; and it is unlikely that Sicily and Italy will ever reunite, because the seas which divide them are always hard at work to prevent this occurrence.

Another military mission was sent to Sardinia which, like Sicily, is famous for its cornfields. From here the Roman granaries draw their earliest and most abundant supplies; Africa itself can scarcely compete with Sardinia and Sicily, even in years when the Sirocco holds off and northerly winds carry rain storms to that thirsty soil, thus assuring a bumper harvest. These precautions taken, Caesar celebrated his victory by a march on Rome. His men were unarmed and far from aggressive, but it was sad to think how it might have been: if only he had been content to conquer Gaul and other northern countries, what a wonderful triumphal procession that would have made! Imagine the military scenes displayed on the decorated wagons: they would have shown the bridging of the Rhine, and the crossing of the Ocean between Gaul and Britain. Behind his tall chariot would have walked Gallic chieftains and fair-haired British captives. Yet by adding Rome to his conquests he forfeited this glory. [1]

The inhabitants of the Italian cities through which he now passed did not flock out to greet him; but every man stood and gazed timorously at the march past. This pleased Caesar, who would hardly have liked them to make much of him.

He came to Terracina perched on its steep hill, crossed the Pomptine marshes and, skirting the sacred grove of Aricia (where Orestes and Iphigeneia introduced the worship of Taurian Artemis), reached the road which the Consuls take when they ascend the Alban Hill during the Latin Holidays. At last he gained a rocky height and saw Rome, his native city, shining afar: a sight denied him ever since he had gone campaigning in Gaul.

He gazed wonderingly, and said: 'Rome, seat of the immortal Gods, can it be true that you were deserted by your entire population when not a single enemy soldier was about? If so, how can any other city in all the world hope to find men to defend it? What a mercy that the fierce Sarmatians, Pannonians, Goths, and Dacians did not then choose to form an Eastern alliance and invade Italy; and that your cowardly commander-in-chief had only Romans against him!'

When he entered Rome, it was paralysed with fear. The people expected him to behave as though he had conquered a foreign city: levelling the walls, firing the houses, and scattering the images of the Gods. Believing that he must be as evil-hearted as he was powerful, they made no attempt to greet him with welcoming shouts, and hardly even felt like cursing him. No constitutional means of summoning the Senate offered, and though a mob of Senators were induced to leave their hiding places and called to a session in the Temple of Palatine Apollo, neither Consuls nor Praetors – the next highest in rank – were available to preside at the meeting; and no other magistrates could be

1. Postponed, not forfeited. He celebrated his Gallic triumph when the Civil War ended.

discovered. Caesar alone represented government, and the Senate had been reduced to a body of private citizens invited to witness his enactments. They were ready to approve anything, even if he chose to claim such titles as King and God, or sentenced their absent fellows to death or exile.

Caesar, fortunately, was more hesitant to give illegal orders than they were to obey; and the spirit of freedom flared up suddenly in one pugnacious Roman named Lucius Caecilius Metellus, who decided to see whether right could resist might. He was a Tribune of the People, and when he saw Caesar's men trying to force the lock of the Temple of Saturn, which housed the Public Treasury, he elbowed his way through the crowd of soldiers and stood with his back to the door.

It was an ironical situation. Nobody seemed to care what happened to the Roman Constitution or dared utter a word of complaint when Caesar defied it, but at this threat to the nation's gold – though gold is mere dross – Metellus dared risk his life in its defence. He shouted at Caesar: 'My lord, call your men off! You shall plunder this Temple only over my dead body, and remember, we Tribunes are sacrosanct. If you shed my blood, the Gods will avenge me. When Crassus marched against the Parthians, a Tribune's[1] curse lay heavily upon him. Come, my lord, out with your sword! You need not fear this unarmed crowd; the civil authorities have abandoned the City. But while I am yet alive, none of your accursed troops is going to rifle this Treasury. Why do you come here and break the peace by robbing Rome? Go back to your own wars in Gaul and Britain. If you are in want of money, plenty of cities remain there to be sacked.'

Caesar's anger boiled up. 'If you expect a martyr's death, Metellus,' he said, 'you are much mistaken. I do not propose to lose my temper and stain my hand with your blood just because you boast about your Tribuneship. Do you consider yourself the sole remaining champion of Roman liberty? Very well, in spite of this political breakdown, the people have not yet sunk so low that they would prefer your support of the Constitution to my suspension of it.' When Metellus still refused to move, Caesar grew even more vexed and looked around for someone with a sword, forgetting his rôle as peaceful citizen. However,

1. Pronounced in November, 55 B.C., by Gaius Ateius Capito, who had done his best to prevent Crassus from levying troops for this campaign.

Lucius Aurelius Cotta saved the situation by making Metellus listen to reason. 'Come,' he said, 'under every autocratic government a nation's liberties are destroyed by the assertion of liberty. They can be preserved, though in name alone, if everyone does exactly what he is told to do. Now that we are conquered we must needs submit to prolonged suppression; and our shameful and un-Roman terror can be excused only on the plea that further resistance was impossible. So let Caesar carry off the wretched sinews of war, as soon as he pleases. A city that continues to enjoy the protection of her own laws certainly feels the pinch once the Treasury runs empty; but reduce her to slavery and the case is altered – a tyrant relieves his subjects of all financial anxiety.'[1]

He led Metellus away, and the Tarpeian Rock began to echo with the grating sound of the Treasury doors being forced. Then Caesar's men hauled out the accumulated wealth of Rome which had been stored in the vaults and left untouched for centuries: the war-indemnities demanded from the Carthaginians,[2] and the treasure taken from Perseus, the last King of Macedonia,[3] or from his father Philip;[4] the treasure which Brennus the Gaul abandoned in his hasty retreat from Rome; and the gold with which Pyrrhus, King of Epirus, vainly tried to bribe Gaius Fabricius – in a word, the entire savings of our thrifty ancestors.

There was, besides, tribute sent by the wealthy nations of Asia Minor, and the Cretan spoils,[5] and the tribute exacted from Cyprus by Marcus Porcius Cato.[6] Finally Caesar's men handled the treasures of the captive Eastern kings,[7] brought from far off to be displayed in

1. A most unlikely speech. Cotta, an ex-Consul, was a maternal cousin of Caesar's and his staunch supporter. Moreover, Caesar had tried to preserve the Constitution by proposing that senatorial delegates should approach Pompey and the Consuls and arrange a conference in which all legal differences might be adjusted.

2. First 1,200 and then 10,000 talents.

3. By Paulus Aemilius in 108 B.C.

4. By Quintus Flaminius.

5. Brought home by Quintus Metellus Creticus.

6. After Cyprus had been declared a Roman province in 58 B.C.; the sum was 7,000 talents.

7. Mithridates of Pontus, Tigranes of Armenia, and Aristobulus the Maccabean king of Judea.

Pompey's Triumphs. All were removed; and this was the first time that Rome became poorer than a Caesar.[1]

Meanwhile, throughout the world Pompey's great reputation had persuaded cities and nations to make the mistake of actively supporting him. To begin with Greece – Phocian troops came from Amphissa and rocky Cirrha, and both peaks of Parnassus; and Boeotians from the swift Cephisus which rises near Delphi, and from Thebes the city which Cadmus founded beside the fountain of Dirce; and Elians from Pisa on the banks of the Alpheus – the river whose god is said to have travelled under the sea to Sicily for love of the water-nymph Arethusa; and Arcadians from Mount Maenalus; and men of Trachis from Mount Oeta where the dying Hercules ascended his pyre; even wild Thesprotians and Dryopians, and the ancient tribe of Sellians from Dodona where the oak-oracle[2] had long been extinct. The levy imposed by the Consuls in Pompey's name almost exhausted Athens' naval resources, yet she could send no more than three warships to join the fleet at Apollonia in Epirus; which made it difficult to believe that she had once defeated the Persian navy at Salamis. Ancient Crete – Crete of the hundred cities, where Juppiter was born – sent archers from the neighbourhood of Cnossos and Gortyna; even the Parthians could not shoot better than they. From Illyria marched the fighting men of Oricum, a city founded by Priam's son Helenus; and Athamanian foresters; and the Enchelians who are called after the serpent into which Cadmus was metamorphosed long ago; and men from Istria where Medea threw the bloody fragments of her murdered brother into the River Absyrtus and sent them rushing down towards the Adriatic.

Thessalians, too, from the cornlands which border the Peneus and the fertile shore of Iolcus – the starting point of the first recorded sea-voyage:[3] the Argonauts, who were drawn from every state in Greece, scorned to remain on dry land and though they knew nothing of seamanship, committed mankind to a struggle with wind and wave, and thus introduced a new manner of death. The mountaineers of Haemus volunteered as one man, and so did those of Mount Pholoë, legendary

---

1. But not the last. Under Augustus there was often more money in the Privy Purse than in the Public Treasury.

2. Since 219 B.C., when the Aetolians felled the sacred trees.

3. Lucan errs. According to Greek mythology (and modern archaeology) the Cretans built sea-going vessels long before the *Argo* sailed.

home of the Centaurs; and the Bistonians of the Thracian River
Strymon, whose flocks of cranes migrate annually to the Nile; and
barbarians from Conë at the mouth of the Danube – there the river
breaks into several streams, one of which, not in Sarmatian territory,
forms the island of Peucë.

Mysia, including the Plain of Troy where the cool Caicus flows down
from Mount Ida, and Arisbe whose fertile soil has been exhausted,
and Pitane, sent every available man. Phrygia sent the men of Celaenae
where Marsyas was flayed by Apollo after unsuccessfully challenging
him to a musical contest: Apollo played the lyre, and Marsyas the flute
discarded by Athene. Others came from the swift, straight River
Marsyas, which joins the twisting Maeander and then finds its waters
carried back again towards its source. Lydians came from the Pactolus
which the Gods allow to rise in mines of gold; and from the Hermus
whose fertile cornlands make it as rich even as the Pactolus. The traditionally ill-fated Trojans disregarded the sad history of their city and,
of course, chose the side destined to lose: they should have remembered
the myth that described Caesar as a descendant of Iulus the Trojan.[1]

Syria also sent contingents from Antioch on the Orontes, from
Nineveh[2] whose prosperity is legendary, from the wind-swept plains
of Damascus, from Gaza in Philistia, from the date-groves of Jericho,
from the city of Tyre, notoriously prone to earthquakes, and from
Sidon, centre of the valuable purple-trade. The navies of the two last-
named Phoenician cities are never steered by guess, since their naviga-
tors observe the Pole-star and keep a straighter course than those of any
other nation. There is a story that the Phoenicians first invented writing
as a means of recording speech; long before papyrus was made from
the river reeds of Memphis – the Egyptians recorded their magical
formulae only on stone, in hieroglyphics representing birds and
beasts.[3]

The wooded Taurus range and the city of Tarsus (founded by the
hero Perseus) were also denuded of men for Pompey's army; moreover
Cilicians came from Corycus (where is shown the rocky cave which
the monster Typhon used as his lair); and from the busy sea-ports of

1. Through Aeneas, son of Anchises, and the Goddess Venus.
2. Long destroyed.
3. Recently disproved; the earliest fragments of alphabetical writing are
Egyptian.

Mallus and Aegae – their ships joined Pompey's fleet as men-of-war, pirates no longer.

News of the approaching war spread to the extreme Orient as far as the basin of the Ganges – the Ganges which the Indians worship as a god, and which is the one river in existence that dares flow towards the Sun and debouch into the Eastern Ocean, defying the gales of dawn. (Here Alexander of Macedon called a halt and confessed himself baffled by the vastness of the world.) The news caused such a commotion in the region watered by the Indus and its many tributaries (which is so broad a stream that the additional waters of the Jhelum scarcely make any difference to it) as to startle the natives to their feet. These strange people suck the sweet juice of the sugar-cane, dye their hair a saffron shade, and wear flowing cotton robes caught at the waist with girdles of different-coloured gems. They also make a habit of building their own pyres and casting themselves alive on the blazing logs.[1] How glorious to hasten death in this way and offer Heaven the remaining span of one's life!

From the Black Sea came the fierce Cappadocians; and Cilicians from Mount Amamus, a region which defies the plough; and Armenians from the Niphates, which rolls down boulders from the hills; and Coatraeans from forests so tall that they seem to touch the sky; and tribes from beyond the Equator who would be surprised to find on their arrival in the strange Roman world that trees throw shadows to the north, instead of the south.

Next, the fever of war spread to the Oreteans of Baluchistan; and the people of Kirman who live so far to the south that part of the Great Bear dips below their horizon. It even reached Ethiopia, where none of the ordinary signs of the Zodiac are visible above the horizon, except a projecting hoof of the Bull, which happens to have one leg doubled under him.[2] It spread also to the land watered by the Euphrates and the rapid Tigris, rising close together in the Persian hills. If they had happened to meet, it is doubtful which of the two would have given its name to the resultant river; but the fact remains that the Euphrates floods and fertilizes the country, just as the Nile fertilizes Egypt,

1. Not merely widows but high-caste Brahmins did so in Classical times; one Calanus burned himself to death in the sight of the whole Macedonian army.

2. Half of the Zodiac, which Lucan wrongly imagined to run parallel with the Equator, lies still farther south than the Bull's hoof.

whereas the Tigris suddenly vanishes underground, reappears from a new spring farther to the south, and eventually enters the sea.[1]

The Parthian armies would not declare for either Caesar or Pompey: they kept out of the war, well satisfied to have reduced the number of Roman rivals from three to two. But the Scythian nomads who wander between the chilly bend of the River Baltch and the enormous Hyrcanian forests, dipped their arrows in poison and set off to join Pompey. The tough Heniochians, who claim descent from Castor and Pollux's Spartan charioteers and had inherited their skill in managing horses, came too; so did the Sarmatians, neighbours of the savage Moschians. Troops also flocked from the banks of the Colchian Rion; from the River Halys, crossed by Croesus in a fatal misunderstanding of the oracle that 'by so doing you will overthrow a mighty empire' – namely, his own; and from the River Don which, rising in the Rhipaean mountains, cuts the world in two by dividing Europe from Asia – one may say that when it verges towards the east it enlarges Europe; and when towards the west, Asia. Others descended from the Bosphorus, where the water that has entered the Black Sea from the Sea of Azov rushes through the straits – a fact which has made geographers challenge Hercules's boast that the Mediterranean connects with the Ocean only in the neighbourhood of Cadiz; they claim that there is another outlet by way of the Sea of Azov and the Finnish Gulf. Hereabouts live the Essedonian Scythians; the Arimaspians whose hair is caught behind in golden loops; the courageous Acians; and the Massagetic Huns who, when famished with hunger after battling against the Sarmatians, open the veins of their horses on which they have ridden from the field, and drink the warm blood.

Never in history had so many kings united under a single leader – even when Cyrus assaulted Babylon; or when Xerxes invaded Greece after ordering each of his men to contribute one dart to the general pile, so that he could count his forces accurately; or when Agamemnon

1. Lucan's geography is hardly better than his astronomy: the Western Tigris rises in Kurdistan near the Euphrates, but the Eastern (which, according to Pliny, disappeared underground for a while) rises three hundred miles away in Armenia. The united stream, which also 'fertilizes the land', joins the Euphrates at Basra before entering the Persian Gulf. It is true, however, that ancient geographers could not decide whether the combined river (now the Shatt-al-Arab) should be called Tigris or Euphrates; only two of them favoured the second choice.

avenged his brother Menelaus's injuries by leading an immense fleet against Troy. And never had troops so variously equipped and speaking so many different languages served in the same army. The Goddess Fortune was summoning these people to join an appropriately long funeral procession which would escort Pompey the Great to his disastrous death. Nor does this end the tale. By order of Zeus's ram-oracle at Ammon, African cavalry came from all over the thirsty land of Libya, which lies between Morocco and the Nile Delta. Caesar was indeed lucky to conquer the whole world at a single blow by defeating Pompey's host on the plains of Pharsalus.

He left the frightened city of Rome and once more hurried his army across the cloudy Alps. Though most of the Gauls were awed by the news that he was on his way, the men of Marseilles, with a courage rare in Greeks, loyally decided to abide by their engagements to the Roman Senate. But first sending envoys to display Athene's sacred olive branch sacred to Athene, they tried to appease the stern and reckless Caesar by pacific argument.

This is what they said:

'My lord Caesar, the history of Italy proves how closely Marseilles has always identified itself with Rome when foreign wars are being fought; so, if you now intend to win triumphs in any distant land, you may count on our armed support. But if you are fighting a civil war, which is an accursed and unlucky affair, we can only weep and remain neutral. While Rome bleeds, no outsider should be allowed to handle her wounds. It is as though a battle had begun among the gods of Olympus, or between the Gods and the ambitious Earth-born Giants. In circumstances of this sort all pious men would refrain from intervening on Juppiter's side either with arms or prayers; their sole intimation of what was going on above would be occasional thunderbolts to prove that the Almighty still held his throne. Moreover, such masses of troops are rushing to battle from every quarter, without considering the wickedness of this course, that you hardly need compel still others to fight against their inclination. We wish that all foreigners would take the same stand as ourselves, and not confuse the destiny of Rome by participating in the dispute. If you recruit none but Roman soldiers, the war will soon end: how could a man bring himself to use sword and javelin when he saw his father or his brothers in the opposing ranks?

76

'Our one plea is that you will leave your terrible Eagles outside Marseilles, and enter as a private citizen, assured of our hospitable welcome: we should like to admit you, while keeping war out. Let Marseilles be the one guiltless city in the Empire, as safe for Pompey to visit as for you: the natural place, in fact, if an armistice can mercifully be arranged, for you two leaders of unconquered Rome to meet and discuss peace terms. And if the crisis is so acute that you must hurry from Rome to Spain, why turn aside here? Ours is a city of no political importance; we have never been successful soldiers. First we went into exile from Phocis, our home in Greece, to Phocaea in Asia Minor; then, when Cyprus's general Harpagus burned us out, we sailed here and built this unpretentious town, whose reputation is based on good faith alone. If you invest its walls and assault its gates, we are ready for the firebrands and missiles that you fling on our roofs; if you cut off our water supplies, we shall dig holes and cool our parched tongues with whatever moisture may rise from the soil; if our grain gives out, we will keep ourselves alive by gnawing whatever filthy and disgusting food we can lay our hands upon. To support the cause of Freedom we are prepared to face even the horrors which came upon Sagunto when Hannibal besieged it.[1] Let our children be torn from their mothers' dry breasts and hurled into the flames; let our wives implore us to kill them; let brothers be driven to exchange death-wounds before they consent to take part in this other kind of civil war.'

Caesar's face had clouded over, and when at last they finished he showed his disapproval by turning to the troops and exclaiming: 'If these Greeks take me to be in such a hurry to reach Spain that I cannot spare the time for destroying Marseilles, they are much mistaken. You will be glad to hear, men, that our march will now be enlivened by fighting. Just as a gale blows itself out unless it can find a dense oak forest to battle against, or as a bonfire dies down for want of fuel, so with me: I feel my pugnacity evaporating when men who might have put up a fight offer to surrender. Although these envoys pretend that they will welcome me into their houses if I meekly enter Marseilles unarmed and alone, their real intention is not so much to keep me out, as to trap and imprison me. So they wish to protect themselves from the disgrace of taking part in this war, do they? I shall teach them that no one is safe nowadays if he refuses to fight under my standards,

1. 218 B.C.

and that whoever chooses peace must suffer the consequences.'[1]

He advanced at once, but found the gates shut against him and a crowd of dauntless defenders mounted on the walls. A wide, flat-topped hill rose not far off, and Caesar saw that here was a safe site for a fortified camp. Because the nearest part of the town stood at about the same level as the hill, from which it was separated by a hollow, he decided on the energetic plan of bridging the gap with an immense earthwork. Then, to invest the place completely on the landward side and so deny the defenders access to their springs and pastures, he built a line of fortifications from his camp to the sea – mounds faced with turf and crowned with numerous turrets.

Marseilles won the eternal honour of being the only town which did not succumb to immediate terror but withstood the headlong rush of Caesar's armies. It was a great feat to delay the workings of destiny and to lose Caesar valuable time in his hasty bid for power, because he captured the place only after immense difficulty. He sent men in all directions to fell forest timber, which would serve as revetments for the soil and brushwood of the earthwork, and thus help to support the additional weight of its assault towers. The axe-men came on an ancient and sacred grove. Its interlacing branches enclosed a cool central space into which the sun never shone, but where an abundance of water spouted from dark springs. Yet this was not the haunt of such innocent country deities as Pan, or Silvanus, or the nymphs: the barbaric gods worshipped here had their altars heaped with hideous offerings, and every tree was sprinkled with human blood. According to the local tradition, no birds ventured to perch upon these trees, and no wild beast made his lair beneath them; they were proof also against gales and lightning, and would shudder to themselves though no wind stirred. The images were stark, gloomy blocks of unworked timber, rotten with age, whose ghastly pallor terrified their devotees – quite another matter from our own rustic statues which are too familiar to cause alarm. Superstitious natives believed that the ground often

1. Lucan does not mention that Caesar marched to Marseilles on hearing that Lucius Domitius Ahenobarbus, whom he had captured but released, had gone to seize the city. While Caesar was treating with its fifteen principal citizens, who pointed out that they owed him and Pompey equal gratitude for past favours, Domitius arrived by sea and took over the command of their war-fleet, part of which he sent away to capture merchantmen and commandeer their gear. Vexed at their duplicity, Caesar besieged the city.

shook, that groans rose from hidden caverns below, that yews were uprooted and miraculously replanted, and that sometimes serpents coiled about the oaks, which blazed with fire but did not burn. Nobody dared enter this grove except the priest; and even he kept out at midday, and between dawn and dusk – for fear that the gods might be abroad at such hours.

Nevertheless, Caesar gave orders for the grove to be felled; it stood too close to his earthworks and, having escaped destruction in all previous wars, was the one patch of forest left in the neighbourhood. Yet the loneliness and solemnity of the grove awed his very toughest soldiers; they shrank from their task, convinced that if they struck at the sacred trees the axes would rebound, turn in the air, and chop off their legs. Caesar, realizing what was passing through their minds, snatched an axe and swung it fiercely at the nearest oak: 'I will take the entire blame for sacrilege,' he shouted. 'None of you need fear any ill consequences.' Then, though the men still felt unconvinced, they weighed the certainty of Caesar's anger against the possibility of divine vengeance, and nervously decided to obey orders. Ash-trees; gnarled holm-oaks; esculent oaks like those at Dodona; alders, whose timber does not rot in salt water; cypresses, which are used only at rich funerals – all were felled. Once their upper foliage had been removed, daylight entered the grove for the first time in history, and the fallen trees lay propped by their sturdy branches.[1] Every Gaul present shuddered at the sight, but the defenders of Marseilles were delighted: they could not believe that such an insult to the gods would remain unpunished. Nonetheless, it often happens that Fortune continues to smile on the guilty and allows the Gods to visit their anger only on the unfortunate; as happened in this case. When enough timber had been trimmed, Caesar's men commandeered wagons and oxen – to the chagrin of local farmers who needed them for the Spring ploughing – and had it carted away.

Caesar then marched off to Spain, leaving Gaius Trebonius to continue the siege, which seemed likely to be a protracted one. The earth-

---

1. To judge from other Druidic groves, the trees were dedicated to the seven planetary powers: cypress to the Sun; holm-oak to Mars; ash to Mercury; esculent oak to Juppiter; alder to Saturn. The two trees missing are willow for the Moon, and apple for Venus, which Lucan may have omitted because they neither grow tall nor inspire fear.

work was revetted with a lattice of timber and two assault towers placed on top at the same level as the town battlements. Watching these structures totter slowly towards them, the defenders thought for a moment that a sudden wind had burst out of the earth behind, and wondered why it had not reached them too. The Romans began to fling missiles into the town from the towers, but were answered with stout javelins hurled by siege catapults; any one of them would burst through a man's breast-plate and ribs, then fly on and kill two or three more of his comrades before losing its impetus. As for the boulders thrown by mangonels, they did as much damage as would a crag shaken by a gale from a crumbling mountain peak: they smashed everything that stood in their path, and not only killed men but crushed their bodies beyond recognition. However, the Romans advanced courageously in tortoise formation with shields, interlocking and over-lapping, raised above their heads, until they came close up to the wall; which was a safer position because the defenders could not easily shorten the range of their catapults and mangonels, and were obliged to topple boulders down upon them without mechanical aid. For awhile the tortoise resisted this shower of missiles, as a roof rattles under a harmless rainstorm; but presently, when this soldier or that grew too tired to keep his shield raised, or lost heart, gaps began to appear.

Next, the Romans brought up wooden mantlets, lightly turfed over against fire-brands and, protected by their roofs and shielded fronts, attacked the walls with crowbars. They also set a battering-ram to work under cover of a mantlet, pounding the solid masonry of the wall and dislodging some of the big stones on which the upper courses rested. But the defenders contrived to crack the mantlet roof with jagged boulders and repeated blows from fire-hardened stakes; and set it on fire; so the besiegers abandoned their attempt and went wearily back to their bivouacs.

The Greeks, who had not hoped to do more than repel the Roman assault on their walls, now took the offensive. They made a night sortie,[1] unarmed but for lighted torches which they screened behind their shields. With these they set fire to the revetments of the Roman earthworks, and a strong breeze fanned the flames. The wood was

1. Lucan does not mention that this was an act of treachery, committed during a truce which they had themselves demanded until Caesar's return from Spain.

green, yet a huge blaze soon started, accompanied by rolling clouds of black smoke, which split the very stones and crumbled them to dust. Caesar's works collapsed outwards, and in their ruin looked still larger than before.

Deciding to repair their fortunes elsewhere, the Romans improvised a fleet from rough timber felled on the hills. These ships had neither paintwork nor ornamental figureheads, but were built with fighting-decks. Decius Junius Brutus Albinus, Caesar's admiral, sailed them down the Rhône to anchor off the Îles d'Hyères, east of Marseilles. The Greeks of Marseilles, equally ready to stake everything on a seafight, recruited even boys and old men for their fleet, which lay in the harbour, and brought it up to strength with condemned hulks.

The rays of the morning sun were glancing on the water under a cloudless sky. No wind blew from any quarter, and the calm sea seemed like a stage set for a sham fight. Both fleets weighed anchor and swept towards each other, every hull quivering to the rapid beat of oars as the tall vessels shot along. On the flanks of the Roman fleet were massed triremes, and other galleys with four and even five banks of oars, which breasted the open sea. In the centre, the remaining vessels, fighting triremes, adopted a hollow crescent formation, and Brutus Albinus's flagship, which had six banks of oars, towered above them.

Nearer and nearer they drew; a confused shout went up, drowning not only the groan of the oar-locks but even the sound of the war-trumpets, as the rowers made a last mighty effort, bending back to the thwarts and pulling the oars close to their chests. A succession of loud shocks followed as beak met beak; but each opposing ship drew away at once, and volleys of missiles flew harmlessly into the sea. Brutus Albinus now deployed his wings and thus increased the interval that separated ships, which allowed the Greeks sea-room for sailing in between. The water was churned up by their passage through the Roman line; as when a river is met at its mouth by headwinds, so that the current and the sea waves run in contrary directions.

By far the more manageable were the Greek ships: they answered the helm at a touch and could be brought about with little trouble, which enabled them to attack and break off the fight at their pleas-ure. On the other hand, the Roman ships were more serviceable once they came to grips with an enemy; their steady fighting-decks gave the soldiers' feet as good purchase as if they stood on dry land.

'Enough of this running fight,' Brutus Albinus shouted to the master of his flagship. 'Why try to compete with Greeks in naval manoeuvres? Signal the fleet to close and turn broadside-on to the enemy!'

His order was obeyed, and the Greeks took the bait. Several of their vessels rammed the flagship, yet none managed either to stave in her oaken sides or back off again. The Romans detained them with grappling irons or chains, and the same thing happened all along the line, so that the battle became stationary. No need now to hurl javelins across the intervening water; fighting was hand to hand, with the sword as the main weapon of offence. Blows were exchanged from the bulwarks; but since it was possible to strike only by leaning far over, the dead tumbled between the vessels rather than on their own decks. Blood now carpeted the sea, and a mass of floating corpses prevented the Romans from hauling the enemy ships closer. Not every man who fell overboard was killed outright; many drowned in a mixture of blood and brine; and numbers of wounded men as they clung to the bulwarks felt their vessels suddenly go down. The sea was alive with struggling figures, and missiles exchanged between opposing vessels often fell short and killed them as they swam.

One Roman ship was being attacked port and starboard; half the crew defended one line of bulwarks, half the other. A soldier named Catus standing on the poop had boldly grasped the stern-ornament of a Greek vessel which was trying to back off, when two javelins flew simultaneously from front and rear and met in his body; a great rush of blood loosened them both and he died of a doubly mortal wound. Then Telo, the ill-fated helmsman of a Greek vessel, steered towards Catus's ship. He was a wonderfully skilful navigator in stormy weather and always knew well in advance exactly what sails he would have to hoist; no man could forecast the weather more reliably than he by observation of the sun or moon. Telo was on the point of ramming the enemy when a volley of javelins transfixed his chest, and he lost control of the tiller. One Gyareus, helmsman of a neighbouring ship, tried to clamber aboard and take his place, but a Roman grapnel caught him in the act, pinning his thigh to the gunwale.

Two Greek twins who fought side by side were destined for different fates. One alone survived, and the parents who had been so proud of both could never again mistake him for his brother; which caused them endless grief – whenever they looked at him, they remembered his twin and burst into tears again. This is what had happened. A Roman ship fouled the oars of the vessel that these twins were in, and one of them reached forward to seize the enemy's gunwale; but had his hand lopped off with a swinging blow. The fingers were so tightly clenched that they continued to hold on until they stiffened; yet this dreadful mutilation served only to increase the twin's courage. He reached for his severed hand with the remaining one, whereupon a Roman sword lopped off his entire left arm; but rather than stow himself away in the hold of the ship, he ran without shield or sword to protect his brother from flying javelins; and several more comrades also owed him their life. At last, mortally wounded, he managed to struggle aboard the Roman vessel; her decks were heaped with corpses, and her hull had been rammed until the water spurted into the blood-stained hold and was rising towards the hatches. The weight of the dying man's body proved decisive: down she went in a gurgling eddy and the sea closed over her.[1]

Many other strange and fearful deaths were reported in that sea battle. When the Romans threw grappling-irons on to a Greek ship, the hooks caught in the body of a sailor named Lycidas. He would have been dragged overboard had his comrades not grabbed at his legs, as he was disappearing, and belayed them to the bulwarks; but the grappling-irons wrenched them off at the thigh and his blood burst out in a torrent rather than a trickle. This was the most spectacularly brutal death of all, because the upper half of his body fell into the sea and could be seen for awhile struggling hard not to drown.

The crew of another ship were so eager to join in the fight that they all crowded to the bulwarks nearest the enemy, where their combined weight made her turn turtle; they were trapped underneath and could not swim away, so there they perished. A most remarkable fatality occurred when the brazen beaks of two ships which were ramming each other struck the same swimmer simultaneously. They crushed his chest and belly, grinding his bones to powder, and forcing blood

1. Lucan has ingeniously combined Justin's heroic story of how Aeschylus's brother Cynaegyrus fought against the Persians at the Battle of Salamis, with a similar story about one of Caesar's soldiers, by name Acilius, who fought not for, but against, the Greeks of Marseilles.

mixed with guts through his mouth; yet clashed together none the less. After the ships had backed off again, water could be seen welling up through the great cleft that the beaks had made in the corpse, which slowly sank. Another Greek vessel went down, and most of the crew escaped and swam for their lives to a sister-ship. A crowd of them clutched at her gunwale and tried to climb aboard, but they were warned off, because she was already overloaded and could not rescue any more men without sinking. When the refugees clung on obstinately, the sailors on deck hacked away their arms, and they slid into the sea again, no longer even able to swim.

Since the supply of javelins had failed, angry soldiers began hurling at the enemy not only oars but an entire stern ornament, the rowers' thwarts and other pieces of timber torn from their ships. They also grabbed at sinking corpses and robbed them of the weapons that had lodged in them. It was not unusual to see a man pull a javelin out of his belly, and stop the rush of blood with his left hand, thus obtaining sufficient strength to throw the weapon vengefully back at the enemy.

But though this battle took place on the water, it was the element most hostile to water that caused the greatest destruction: fire, spread by resin-smeared pine torches which an undercoating of sulphur kept ablaze. The pitch on the hulls and the wax caulking of the decks made both fleets highly inflammable, and because the sea did not extinguish the flames once they had gained a hold many ships were soon drifting about on fire. It has been observed that when death appears in more than one form simultaneously men are apt to concentrate on escaping from the first that presents itself. In this case, those afraid of being burned swamped their ships, while those afraid of being drowned clung desperately to the blazing planks. Nevertheless, courage did not desert some of them even in the water: they retrieved javelins from it and handed them up to friends who were still afloat, or made feeble efforts to fling them at the enemy. A few, for lack of any other weapon, used the sea itself; a man would grapple with a shipwrecked opponent and be content to drown if he might only drag the other with him. One Greek was such a fine swimmer that he had been in the habit of searching the sea-bed for lost objects, and could hold his breath for a considerable time; also, if an anchor had fouled some underwater obstruction and resisted the tug of its cable, he would dive below and release the flukes. He now seized a struggling Roman and hauled him down to death, then rose victoriously to the surface, but struck his head against a ship's bottom and disappeared for good. Others were seen hugging the oar-blades of enemy ships, to immobilize them. The ruling obsession, indeed, was to make the best possible use of what life remained; thus a dying man would lash himself to the stern of his ship, and so provide a fender, should an enemy beak ram this vulnerable part of her hull.

An Etruscan soldier in Caesar's fleet was standing high up in the bows when a Balearic slinger named Lygdamus aimed at him sideways and knocked out both his eyes with a leaden bolt. He stood there in astonishment, thinking: 'This must be the darkness of death,' until he realized that he could still move his limbs. Then he cried: 'Comrades, I have lost my sight; but point this javelin towards the enemy and let me hurl it just as you are hurling yours, because I do not want to waste what life I still have. This carcase of mine can yet be of some military use: it will attract weapons that might otherwise be aimed at those of you who remain whole and active.' They gave him the general direction, and he let fly; his javelin struck a young Greek nobleman named Argus just above the groin and, as he fell forward, the point drove deeper into his flesh. Resistance had ended on this Greek ship, and from the stern hurried Argus's father, who had seen him fall. In his prime, this old man had been as fine a fighter as any in Marseilles, but now he had grown so feeble that he could only direct the battle, not take part in it. He stumbled past the rowers' benches and found Argus only just alive, but he neither wept nor beat his breast: he merely stiffened and spread out both hands in despair. Argus weakly turned his head and dumbly implored the old man to kiss him and close his eyes. However, a thick veil of darkness clouded the father's vision and, being unable to distinguish his dying son, he could not do as he had been asked. Presently the darkness lifted, and he cried sorrowfully: 'Argus, forgive your poor father for seeming to refuse you a parting embrace! But I see that blood still oozes from your wound and your breast still heaves: you may yet survive me.' With this, he first drove a sword up to the hilt into his own body, then leaped overboard – so determined on predeceasing his son that he trusted no single form of suicide.

The issue of the battle was no longer in doubt. Most of the Greek fleet had been sunk, and the rest captured; or all but a few ships, which made good their escape to the docks.[1] The whole shore rang with the shrieks of mothers who had lost their sons, and every eye was wet. Some wives mistook washed-up Roman corpses for their husbands and clasped them close, not recognizing the mutilated features. One angry quarrel sprang up between two fathers for the possession of a headless body, each claiming it as his son and wanting to burn it upon a pyre.

But Brutus Albinus had the satisfaction of having won the first naval battle for the Caesareans.

1. Nine ships out of seventeen were lost. Lucan does not mention that the Greek fleet was largely manned by a neighbouring Gallic tribe of Albician mountaineers. Trebonius pressed the siege of Marseilles until Caesar's return from Spain, where he had taken only forty days to overcome Pompeian resistance. The defenders then capitulated and surrendered all their treasure, arms and remaining ships; the spoils of Marseilles were later displayed in his Triumph. But he confirmed the city's freedom.

BOOK FOUR[1]

CAESAR, meanwhile, carried on his war in the far West; and though little blood was shed, the campaign proved to be of critical importance. Lucius Africanus and Marcus Petreius, close friends who shared the Pompeian command in Spain, had resolved to hold the province against him. Their troops were regular Roman legions, reinforced by native auxiliaries – energetic Asturians, and Veltonians from Portugal, besides Celtiberians, a nation formed by the intermarriage of Iberians with an ancient tribe of Celtic immigrants from Gaul.

The old city of Lerida stands at the top of a gently sloping, fertile hill; below it flows the placid Segre, which is quite large for a Spanish river and spanned by a stone bridge built with massive piers and an enormous arch to resist the winter floods. Pompey's standard had been raised on a steep hill near the city; Caesar encamped on another of much the same height across the river. Eastward, a level plain stretched nearly to the horizon, but was cut by the swift Cinca, which cannot be said ever to reach the sea, since it runs into the Ebro – the river from which Iberia takes its name – and loses its identity at their confluence.

No fighting took place that first day: a sense of shame still restrained the generals on either side from breaking the laws of Rome by any act of civil war, and they spent the time in calculating each others' fighting strength. However, when evening drew on, Caesar decided to take up a position closer to the enemy and defend it with a broad fosse; this was secretly dug by his reserves, while the forward battalions stood to arms within observation of the enemy and screened the manoeuvre. At dawn he ordered an assault on a rocky ridge commanding the approaches to Lerida. Africanus and Petreius realized their danger and would have been ashamed to let Caesar occupy a feature of such tactical importance; so they hurriedly sent troops to forestall him. It soon became clear that the assault would end in catastrophe, because

1. These next seven books were unrevised at Lucan's death.

the Pompeians had the advantage of being already in position. The Caesareans climbed the rocky hill-side in full equipment, and kept themselves from backward tumbles by clinging to knobs of rock or tree-stumps, and helping one another up difficult slopes with their shields. No one had an opportunity to use his javelin as a weapon of offence, rather than as a staff, or even to draw his sword. But Caesar sent cavalry to create a diversion on the left flank and managed to recall his assault troops without loss; the Pompeians did not pursue but remained in possession of the ridge.[1]

This was the last skirmish before winter set in with numbing frosts and parching northerly winds. Snow nipped the mountains, and every morning the plains were white with hoar-frost which melted as soon as the sun rose; the whole Spanish countryside grew hard and dry. But when the Spring Equinox came round and the Sun rose again in the Ram – the magic ram off whose back Helle once fell and drowned in the Hellespont – the new moon turned reddish and brought a change of weather. The wind veered from North to East, and not only the clouds collected in Northern Arabia, but all the mists sucked up by the Sun from the Ganges region, until they darkened the sky and shaded the Indians, were now hurried westward in the form of storms – which did not break before they reached their distant goal. Gaul and Africa escaped the currents of moist air; they came streaming on towards Spain, the land where West Winds originate and where the sea has a higher horizon than anywhere else in the world. There seemed hardly room between heaven and earth to contain such an accumulation of dense black clouds, and when the pressure from above and below burst their envelopes, rain fell in such torrents that it quenched even the incessant flashes of lightning. Once a half-rainbow appeared; it shone very feebly for want of adequate light, and was busily engaged in sucking up the Atlantic waves and pumping back into the sky whatever rain had fallen there. Warm winds melted the ice and snow on the Pyrenees, which had so far defied the power of the Sun, and sent streams running down the cliffs; whereupon the mountain torrents overflowed and an immense head of water came rushing at Caesar's camp, washed away the ramparts and formed enormous pools inside.

1. Lucan has confused this attack, in which cavalry played no part, with another made later at Lerida by the Ninth Legion – when the cavalry covered a retirement.

The troops were, so to speak, shipwrecked on dry land. Tracks vanished, and foraging parties returned to camp empty-handed after wandering vaguely about the countryside: they had been unable to requisition cattle, and the fields, being now under water, offered no food either for man or beast.[1]

Famine, the leading attendant in Disaster's train, soon made her appearance, and proved a cruel enemy. Though there was no fighting, the soldiers starved; and even those ordinarily careful with money were ready to surrender their entire savings for a handful of corn. (Avarice is a cursed vice: offer a man enough gold, and he will part with his own small hoard of food, however great his hunger.) Soon a vast lake spread over the plain, hiding every mound or hillock; sweeping the very wild beasts from their lairs and drowning them; the rivers roared as they swirled down to the sea, the waves of which retreated before such violence. Dawn brought no relief, all natural distinctions between night and day being confounded by the hideous weather. Caesar's men might just as well have been encamped in the barren Antarctic snows where perpetual winter reigns and no stars shine; and the ice serves merely to cool countries nearer the Equator. This weather was sent as a warning by Almighty Juppiter, and by his brother Neptune who, when the three Gods cast lots for Sky, Sea, and Underworld, drew the second choice. Ah, if only Juppiter had pledged the sky to endless rain, and Poseidon had ordered every stream to continue running, but forbidden the sea to accept any further flood water! And if earthquakes had then deflected the course of rivers, so that Rhine and Rhône cascaded into Spain, carrying with them the melted snow from the Riphaean Mountains in Scythia besides the contents of every pond, lake, and marsh in the world! That would at least have freed our unhappy country from civil war.

However, the Goddess Fortune had been no more than teasing her favourite; after this scare she quickly returned to his side and any grudge that he might have borne the Gods was soon forgiven, because they rallied wholeheartedly in his support. Out came the sun; fleecy white clouds replaced the dark ones; red dawn gave promise of a fine day. The elements resumed their normal positions, the waters which

---

1. The floods swept away the bridges across the Cinca and the Segre, already unfordable; no corn supplies could therefore reach Caesar, and the Spanish cattle in the neighbourhood had been driven to high ground.

had been caught up into the firmament until they obscured the stars were now back again in a lower station. Trees and hills began to emerge from the floods and the valleys emptied themselves at sight of the sun. No sooner was the Segre back in its bed than Caesar ordered the willows growing on its banks to be polled and the clippings steeped in water. These osiers were then plaited over timber frames and covered with ox-hides, to form coracles: a type of boat used by the Venetians on the River Po, by the Britons on their wide Ocean, and by the people of Memphis on the flooded Nile – though at Memphis papyrus reed replaces wicker-work. Caesar's men ferried themselves across the Segre in the coracles, and began hastily to build a wooden bridge; but, for fear of another flood, they planted its piers well back in the fields; and took the further precaution of dividing the river into channels, to punish its recent impetuosity.

When Petreius observed that all was going well for Caesar he evacuated Lerida but, reluctant to stay in the settled areas of Spain, marched towards the interior, a region inhabited by savages who could be counted upon to despise death and never shrink from battle. Caesar soon discovered that the enemy had abandoned their position; he ordered his men to waste no time in searching for fords or even using the bridge, but to swim across the stream. They eagerly undertook a feat from which they would have shrunk had this been a retreat rather than a pursuit.[1] Arriving on the farther bank they rearmed, and broke into a double because the water had been numbing. They pressed on until noon. By then Caesar's cavalry were already harassing the enemy rear-guard, who could not decide whether to stand or continue their march.

A narrow defile led from the plain into the hills, between two rugged cliffs. This was the beginning of a sheltered track which wound upward into unsurveyed country. Realizing that once the Pompeians gained the defile in safety the war would pass beyond his control, Caesar gave the order: 'Break ranks and press on individually as fast as you can. If the enemy cannot be halted, we are lost. When you have headed the cowards off, turn and force them to fight; they are running away in

1. They did not, as a matter of fact, swim the river. Though the stream was deep even after canals had been dug to drain off some of the water, they forded it with the help of a cavalry breakwater, such as had been used in the passage of the Rubicon and had no casualties.

terror now, but they will soon have to meet your swords and die like men.' This operation was successful; Caesar's vanguard made a wide circuit, yet managed to reach the defile first.

That night the two armies encamped close together, separated by a narrow trench across which faces could easily be distinguished, and at once the real horror of civil war became apparent. Though for awhile camp discipline ruled out all parley, and friend greeted friend with a nod or the waving of a sword, soon personal feelings proved stronger than standing orders. Soldiers of both camps scrambled over the stockade to shake hands with men they knew: one called a friend by name, another shouted to a neighbour or recognized a former play-mate, and whoever found no acquaintances among the enemy failed to pass as a true Roman. Men sobbed with emotion and let tears fall upon their weapons as they embraced; and though Caesar's men had not so far disgraced themselves by murder, they shuddered to think what might have been. Fools! Why did they beat their breasts and groan and weep? Why not admit that they had chosen to obey Caesar's criminal commands; and that they had no need to be so terrified of him, since only their eagerness to follow made him seem terrible? They had merely to stop their ears against the cruel bugle blast and, when the standards moved ahead, stay where they were. Thus they could have brought the madness of civil war to a sudden end and Caesar, once more a private citizen, might have embraced his son-in-law. What an opportunity for Concord, the spirit of everlasting and universal love which alone can save this world, to appear and set a glorious precedent for future ages! The mask had been torn from the face of evil: the soldiers recognized their own friends and were left no excuse for further error. Yet the accursed Goddess Fortune used her malignant powers to make this short respite from war a prelude to even worse disasters.

An armistice having been tacitly agreed upon, the troops fraternized freely, strolling at leisure between the two camps. Together they pic-nicked around hearths built of turf, mixed their wine rations, and poured libations to Bacchus. They lay side by side and kept one another awake all night by telling stories of the war: first engagements, feats with the javelin, and so forth. A deal of boasting and friendly argument could be heard, but Fortune succeeded in her principal object of mak-ing them friends once more, so that when hostilities began afresh their guilt would be enhanced by this temporary conciliation.

What happened next was that Petreius, informed of this unofficial truce and realizing that the Senatorial cause had been betrayed, armed his servants and a crowd of Spanish auxiliaries, with whom he launched a sudden infamous attack on the unarmed Caesareans who were fraternizing with his men, and brutally disturbed the peace by massacring them.

His provocative speech went as follows: 'Men, have you forgotten your country and the Eagles before which you swore loyalty? If you cannot uphold the Senate's authority by defeating these rebels and saving Rome, at least you can fight and die. Will you accept Caesar as your master and treasonably put your standards at his disposal without even matching swords with his men or shedding a drop of blood? And will you beg him to treat you no worse than his other slaves, and show equal mercy to your generals? No: we refuse to betray Rome at the price of our skins; nor is the object of this civil war to keep us alive. You have handed us over to Caesar in the name of peace – as though anyone would trouble to dig iron ore from deep mines, or fortify cities, or train cavalry, or launch ships on every sea, if it were ever right to barter liberty for peace. It seems that our declared enemies still consider themselves bound by the wicked oaths they swore; whereas you do not, because you are fighting in a just cause and can expect to be pardoned by him. Alas, the shameful death that honour has died! Even as I speak, Pompey is raising levies throughout the world and persuading distant sovereigns to join him, unaware of what has happened here. Perhaps you have already bargained with his enemies that if you surrender, his life too will be spared?' [1]

Petreius's words had the effect of turning the men into savages. One may tame wild beasts by keeping them in a cage and teaching them docility and good manners, until they forget how they used to behave in the forests; but once let their thirsty mouths taste blood again, and they will rage and snarl for fury, baring their gums, until the terrified keeper finds it hard to control them. So the Pompeians, blindly obey-

[1]. The Pompeian soldiers had thanked Caesar for not massacring them at the entrance to the defile; regretted not having deserted to him earlier; and, to avoid the infamy of handing over Africanus and Petreius to his vengeance, begged him to let them go free. When he consented, they offered to carry their Eagles into his camp and draft a peace treaty; but at this point Petreius suddenly attacked.

ing Petreius's orders, committed in cold blood such horrible crimes as
it would have disgraced the Gods to sanction even in the mad heat of
battle. They murdered the very comrades with whom they had shared
food, drink, and couches; and though at first hating to draw their
swords, yet the feeling of a hilt grasped in the hand was an irresistible
provocation to evil. Every man conceived a sudden loathing for former
friends, and every blow struck strengthened his wavering purpose.
The whole camp rang with the uproar and, as though it were not
enough to keep such crimes dark, Petreius's troops actually paraded
them before him, glorying in their wickedness.

Caesar lost a number of men, but recognized the hand of Heaven
behind this outrage. Never, indeed, did he have a luckier day – the seafight at Marseilles, and even the great battle at Pharsalus, were nothing
by comparison. It had made the cause which he championed the more
righteous of the two.

Not daring to stay in the neighbourhood of Caesar's camp after
what they had done, the Pompeians hurried away and tried to retake
Lerida; but unsuccessfully, because Caesar's cavalry went in pursuit,
driving them off the plain and forcing them to seek refuge in the thirsty
hills. Caesar then boldly hemmed them in with fortified works; and
their panic changed to desperate courage when they found themselves
cut off from the river and all other sources of water. Having killed
their horses, which would be useless in a siege, they made a suicidal
sortie. But Caesar shouted: 'Men, they are rushing at us in the hope of
being killed. Do not oblige them! I want no casualties in my command.
Men who do not mind being killed are dangerous customers. Look,
they are selling their lives cheap and expecting me to buy! No longer
afraid of wounds, they will fling themselves upon your swords and
rejoice in the act. Let us damp their enthusiastic desire for death.'
Thus, by refusing battle, he silenced the Pompeians' excited threats.
Finding, as darkness drew on, that they had lost the chance of killing
and being killed, their resolution slowly waned and the anticlimax
depressed them. Much the same thing can be seen in the amphitheatre:
a gladiator shows far greater courage when he has just been wounded
and the gush of hot blood increases his muscular strength, than when
his wounds are beginning to scab over and the skin shrinks on the
bones. Indeed, if his opponent, once he realizes that the thrust has gone
home, stands back and refrains from further punishment, the wounded

man will gradually go numb with pain and become incapable of retaliation.

Water now ran so short that the Pompeians began to cut trenches in the hope of discovering some underground spring, and worked with swords as well as picks and mattocks. They dug down to the very level of the plain; not even the pallid Asturian miners burrow so deep when they mine for gold in their dark tunnels. But no faint sound of a sub-terrene stream reached their ears and, hard though they pounded at the rock, nothing spouted out. They searched in vain for signs of water on the walls of their excavations, or for a thin trickle in the gravel beds. Diggers were hauled up in a sweat of exhaustion after laboriously hack-ing at the flinty soil; and this vain search for water made their mouths still drier. None could face the food that might have restored their strength but, as it were, staved off thirst with hunger. Wherever they found a patch of soft soil they snatched handfuls of it and squeezed the moisture into their mouths, or flung themselves down in agony beside stretches of foul stagnant mud and eagerly lapped water at which they would have shuddered had they seen any prospect of sur-vival. Like beasts they pulled at the udders of their slaughtered mares, and finding no milk in them sucked the corrupt blood instead; or they bruised grass and leaves, pressed juice from the green shoots and pith of trees, and collected dew drops from the branches.[1]

Those Romans who in previous campaigns drank at springs bar-barously poisoned by the retreating enemy,[2] had been comparatively fortunate; for even if Caesar had openly dropped carrion and Cretan aconite into the Segre and invited the Pompeians to drink, they would have done so. Thirst burned like a flame in their vitals, their mouths were leathery, their tongues scaly; their veins shrank, the dryness of their lungs made them wheeze and every gasp hurt their cracked palates; yet they forced themselves to breathe despite the pain. And, though the whole country had been flooded only a few days before, they yearned for another downpour and gazed without hope at the rainless clouds overhead. What made their situation still more distress-ing was that they were not encamped south of the broiling tropical island of Meroë, and under the sign of the Crab, where the naked

---

1. It would have been more sensible to dig under the trees for the water accumulated there during the floods which had caused the shoots to sprout.

2. Such as Pyrrhus, Jugurtha, Mithridates, and Juba.

Garamantians plough their fields,[1] but between the brimming Segre and the swift Ebro, which were in full view as, one by one, they died of thirst.

Finally their generals had to capitulate; but it was Africanus who took the initiative. Despairing of further resistance, he came out under a flag of truce, leading his half-dead squadrons into the enemy camp, and stood before Caesar as a suppliant. Nevertheless, he kept his dignity in this humiliating position – the dignity of a man who has held high military command and, though defeated, remains unbroken in spirit – and confidently sued for pardon.

'If it had been my fate,' he said, 'to be overcome by a dishonourable enemy, I should have killed myself without hesitation; and the sole reason for my asking you to let me live is that I consider you worthy of this request. None of us is a sworn partisan of Pompey's, nor have we taken up arms from any dislike of your aspirations. We fought because this is a civil war; and, owing loyalty to the Senate who appointed us, we held out as long as possible. But since Fate cannot be gainsaid, we surrender the West; and you may now invade the East, confident that your rear is secure. This has been a bloodless victory: you were spared recourse to massacre, and if one crime deserves your pardon it is that we are beaten by you. I make modest demands: allow my exhausted troops to refresh themselves, and grant them their lives since they have laid down their arms. Think of them as battle casualties; now that you have subjected them to the disgrace of becoming your prisoners they are debarred from sharing in your triumph. My command has ceased to exist; and I beg you not to enrol us forcibly in your victorious army.'

Caesar cheerfully did as Africanus asked: excusing the men from service in his own forces and from all punishment.[2] As soon as satisfactory articles of capitulation had been signed, he let the Pompeians rush down to the now unguarded river and fling themselves on their faces, muddying the stream in their haste. They drank so long and greedily that the water lodged in their wind-pipes and made them

1. A geographical error. The Garamantians (now the Karamatse of the Niger Bend) were then living in the Fezzan Oasis of the Sahara, hundreds of miles nearer Spain than the people of Meroë in the Sudan, which lay seven degrees south of Fezzan.

2. Lucan does not mention that Africanus and Petreius broke their parole and went to join Pompey; both were killed in the last campaign of the war.

choke for breath; and even then they could not rid themselves of the burning sensation in their throats. Although their stomachs could hold no more water, they still felt a craving for it.

Eventually they recovered their strength, and gourmets may learn from this incident that Nature is easily satisfied: to keep alive costs very little. There is no need for luxurious eating and drinking – ransacking the ends of the earth in search of extravagant delicacies. These Pompeians were not resuscitated by famous vintage wines, bottled during some long-forgotten consulship and served in gold or myrrhine ware: it was plain water that saved them. Spring water and bread are quite sufficient to preserve the life of man. [1]

However, the soldiers whose wars had yet to be won were the unlucky ones. The defeated Pompeians, after surrendering their weapons to Caesar, strolled harmlessly home to their own cities and, though no longer wearing breast-plates, felt perfectly safe and cheerful. Being civilians again, they greatly regretted ever having hurled javelins, or endured thirst, or prayed in vain to the Gods for victory. The Caesareans still had many hard battles and heavy labours awaiting them in distant lands; even if fickle Fortune continued to support Caesar, they must win engagement after engagement and shed quantities of blood as they shared his trials. Yes, these fortunate Pompeians knew that they could settle down in their own humble homes, welcomed by wives and innocent children, while the rest of the world tottered to its fall. There they would be allowed to sleep through the trumpet-blasts that summoned neighbours to battle, nor were they sent as colonists to some foreign region: relieved now of the need to take sides – they had followed Pompey, true, but their lives had been spared by Caesar – they found themselves the only Romans who could wish the cruel war to end in victory for neither faction.

However, this is not to suggest that Caesar's cause was everywhere successful; in the Adriatic, for instance, he suffered a setback. The straggling town of Spalato looks west across this sea, beside the mild river Giadro; and some seventy miles to the north Lucius Antonius (one of Caesar's generals) was encamped on the island of Curicta. He did not fear an enemy landing, so long as he could fend off attacks by the Goddess Hunger, who can be counted upon to take every city

1. I suspect that this passage was salvaged from an early rhetorical exercise written by Lucan for his tutor, the Stoic philosopher.

that she besieges. No corn grew on the island and it provided no pasture for cattle; the starving soldiers had cropped close what green stuff they could find, to fill their own bellies: they had even torn the withered tufts out of the sods that faced the rampart. At last they observed a friendly force on the mainland opposite, commanded by Lucius Minucius Basilus, and at once contrived a means of escape. They built three transport floats without either ribs, poops, or sterns, consisting of a deck supported on double rows of empty barrels, chained together and capable of carrying a heavy load. The crews (who were screened from javelin volleys) would use their oars in the wide gaps left in the deck between the rows of planks laid transversely across the barrels. Thus the float presented a remarkable sight: it ploughed steadily forward without sails or any visible means of propulsion. Antonius's men kept a close watch on the straits and, when the tide began to ebb from the beach, manned and launched the three floats, which slowly drifted seaward. Each float carried a tall wooden artillery-tower, and screened platforms from which men could fight.

Marcus Octavius, Pompey's admiral, who was blockading the island, did not attack immediately but waited until the enemy had been tempted, by a successful trial run, to embark greater numbers of men than at first. This is how a cautious huntsman works, while netting the wood in which he knows that stags are lodged: he uses a 'scare-foil' of stinking vulture feathers dyed a bright red, and ties the foils to stakes; to avoid startling the quarry, he muzzles his noisy Molossian hound, and keeps the Laconians and Cretans on a leash. The only hound allowed to go nosing through the undergrowth is one that can follow the scent in silence and refrain from barking even when he has traced a beast to its lair; he merely gives the leash a warning tug.

The floats recrossed the straits to the island, and at dusk the main body of troops eagerly embarked. Pompey's Cilician levies displayed their old piratical skill by preparing a trap: they rigged up a rope-boom, belaying the ends to rocks on either side of a channel, and letting the middle part droop below the surface. The two leading transports managed to negotiate the obstacle, but the third fouled the cable and found herself being hauled ashore at a point where wooded cliffs over-hang the sea and always seem about to collapse. Underneath are caves in which wrecks and dead bodies often gather after a northerly gale, but when the water inside comes spouting out, as furiously as from the whirlpool of Charybdis in the Straits of Messina, these are set adrift again.

The soldiers aboard this float, who were Gauls from Oderzo, a town to the north of the Po, found themselves attacked on all sides by ships recently arrived on the scene, and by troops that swarmed over the rocky shore. A tribune named Vulteius commanded the float and when he realized that it had fouled the boom he tried unsuccessfully to cut the cable with his sword; then he ordered his men to their battle stations, but could not guess from which quarter the main attack would develop. The Caesareans did all that brave men could do in such diffi-cult circumstances; although barely six hundred strong they fought against the several thousands of Pompeians milling around the float, and the battle continued until darkness supervened.

Vulteius preserved discipline by a heartening address to his men, who were appalled at the prospect of imminent death. 'Lads,' he cried, 'we will remain free for this short night alone; but let us make good use of the respite by deciding what course to follow. Nobody need complain that he has only a few hours of life left; these are enough for suicide, and the glory of such a deed cannot be diminished by the thought that he would soon have been killed in any case. The future is always unforeseeable; and though it is a noble act to cut short a long expectancy of life, it is no less noble to sacrifice one's last few hours deliberately.

'I am not compelling you to choose death. But since we have no retreat, and since our fellow-citizens who surround us are bent on slaughter, we had better face the inevitable. Make up your minds to die and you will lose all fear. And we are not fated to fall in the dusty confusion of an ordinary battle, when two armies are locked together and murderous javelins fly blindly here and there; on such occasions nobody notices particular acts of courage and the casualties are entered in the common ledger. This is a very different case: we are stationed on a vessel under direct observation of Basilus's men in one quarter and Octavius's in the other; and our fight will be witnessed from both the shore and the cliff-top. I do not know how memorable our end will be; I know only that you will transcend all recorded examples of soldierly devotion to duty. It is not enough for us merely to fall on our swords in Caesar's cause, though our present plight makes this the surest pledge of loyalty that we can offer. And whereas we may forfeit a great deal of glory in not being tempted to surrender by the presence of our parents or children, and proudly rejecting that temptation, we can still teach the enemy that the same mad courage which makes us welcome death also makes us invincible, and that they are fortunate not to have trapped the other two floats as well. Let them by all means try to entice us with inacceptable terms of surrender. I hope that they will even offer us free pardons, because if we then insist on suicide, they will know that this was no act of despair; and we shall be more famous yet. I also hope that when the news of our last stand reaches Caesar he will regard it as a disaster, although our numbers may be negligible by comparison with the total casualty list.

'Even if we were fated to survive tomorrow's battle, I should feel small satisfaction in doing so. Comrades, I have already said goodbye to life, and the longing for death has become an obsession with me; but this longing can be experienced only by those who feel their doom approach. The Gods conceal the beauty of death from those destined to escape it, and thus encourage them to go on living.'

The effect of Vulteius's speech on the noble-hearted Gauls was remarkable. Before he spoke, they had been sorrowfully watching the movements of the stars and dreading the time when the Great Bear would change her position in the sky; but after this encouragement they yearned for day. Nor did they have much longer to wait, since the Sun was now in the House of the Twins and passing into the Crab, where he attains his midsummer zenith. Cheiron the Thessalian Centaur, who was raised to Heaven as the Archer constellation, shone above the horizon all that brief night.

Dawn revealed Istrian forces posted on the cliffs above, and the enemy further reinforced by shiploads of savage Liburnians. No immediate attack was launched, however, because the Pompeians expected that a postponement would make their enemies appreciate life the more; and as Vulteius had hoped, peace terms were offered. Nevertheless, the Caesareans stood firm and did not in the least dread the approaching battle, since they had unanimously pledged themselves to die by their own hands if they failed to fall otherwise. They greeted the enemy's war-cries with contempt and continued to repel the attacks of vastly superior forces; but feeling satisfied at last that enough blood had flowed, turned their backs to the enemy and became one another's executioners.

Vulteius now bared his throat and cried: 'Is anyone here worthy to kill and be killed by me?' No more was needed: several comrades stabbed him and earned his dying praises; but he showed a deeper gratitude to the first assassin by dispatching him in return.

The survivors then enacted the horrible drama of civil warfare, though every soldier belonged to Caesar's party. This scene recalled the fratricidal blows exchanged between the armed men sown by Cadmus near Dirce's Fountain, which set so unfortunate a precedent for their Theban descendants, the brothers Eteocles and Polyneices. It also recalled a similar scene at Colchis, where another crop of soldiers, sown by Jason from the remaining teeth of the same dragon and inflamed to anger by Medea's magic spells, hewed at one another until the furrows from which they had sprung ran with blood. Medea herself shuddered at the crime which her pharmaceutical experiments had prompted!

The Caesareans fulfilled their compact of mutual murder by trying to kill at the same moment as they were being killed, though the former was a far more painful experience. None failed to strike home even though mortally wounded, and the victim helped him by thrusting his own breast or throat against the sword point. Father paired off with son in this ghastly massacre, and brother with brother; and none betrayed any reluctance to perform his sacred duty, which was to ensure that no second blow would be needed. Mortally wounded men now began to drag their entrails along the fighting platforms and let their blood spurt into the sea. They could take a brief pleasure in smiling at the daylight which they had bartered for eternal darkness, and in glowering defiance at the enemy. When the float was heaped with dead and dying, the Pompeian generals Octavius and Libo, amazed that any general could inspire such extravagant loyalty in his men as Caesar had done, collected the corpses for honourable cremation. No ship's company had ever earned comparable praise; yet even this glorious precedent has not taught cowardly nations how easy it is to escape servitude by self-immolation; because when tyrants impose their will by terror liberty shrivels, until nobody realizes that the purpose of the sword is to secure individual freedom. If death were only the exclusive reward of brave men, denied to cowards!

War flamed up hotly in Libya too. Gaius Curio, whom Caesar had sent to Sicily, sailed from Lilybaeum and light northerly breezes brought him to a point on the African coast, between the ruins of Carthage and Clipia, famous for Cornelius Scipio's stay there. Curio pitched his first camp at some distance inland, where the river Bragada makes its slow way through the sandy waste. Then he marched up to a rocky hill, pitted with caves, traditionally known as the 'Tomb of Antaeus'. When Curio asked the reason for this name, an untaught peasant told him the story as it had been handed down from father to son for many generations.

'Mother Earth, who was not yet past child-bearing even after giving birth to the Giants, conceived a frightful monster in a Libyan cave. She had as much cause to be proud of her huge son Antaeus as of his elder brothers Typhon, Briareus, and Tityus. The Gods were lucky that Antaeus did not come against them with the rest of the giants on the plains of Phlegra, because not only was he of enormous strength but his mother had endowed him with the power to renew it, whenever he grew tired, merely by touching her.'

At this point the countryman showed Curio the cave which Antaeus had made his den, and continued: 'He is believed to have sheltered under this tall cliff, feasting on the lions he caught. When he went to sleep, he had no use for skins or leaves as bedding, but stretched out on the bare earth and so maintained his vigour. He killed numerous Libyan farmers, and any strangers who landed on the coast, and it was long before he availed himself of the power bequeathed him by his mother; since no wrestler could throw Antaeus when he stood upright, he did not need to fall deliberately.

'At last Hercules, who was then engaged in ridding earth and sea of monsters, heard of this bloodthirsty ogre and crossed the Libyan border to wrestle with him. As soon as they met, Hercules cast off the lion's pelt which he had won at Nemea; and Antaeus his Libyan one. But while Hercules rubbed oil on his limbs, as Olympic wrestlers still do, Antaeus decided not to keep contact with Mother Earth through the soles of his feet alone, and therefore began to sprinkle hot sand all over his body.

'They locked arms and grappled, heads held steady, each trying unsuccessfully to secure a neck-hold and surprised that he had finally found his match. Hercules contented himself with wearing Antaeus down; making him pant and sweat, until finally his neck tilted backwards and Hercules, leaning over him, lifted a knee and struck one of

his legs just below the hip. Antaeus tottered and Hercules caught him
tightly about the waist, parted his thighs by kicking the legs apart, then
threw him fairly at full length. But as soon as the sand had absorbed
Antaeus's sweat, fresh blood coursed through his veins, his muscles
bulged, his body regained strength, and he managed to free himself
from Hercules's grasp. Hercules was astounded at this recovery. He
felt far more apprehensive than when he had struggled with the
hundred-headed Hydra in the Lernaean swamps, chopping off her
snaky heads, only to see them grow again; and in those days he had
been an inexperienced fighter.

'So the match continued, Hercules relying on his own strength,
Antaeus borrowing his from the earth. Never had Hercules been in
greater danger of death and his implacable step-mother Juno felt keen
satisfaction as she watched exhaustion overcoming him and making
the sweat start from his neck. This had not happened even at the time
when he bore the whole weight of the heavens, as substitute for Atlas
the Titan. Now Antaeus, wearying once more, did not wait until he
was thrown but deliberately lay down and rose up stronger than ever,
with all the vital fluid that Mother Earth could supply coursing through
his veins. One might say that she herself felt worn out by the strain of
this wrestling match. At last Hercules realized what was happening,
and gasped: "Very well, henceforth you must remain upright. I shall
keep tight hold of you and if you fall it must be on me, rather than on
the ground."

'With that, he heaved Antaeus high into the air and resisted his
frantic efforts to cast himself down. Gradually he felt the giant's body
stiffening but continued to hold it aloft, and thus prevented Mother
Earth from reviving her dying son.'

The peasant concluded: 'We pride ourselves on the ancient tradition
which has given the hill its name. Yet a still greater name was conferred
on it by Scipio Africanus when he landed here during the Punic Wars
and, by his victories over the Carthaginians, forced them to recall
Hannibal who already threatened the cities of Latium. This is the very
spot where he first encamped; and yonder are the remains of his
entrenchments. Ours was the earliest Carthaginian district occupied
by him.'

Curio, convinced that he must win the campaign merely because he
had struck such a lucky site for his camp, delightedly told the troops as

much; not realizing that he had brought ill luck with him, and was by no means strong enough to challenge the resolute Publius Attius Varus who commanded Pompey's forces hereabouts. All civilized Africa now acknowledged the Senate's sovereignty: Varus, having escaped from Osimo, as related above, and crossed into Africa, had become governor of the Province, where he not only raised two legions from the Roman settlers but induced King Juba to levy troops throughout Numidia. Juba ruled the most extensive kingdom in the world; it consisted largely of burning desert sands, and stretched from Mount Atlas, as far westward as Cadiz, to the Indian Ocean in the east, being bounded on the north by the Mediterranean, and on the south by the Oasis of Ammon, which lies a great distance inland from the Gulf of Sirte.

Numerous tribes arrived at Varus's camp: Autoleans from Tangier, Numidian nomads, bareback Gaetulian horsemen, Moors as brown as Indians, needy Nasamonians, swift-riding Marmaridaeans, sunburned Garamantians, Mazagian javelin-throwers whose aim is as true as any Persian archer's, Massylians who ride bareback, too, and guide their horses with switches, not bit and bridle; finally a contingent of those African lion-hunters who never travel without their huts, and throw cloaks around the heads of the roaring beasts before venturing to spear them.

It was private resentment no less than partisanship that brought King Juba to Pompey's support. Curio, in the year of his Tribuneship, when he disgraced himself in the eyes of Gods and men by covertly trying to make Caesar a despot, had introduced a bill to remove Juba from his ancestral throne. Since Juba believed that the civil war had been occasioned by the failure of this attempt, news of his approach caused Curio some anxiety. Besides, many of his men were lukewarm in Caesar's cause, and had never fought under him on the Rhine, being troops who had deserted to him at Corfinium. He feared that they had no greater attachment to their new cause than to the old, and indeed felt little love for either. Observing the half-hearted way in which they carried out orders, and their widespread dereliction of sentry duty on the ramparts at night, he grew thoroughly alarmed and spoke to his officers as follows:

'The best mask for demoralization is daring; so let us take the offensive. While we can still control these troops, I intend to march them across the plain. Idleness breeds unreliability, but once they are committed to battle we need fear no rebellion. Give a man a sword and a helmet to hide his blushes, and the passion for bloodshed will soon rise in him. Instead of stopping to consider whether Pompey's or Caesar's cause may be the more righteous, he will fight for the side that happens to have enlisted him. It is the same with gladiators in the arena: they nurse no political grudges but merely hate whatever opponent is pitted against them.'

Curio then marshalled his forces on the plain, and Fortune, though planning to ruin him later, smiled on him that day: he was allowed to drive Varus ignominiously from the field and chase him back to camp without meeting any opposition from his rearguard.

The news delighted King Juba, who rejoiced to think that the glory of this campaign would now be his. He marched off in haste, enforcing the strictest secrecy about all military movements; his only fear being that Curio's men, flushed with success, would hear of his advance and be sobered into caution. He then sent forward his second-in-command, Suburra, to skirmish with the enemy at the head of a small cavalry force and make them mistake this for an unsupported action. Juba's main body, meanwhile, massed out of sight in a valley. Thus the crafty ichneumon makes an Egyptian snake raise its head by provocatively waving his tail; then in a flash, turning his own head sideways, catches the snake by the throat, and forces the poison to trickle harmlessly from its mouth.

King Juba's tactics proved equally successful. That night Curio rashly ordered his cavalry to fan out across the plain, which he had not troubled to reconnoitre; and though repeatedly, if vainly, warned never to trust the Numidians who, like the Carthaginians, were adepts in every kind of stratagem and ruse, he sounded the infantry's advance at the first signs of dawn. Curio's men were doomed, and so was Curio himself, the prime instigator of the civil war. He led them along a dangerous path, over rocks and crags until at last he caught a distant sight of the enemy from a hill-top. The Numidians showed their native cunning by a gradual retirement, drawing him down from high ground and making his troops straggle through open country.

Curio thought that they were trying to escape and descended confidently to the plain; whereupon the Numidian light horse occupied the surrounding heights, with so rapid an enveloping movement that cowards in Curio's ranks were too stupefied to run off, and brave men to show fight. Moreover, the Roman cavalry had exhausted themselves. When the trumpets sounded the charge, their horses failed to respond as usual: there was no kicking up of heels until the stones flew about, no champing of bits, no tossing of manes, no pricking of ears, no refusal to stand still. The poor beasts merely hung their heads; their legs reeked of sweat, their tongues lolled from parched mouths, their lungs wheezed and their flanks laboured, their bits were caked with foam and dried blood. They were forced into a trot, not only by blows of the whip, digs of the whip-handle and pricks of the spur, but by sword stabs; yet to little purpose, since no effective charge could be launched. All that happened was that their riders came just near enough to offer the enemy an easy target for a volley of javelins.

On the other hand, the Libyan counter-attack made the plain re-echo with a fierce drumming of hooves on the baked soil. A cloud of dust, like those raised by Thracian whirlwinds, rose and darkened the sky. From that moment, the unfortunate Roman infantry had no hope of survival, for death pursued them mercilessly. They could not rush forward and come to grips with the enemy because, simultaneously attacked in flank and rear, they were subjected both to javelin thrusts from close quarters and to a storm of javelins, hurled from a distance, which bore them down by sheer weight of metal. As a result, the two legions bunched together for protection, and any front rank soldier who tried to retreat came up against the drawn swords of his comrades pressing behind. Gradually the net tightened as Juba's men closed in, crowding the Romans until they no longer had room to use their weapons. The crush was so great that breastplate cracked against breastplate; yet the Numidians were denied the glorious spectacle offered by their victory – torrents of blood and men collapsing from suffocation – because no corpse had even space to fall.

This massacre of Romans in a Roman cause on African soil served as a propitiatory sacrifice to the murderous shades of Hannibal and those other Carthaginians who had suffered such hardships at the hands of our ancestors. Yet how outrageous that this disaster should have been to the advantage of Pompey and approved by the Senate! Far better if those Africans had defeated us in pursuit of their own national ambitions.

When Curio saw that the troops were being massacred before his eyes and, as it were, laying the dust of battle with their blood, he did not have the heart to escape. He welcomed death and, emboldened by despair, died in the thick of the fighting. What solace was it to him that he had inflamed popular feeling and armed all the nations of the world by his eloquent speeches from the Rostrum, which the Tribunes of the People had made their stronghold? Or that he had betrayed the Senatorial cause by accepting Caesar's bribes and thus made the clash between him and Pompey inevitable? There lay Curio; never to witness the climax of that fatal feud on the battlefield of Pharsalus. Such is the penalty that powerful men like him force their unhappy countries to exact: they pay with their own blood for the wars which they have instigated. How fortunate Rome would be, now and for all time, if the Gods were always as careful to preserve her freedom as to avenge it!

Curio died well, and though his body was left unburied for the Libyan carrion birds to tear, I cannot omit here to touch upon those good actions of his which will always be remembered; and therefore give praise where praise is due. No Roman of greater natural gifts had ever been born, and none deserved better of his country while he still respected the Constitution. But his character proved to be unstable, and in that age of ambition, luxury, and destructive wealth, he was swept away by the torrent of corruption. Curio ceased to be Curio when, dazzled by the gold that Caesar had won from the Gauls, he began meddling in politics.

Sulla won his sovereignty by the sword, as also did bold Marius, bloody-minded Cinna, and the long line of Caesars; yet none of them had the opportunity of doing what Curio did. They all bought the City; he sold it.

BOOK FIVE

By thus judiciously alternating victory with defeat, Fortune kept an even balance between Pompeians and Caesareans; ensuring that when the two main armies clashed in Thessaly, they would be well matched.

Mount Haemus was already sprinkled with snow, the Pleiads had set, and January approached, the opening month of the Calendar, when the new Consuls elected would give their names to the next twelve; so the Consuls of the expiring year sent out messages convening all Senators, whatever military duty they might have undertaken abroad, to a meeting in Epirus. The building in which the noble Senators now assembled as guests of a foreign country, to discuss State affairs, was mean and looked un-Roman. I hesitate to describe it as a camp headquarters because the presence of the Consuls with their axes and fasces (the symbols of sovereignty authorized by the laws of Rome), and of the worshipful Order of Senators, proved that these were not partisans of Pompey's, but contrariwise, he of theirs.

Lucius Cornelius, from his raised chair, interrupted the first gloomy silence.

'My lords,' he said, 'be worthy of your old Roman blood: forget for awhile that you are exiles here in Epirus, far from our conquered City. Look around you, rather, and pass this preliminary decree, as you have every right to do: that this assembly constitutes the Senate, and that all foreign kings and nations are expected to recognize it as such. Wherever the fortunes of war may take us, whether to the far North, or to the hot and humid South where the days and nights are always of equal length, the State moves with us, and imperial authority remains in our hands. Once, when the Gauls set fire to the Capitol, Camillus made Veii his headquarters; so that, for the time being, Veii became Rome. The Senate has never forfeited its sovereignty by a mere change of venue. Granted, Caesar is master of Rome, but the buildings where we used to transact our business are now empty and silent; as are also the Law Courts in the Forum, closed by this long and dismal holiday. No Senators are available for a meeting in the House, except perhaps those few whom we expelled before coming to Epirus. Every member of this venerable body who is not still living as an exile – in Italy! – may be seen here to-day.

'A reign of uninterrupted peace had made us grow up ignorant of what civil war implied, and the sudden fury of revolt consequently scattered us in all directions. Yet behold us again – lopped limbs, as it were, magically assembling and being reunited to the parent trunk. I need not remind you how Heaven has repaired our loss of Italy by persuading every army in the world to assist us. Moreover, some of our enemies lie sunk beneath the Illyrian waves and Curio, Caesar's chief Senatorial supporter, has fallen on the stricken fields of Libya.

'My lords, raise your standards, hasten the march of destiny, trust the Gods! You fled from Caesar because you knew that your cause was righteous; let the fortune that has since attended our arms confirm you in this knowledge. The calendar year is drawing to a close, and my colleague and I must resign our powers; but your powers are inalienable. I now therefore move that, for all our sakes, you appoint Pompey a dictator!'

Hearty applause greeted this speech, and the Senators laid the fate of Rome, and their own fate too, in Pompey's hands. Next, they awarded honours to such kings and nations as had earned their gratitude – among them the Rhodians, Apollo's favourites, and the dour Spartans who live beyond Mount Taygetus. Then Phocis was created a free state, in recognition of the heroism and loyalty shown by Marseilles, her daughter-city, and compliments were also bestowed on the famous old city of Athens; on Sadales and his brave father Cotys, King of Thrace; on Diotarus, King of Galatia; and on Rhasipolis, who ruled a chilly district of Thrace between Mount Rhodope and the sea. Another Senatorial edict placed all Libya under the sole sovereignty of King Juba; and finally – how cruel is Fate! – Ptolemy XII was authorized to wear the crown bequeathed his ancestor Ptolemy Lagus by Alexander the Great. The treacherous Egyptians deserved to be ruled by this new Ptolemy, who accepted the sword of state and later used it remorselessly against them. If only they had been the sole sufferers! But his reign proved a disgrace to Fortune and to the Gods because the Senate, in conferring the throne on him, unwittingly added the life of Pompey to their award. Moreover, this decree deprived his sister Cleopatra of her joint-rights in the kingdom and, as it proved, spared Caesar the odium of murdering his son-in-law.

The meeting then broke up, and the Senators went off again to assume their military commands. But while every nation and every leader prepared for the coming struggle, careless of the future, Appius Claudius Pulcher alone shrank from taking arms until he had asked advice from Heaven. He approached the Delphic Oracle, which had been closed to the public for many years, and consulted the god Apollo. The town of Delphi stands on Mount Parnassus, the only mountain that showed above the waters during Deucalion's flood; even so, one of its twin peaks was submerged. These peaks rise exactly midway between the eastern and western limits of the world and are sacred to Apollo and Dionysus, whom the Theban Bacchantes regard as respectively the immortal and the mortal aspects of the god celebrated in their triennial festival. Delphi was once the lair of the Python, whom Juno sent to persecute Leto when Juppiter had got her with child. Leto's son, Apollo, came here soon afterwards to avenge her and, though not yet a practised archer, shot Python dead. At that time the Oracle belonged to Juppiter's aunt Themis; but Apollo, understanding that a vapour which rose from the Delphic chasm made anyone who inhaled it speak divine truth, seized it from her for his own prophetic use.

Which of the immortal Gods, I wonder, has condescended to leap down from Heaven and ensconce himself in those dark subterranean grottoes, with the weight of the mountain piled upon him? He must be very powerful, because he knows every link in the eternal chain of events; and has a divine share in the secret knowledge of things to come; and also very obliging, because he makes revelations to all mankind. It is doubtful, of course, whether this god merely predicts the future or whether he directs it by his oracular declarations. Perhaps a large element of the divine is embedded in the earth and acts as its ruler, incidentally supporting our terrestrial globe as it floats on empty space; and that, though closely associated with Juppiter on high, this essence seeps up from the chasm at Delphi. There the priestess inhales it, and when it reaches her heart she bellows prophecies for all to hear; very much as the flames in the crater of Etna send lava boiling over its lip; or as the Giant Typhoeus, who lies everlastingly buried under the island of Ischia,[1] scorches the rocks of Campania in his struggles to escape.

Every honest visitant may approach this holy spot, but it must never be defiled by criminals. Moreover, no wicked requests are whispered here, since prayer is banned – the god merely announces irrevocable doom. He shows favour to the just; indeed, he has often allotted new homes to the entire population of cities which have had to be abandoned – Tyre, for instance. He has also encouraged others to fight in self-defence, as he did for the Athenians before the Battle of Salamis; and ended famines by disclosing the remedy, or epidemics by explaining their origin. The world suffers no heavier loss than when, at times, the Delphic Oracle is closed because certain great ones, afraid of the future, have stopped the god's mouth.[2] His priestesses alone do not regret the ban, since the oracular frenzy – which is both a gift and a punishment – shortens their lives; the vehemence of the inspiration proving too much for flesh and blood to endure indefinitely.

When Appius came to consult the Oracle, intent on learning the secrets of Rome's destiny, no priestess had occupied the sacred tripod for many years and silence therefore reigned on the towering crag. However, he ordered the priest to open the Temple and usher the Pythoness into Apollo's sacred presence. Her name was Phemonoë, and she was strolling idly from the Castalian Spring towards the laurel grove when he seized her, dragged her to the shrine and pushed her inside; but being afraid to enter the innermost sanctuary, she tried to discourage Appius's curiosity by prevarication. 'Appius,' she said, 'why do you take it upon yourself to demand the truth? Responses no longer come from the chasm; it is as though the god lay buried far

1. Two early attempts to colonize Ischia were defeated by earthquakes and minor volcanic eruptions.

2. Pyrrhus, King of Epirus, is said to have temporarily silenced the Oracle; but, although the temple was plundered by Sulla, it continued in operation until Nero consulted it more than a century later. Nero was refused a response, on the ground that he had killed his mother and that the countenancing of so notorious a crime would defile the sacred precincts. In revenge he closed the temple, after sacrificing an ass to Apollo (who liked ass-sacrifice), and stole five hundred bronze statues; but it was reopened after his death, and Pythonesses continued to serve the Oracle until the reign of the Christian Emperor Theodosius, who finally abolished it.

below. Perhaps the spirit of inspiration has deserted the oracular vent, and found an outlet in some distant country; or perhaps, when the Gauls sacked and burned this Temple, the ashes drifted into the chasm, blocking Apollo's path. It may even be that the Gods themselves have silenced the Oracle, on the ground that the Sibylline verses entrusted to you Romans should be sufficient for your purposes. Or is it that Apollo, who forbids criminals to enter this Temple, has found no living person worthy of his confidences?'

Phemonoë was clearly not telling the truth; her very agitation suggested that the god must still be at work. So the priest tied one laurel wreath, bound with white wool, above her brow in the form of a fillet, and used another to secure the long tresses behind. But Phemonoë, as yet unwilling to seat herself on a tripod in the innermost sanctuary, came to a sudden halt just beyond the Temple threshold, pretending to be possessed. What she said was uttered neither wildly nor incoherently, as it would have been had the god taken possession of her; and this new subterfuge wronged the oracular credit of Apollo even more than Appius. The sound of her voice, which did not echo tremendously through the Temple vaults; the laurel wreaths which stayed on her head instead of being tossed off by the bristling of her hair; and the failure of the Temple threshold to shake or the laurel grove to quiver – all these signs convinced Appius that she shrank from submitting to Apollo's power. He shouted angrily: 'You impious creature, I have come to inquire about the fate of this distracted world. Unless you stop speaking in your natural voice and go down at once to the chasm for true inspiration, the gods whose Oracles you are taking in vain will punish you – and so will I!'

Appius's violence terrified her into action. She approached the lip of the great chasm and seated herself on the tripod. Then for the first time she experienced the divine afflatus, still active after so many centuries, and Apollo genuinely possessed her at last. He forced his way into her heart, masterful as ever, driving out her private thoughts and draining her body of all that was mortal, so that he could possess it wholly. She went blundering frantically about the shrine, with the God mounted on the nape of her neck, knocking over the tripods that stood in her path. The hair rose on her scalp and when she tossed her head the wreaths went flying across the bare floor. Apollo's fury was so fierce that fire seemed to boil from her mouth. He whipped her, goaded her, darted flames into her intestines; but at the same time kept her on the curb and prevented her from disclosing as much as she knew. Countless centuries crowded tormentingly in her breast; rival secrets contended within her for utterance. She understood all that was or would be, from the beginning of the world to its very end, and could have revealed the laws that govern the Ocean or the number of sands on every shore in existence. But just as the Sibyl of Cumae (a Euboean colony) disliked being made the repository of so many national destinies, and therefore haughtily chose that of Rome for sole revelation – so Phemonoë went through a distressing search among the fates of far more important men than Appius before she finally came upon his own. As soon as she recognized it, her mouth foamed frenziedly; she groaned, gasped, uttered weird sounds, and made the huge cave re-echo with her dismal shrieks. In the end Apollo forced her to use intelligible speech, and here is the response she gave:

'Appius, you shall avoid the tremendous perils of warfare,
Taking your lonesome ease in Euboea, that haven of refuge.'
This was all, because Apollo cut short the prophecy.

I wonder why the divine oracles, capable of universal truth, especially the Oracle of Apollo, from whom the Gods hide no single secret, were disinclined to reveal the closing chapter in this fatal history – the fall of generals, the death of kings, the ruin of so many nations, which Rome's civil war implied. Was it that the Gods themselves had not yet decided on this catastrophe, that the stars were equally doubtful whether or not Pompey should be killed, and that therefore the fate of multitudes could not yet be confidently predicted? Or was the silence due to policy: a decision to let Fortune have her own way and – because a Brutus once took heroic vengeance on the tyrannical King Tarquin – to give no warning that might deter another man of the same name from curtailing the mad ambitions of Julius Caesar?

The Priestess ran full tilt against the Temple doors, broke them open and rushed out. She was still in an ecstasy, not having been able to expel the god; who continued to prevent her from telling Appius the full story. Her eyes rolled wildly as she gazed at the sky, and her expression changed continuously: never placid, but varying between alarm and menace. Her cheeks were alternately scarlet and deathly pale, and this was a paleness which induced rather than registered fear. As yet she felt no relief after her labours, but was shaken by heavy sobs, as the sea goes on roaring hoarsely even when a northerly gale has dropped; and before her spirit could be restored to the common light of day, a spell of unconsciousness intervened. Apollo was washing her mind with Lethe water, to make her forget the fateful secrets she had learned during his effulgent visitation. The spirit of divine truth departed and returned whence it had come; Phemonoë collapsed on the floor, and was revived with difficulty.

The oracle, however, being ambiguous deceived Appius into think-ing that he stood in no danger of immediate death. Though none could yet foresee who would be master of the world, he cheerfully decided to make himself master of Chalcis in Euboea. The fool never thought to ask what god, save Death alone, could assure his escape from the shock of war and the widespread suffering that this would entail. He was fated to take his 'lonesome ease in Euboea, that haven of refuge' by being buried in a sequestered but famous tomb near the asbestos quarries of Carystos. It faces across the narrow sea towards Rhamnos in Attica – a town sacred to Nemesis, the goddess who punishes human ambition. In between lie the so-called 'Hollows of Euboea', where the sea is disturbed by the rapid, constantly-shifting current from the straits: the same current that sets the ships of Chalcis adrift and swings them across to Aulis in Boeotia – the fatal shore whence Agamemnon's fleet once sailed to Troy.

Meanwhile Caesar had completed his pacification of Spain and was about to march elsewhere, when the Gods nearly put an end to his run of successes, at Placentia. Although he had never been defeated in war, he all but forfeited the rewards of wickedness by a revolt of the very soldiers who had served faithfully in so many of his campaigns, but who at last wearied of bloodshed and prepared to desert him. It is an arguable question whether the brief respite from fighting – the silence of the trumpet, the sword tamely sheathed – caused this change of heart; it may rather have been that, in repudiating Caesar's cause, these wretches were hoping to sell their swords back to him again, at a higher price than before. At all events, Caesar had never known better than now how insecurely he was placed; he could feel the pinnacle, from which he gazed down on the rest of the world, sway under him. Though trying to involve so many nations in war, he found himself deserted by his troops and practically reduced to using his own sword; the moral being that once war has been declared, it is the common soldier, not the general, who counts. Fear of their officers no longer obliged the troops to bottle up their secret anger or express it only in timid grumbling; and it ceased to be a case of every man thinking that he alone resented Caesar's high-handedness. Dissatisfaction had become so widespread that, on the contrary, the men inspired fear in the officers. Their very numbers were an encouragement to mutiny: if thousands joined in, it was argued, they could not all be punished.

They shouted at their officers: 'Release us from this wicked war. Caesar thinks nothing of our lives; he drags us with him across land and sea, taking it for granted that we will support him in whatever quarrel he picks. Some of us fell in Gaul, some in those hard Spanish campaigns, others in Italy; he wins victories throughout the world, but we pay for them. We march north and reduce the Rhône and the Rhine – and how does he reward us? By committing us to civil war! Yet when we drove the Senate from Rome, and captured it, he forbade us to plunder either temples or private houses. He hounds us on from one crime to another, but though we are guilty of bloodshed, nobody can accuse us of making money that way. Is there no limit to his ambitions? Why was it not enough for him to become master of Rome? We have gone grey in his service. Look: these are already the hands and arms of old men! Let him disband us and allow us to end our days in peace, now that we have wasted our prime in fighting and missed all the pleasures of life. That surely is not much to ask!

'We want to be spared the fate of lying mortally wounded on the hard ramparts of a camp: from breathing our last with helmets still tightly pressed on our heads, after calling in vain for a friendly hand to close our eyes. Let each of us die at home, pillowed on the breast of a weeping wife, while an individual pyre stands ready to burn the corpse – no more of those communal pyres for us! Why not succumb to an ordinary sickness instead of always falling in action? Caesar lures us on with vain hopes, as if we were too stupid to realize for what horrid feats he is training us.

'Does he think we are the only serving soldiers who do not know how traitors can best enrich themselves – which is by murdering we need not say whom? Neither the oath of loyalty we swore, nor the laws of Rome, can prevent us from saying that though Caesar commanded on the Rhine, here he is merely our fellow-citizen; because the crime of invading Italy has cancelled distinctions in rank. Besides, all our courage is wasted if he ungratefully attributes to Fortune the hard victories we win.

'Caesar must understand, in fact, that his fate depends on us veterans. It is useless to count on the Gods' favour; if he provokes our anger, the war will end here and now. His campaigns have been fought in vain if he has not yet learned that we stick at nothing.'

They ran furiously through the camp, bawling for Caesar. At this point, where loyalty and duty had alike broken down, and the only hope for peace lay in Caesar's assassination, the Gods might surely have encouraged such a grave breach of discipline; yet they refrained.

I can think of no other general in history who would not have been terrified by a mutiny on this scale. But Caesar was always ready to run extraordinary risks and stake his entire fortune on a throw. Instead of waiting for the mutineers to calm down, he left his quarters at once and defied their rage. Doubtless he would not have grudged them leave, if necessary, to sack cities, plunder temples – even that of Capitoline Juppiter himself – or outrage the mothers and daughters of senators; on the contrary, he would have been delighted had they asked his permission to commit every sort of atrocity. He wanted them to consider the spoils of war worth winning; for this sudden violent return to their senses had taken him aback. He should, really, have blushed to be in favour of war when everyone else had so roundly condemned it. Why should it be his soldiers who wearied of bloodshed and rejected the rule of the sword, while he was still eager to carve out his fortune for good or ill? Why could he not have taken a rest and enjoyed the benefits of peace, bringing the wicked war to an end? Why this merciless insistence on glory, this forcing of men to fight against their wills?

One would have thought that he had lost control of the situation, until he climbed to the top sods of a rampart and stood there so calmly that his bravado frightened them all. 'Men,' he said, 'just now you brandished your swords and yelled threats at me – in my absence! Very well, here I am, and if you really wish to finish this war, here is my bared breast; I give you leave to stab me through, and then slink off. But no! I can see that you have no fight left in you; this is one of those mutinies that begin and end in talk. Call yourself soldiers! All that you ever think of is running away. I have never lost a battle, and yet you are battle-weary! Be off, cowards, and let me carry on this war by myself. It will be easy to enlist new troops and arm them with the swords you discard. In fact, I shall be delighted that brave men are using them for a change.

'Listen: if a large fleet and a great number of Italian troops have joined Pompey even since his abandonment of Rome, what can I not expect? My victories will enable me to enlist as many men as I need, anxious to win the rewards of this war – which is already as good as won – and so deprive you of them, after your so-called hardships. They are the fellows who will walk in triumphal procession behind my laurelled chariot, though without a wound to show for their victory, and leave you poor old wretches standing in the gutter among the rabble of Rome, to watch us go by! And I will certainly not miss you for a moment, now that you have deserted me. It is as though all the rivers went on strike and threatened not to flow into the sea. Do you think that the sea-level would be appreciably altered, whatever their decision? And when did your courage ever save the day while I was your commander? It would be beneath the Gods' dignity to spare a thought for the lives of rascals like you. Great events are the work of a few great men; and humankind exists only for their sake. While you were known as Caesar's soldiers, I made you the terror of the Iberians and Gauls; had you been Pompey's, you would have run away. Titus Labienus was a fine general when he served under me; but he has thrown in his lot with Pompey, and now look at him! Labienus is on the run, and utterly worthless.[1]

'I shall have no better opinion of your loyalty, even if you remain neutral in the war. Whoever deserts my standard without joining Pompey's forces shows an inveterate dislike of me! So I thank the Gods for to-day's favour; they clearly intend to give me a change of troops before the decisive battle takes place. I have had a great many anxieties of late, and it comes as an immense relief to me that I can at last decently disband you greedy and ambitious rascals, and thus feel free to fight battles when and where I please. So get out, and leave these standards for real soldiers to follow – you pack of cowardly civilians!

'Nevertheless, a few of you must stay here – not to serve, but

---

1. Later, after murdering the Caesarean prisoners taken at Dyrrhachium, Labienus helped Pompey to lose the battle of Pharsalus; shared the defeat of Cato and Scipio at Thapsus; and was finally killed at Munda, which he also helped to lose.

to die. I intend to execute every tenth man. Down on the ground, traitors – prepare to lose your heads! And since the backbone of my army will henceforth be formed by recruits, all recently enlisted men are ordered to stand fast and witness the executions. They may as well learn at once how to kill and be killed.'

Caesar's violent threats cowed the mutineers. Nothing would have been easier for so many thousands of men than to degrade him from his command. Yet he inspired such terror that he seemed able to make every sword obey him, even though the owner himself might refuse to handle it. Caesar felt a certain anxiety that no one would come forward to implement his command; but since the strongest bond that unites criminals is the rule of 'kill and be killed', the troops put up with more than he had dared hope. Eventually he consented to re-enlist the disbanded mutineers, without decimation, if they would hand over twelve ringleaders to justice; which they did. Order was restored and the veterans discovered that every one of their grievances had been settled by the executions.

He now sent his army to Brindisi by forced marches, allowing them nine days on the road. They must also commandeer all vessels which could serve as transports, and direct them to the same port. Detachments were sent for that purpose to Otranto and Leuca in remote Calabria; to the ancient Sicilian city of Taranto; to Salapia which is backed by a marsh, and Sipuntum which is backed by a hill – both Apulian ports in the neighbourhood of Mount Garganus. This promontory with its famous oak-woods, where immense herds of pigs fatten, juts out into the Adriatic and catches the full force both of the north wind blowing from Dalmatia and of the south blowing from Calabria.

Caesar himself, without troops, but no less safe for that, hurried to Rome, which he had terrified into obeying him even though he arrived in civilian dress. Yielding to what was allegedly a popular demand, he assumed the name of Dictator and let himself be named co-Consul with Publius Servilius – what an honour for the Calendar! – which was when we first began pretending that the titles bestowed on our emperors are constitutional. Caesar wished, in fact, to justify his illegal use of a provincial army, by fraudulently adopting the rank of Consul and thus adding rods and axes to his armoury! It was appropriate that this legal fiction made the year notorious: for no man had a better right than Caesar to name the year in which Pharsalus was fought!

The annual election on the Campus Martius had been a farce. A herald ceremoniously announced the names of tribes entitled to vote, put pebbles bearing these names into an urn, shook them up, and presently read out one by one the order in which the tribes would vote – although all were excluded from the Campus, so that, when it came to the point, no voting took place. What was more, the College of Augurs had been forbidden to make any prognostications which might postpone the elections; even if a thunderstorm broke, or an owl appeared on the left hand, officially all signs would be favourable. Thus for the first time the once venerated office of Consul lost authority and began to decline – the only reason for its continuance to-day being that each new year is required by the Annals to have a distinguishing name; which means that we now have a so-called 'Consul of the Month'. And though Caesar celebrated the Latin Holiday, ending with the traditional bonfire to Latin Juppiter – patron of Alba Longa, the town founded by Ascanius the Trojan – this was most ironical, since Latium had become a conquered country. He settled his business at Rome and hurried over the fields of Apulia (which the negligent local farmers no longer hoed, having let the cornland revert to pasture) until he reached Brindisi. There he found the fleet at anchor and afraid to venture out while the winter storms still reigned. It shocked him to think that, at the very time when the war should have been brought to a rapid conclusion, his men were making the weather an excuse for their idleness; whereas his enemies, though less favoured by Fortune, sailed in any direction they pleased. He addressed the transport commanders, none of them seamen by profession, saying: 'You ought to have realized how much safer it would be to sail at this season than during the rainy Spring when the wind constantly changes its quarter. At present it is violent but steady, and we need not row cautiously along the shore. Let us run straight across the Adriatic with a following wind. The harder it blows, the better; I should like to see it blow until each top mast bends. By running over at full speed we will be safe from Pompey's galleys which are based on Corfu. Now, then, cut the cables and let us be off at once on our voyage of victory, before we lose the protection of the stormy weather.'

The sun had sunk in the western waves, the first stars were already in the sky, and the full moon threw shadows, when Caesar's fleet weighed anchor. His crews unfurled the sails, bent the yard-ends to port, thus slanting the canvas to the wind, and hoisted the top-sails to take full advantage of what breeze might be blowing aloft. A land-breeze sprang up and carried the fleet out of port; but presently deserted it, letting the sails droop idly against the masts. A dead calm reigned; the water was as motionless as a stagnant pool; or as the Black Sea when it is covered with icebergs, and the frozen Danube no longer rushes into it, and the Bosphorus has ceased to flow – when every ship is imprisoned by black frost, and the Bessian nomads can drive their carts across the Sea of Azov, now a solid sheet of ice.

A sullen silence prevailed. The Adriatic seemed deserted by the lively powers of Nature; it forgot to ebb and flow, or even to ripple; and no moonbeams danced on its surface. Caesar's fleet lay in great peril, an easy prey to Pompey's galleys had they rowed out – and to famine too, being as it were beleagured by the flat calm. The soldiers were offering unusual prayers for protection against this unusual danger: prayers for a violent storm to rouse the stagnant water and transform it into a real sea again. No indications of a change were visible; the night sky remained cloudless, and even shipwreck would have seemed a welcome alternative to these doldrums. But when dawn broke bright and clear, a breeze set the sea in motion and brought the distant Ceraunian mountains a little closer. Presently it freshened, the ships gathered way and began to leave a wake behind, until at last they were bowling along with their sails a-bulge, to drop anchor safely in the bay of Palaeste.

The first region where Caesar and Pompey encamped near each other was the part of Illyria watered by the Iskumi and Crevasta. Whereas the Crevasta flows slowly and quietly out of a lake, and can therefore be navigated, the Iskumi is a rapid stream which drains the mountains whenever sun or rain thaws their covering of snow. Neither river has a long course, the coastal strip being narrow at this point.

Here, then, Fortune matched the famous rivals, but unhappily the world was deceived in its hopes that, when separated only by the cramped valley of the Crevasta, they might reconsider their wicked feud and come to terms. Each could see the other's face and even hear his voice, nor had Caesar ever enjoyed so close a view of his affectionate son-in-law since the family tie was dissolved by the death of Julia and her two poor children – and never would again, either, until Pompey lay dead on the sands of Egypt.

Though Caesar was desperate to take the offensive, the behaviour of his followers in Italy obliged him to postpone this evil intention. Bold Mark Antony who commanded there was already – so early in the civil wars – plotting to turn against him, as he afterwards turned against another Caesar at Actium.[1] Caesar sent Antony constant messages, alternately threatening and pleading, in demand of immediate reinforcements. 'I must make you responsible,' he wrote, 'for all the present misery. Why do you try to alter the course of destiny, which the Gods have mapped out? I have made every possible preparation with my usual speed, winning victory after victory; nothing needs to be added but the finishing touch, and you alone can give it. Anyone would think that I was somewhere in Libya, cut off from you by the shoals and quicksands of the Gulf of Sirte. Have I asked you to risk your army by taking it over a sea that I have been afraid to cross myself, or exposing it to unknown dangers? I led the way when the Pompeians not only controlled the Adriatic but were able to prevent my landing. Are you still afraid to join me, now that I have consolidated my position? You are squandering the precious days which fate has granted me; you force me to spend my time praying for the waves to subside and the winds to blow fair. Why do you discourage your brave men from attempting the passage? Unless I am much mistaken, they would face even shipwreck if it brought them alive to my camp. Let me reproach you by pointing out how unfair a division of territory this is: you rule all Italy, whereas I have to share Illyria with the Senatorial forces!'

Since this stream of messages failed to rouse Antony, Caesar, who always believed that the Gods were more loyal to him than he to them, did voluntarily what Antony had shrunk from doing even when ordered. Experience had taught him that Fortune favours the brave, and he prepared to defy the night sea by launching a small boat in weather that would have terrified the commander of a fleet.

Silence reigned in the dark camp; the third hour had come, and though the second watch was supposedly on duty, every man had fallen asleep, exhausted by the camp routine. Night gave a brief

1. 31 B.C., where Mark Antony and Cleopatra fought against the fleet of Caesar's heir Octavian, afterwards Augustus.

respite to the poor fellows who were able to forget their troubles in this way, being only private soldiers without responsibility. Walking cautiously through the silent gloom, Caesar did what even a desperate slave would hardly have attempted: he broke out of camp unarmed and quite alone except for the companionship of the Goddess Fortune. He skirted the tents, stepping over the recumbent sentries (however vexed that he could evade their vigilance so easily); then slipped out of a gate and walked along the coast until he came upon a dinghy moored in a small cove. Amyclas, the owner and skipper, lived in a near-by shack, built of rush-and-reed hurdles without timber supports; only the seaward side was protected against the weather by an overturned boat.

Caesar banged at this makeshift door until the roof shook, and at last woke Amyclas, who was asleep on a soft couch of seaweed. 'Is that a shipwrecked sailor?' Amyclas shouted. 'Or has some other distressed person happened to find my hut?' He pulled an old rope-end from under the ashes of his fire, and blew softly on the smouldering butt until it burst into flames. Amyclas was not frightened of the visitor, knowing that humble shelters like his own were not plundered even in times of civil war. Though poor, he lived a safe and peaceful life; and it is a comment on the lack of appreciation with which most people view the bounty of nature, that no temple and no fortified town could then have said with Amyclas: 'When Caesar knocks, why should I feel alarm?'

He opened the door and Caesar entered, disguised as an undistinguished traveller, though he found it difficult to speak like one. 'Young man,' he said, 'I bring good news. You can look forward to being richer than you ever dreamed. I want you to take me across the sea without delay. If you land me safely in Italy you need never again rely on your dinghy for a livelihood; in fact, I undertake that you will have no cause to complain of poverty even in your old age.'

Amyclas answered: 'I do not trust the sea to-night, after the adverse signs I saw before going to bed. When the Sun sank, his disk was cut by a dark horizontal patch which prevented the rays from forming a symmetrical ring about it; he shone dimly and no crimson clouds rode overhead. Then, when the Moon rose, instead of shining bright and clear with sharp, well-defined horns, she looked sallow, sad, and reddish – which is a sign of wind – and soon disappeared behind a cloud bank. Listen, do you hear the soughing in the tree-tops and the roar of breakers on the coast? What is more, I noticed that the dolphins were gambolling oddly as though challenging the waves to rise; and that the gulls had taken refuge ashore; and that so had the cormorants, which usually fly above the sea and dive for fish; and that a crow was lurching about on the beach and getting its head wet with spray – a sure sign of rain! I do not at all like the look of things. Nevertheless, if your journey is one of exceptional importance, I cannot very well refuse my help; so let us go where you want, until wind and waves prove too much for us.'

They went out to the dinghy, Amyclas unmoored her and, as soon as they were both aboard, hoisted the sail. By now the wind was blowing so hard that it seemed not only to change the course of the meteors as they streaked across the sky, but to shake the very stars. The black water shuddered, an enormous swell arose, and the long ugly waves driving this way and that showed that a hurricane was brewing.

As the boat pitched and tossed, Amyclas said: 'We are in great danger, but the sea is so choppy that I cannot tell from which quarter to expect the wind. The clouds suggest a southerly gale, but the roar of the sea inclines me to think that it will be a north-wester. We shall never reach Italy in such weather, even if we are wrecked and try to swim ashore. Our sole hope of survival is to abandon this impossible attempt; and if you do not let me turn about at once the dinghy will be too badly battered to make land anywhere.'

Yet Caesar was still confident. 'Pay no attention to the sea,' he shouted, 'and spread all your canvas! Although Heaven may forbid you to sail for Italy, such are my orders. Your sole excuse for fear can be that you have not recognized me; as the man whom the Gods never desert, and whom Fortune would never dare ill-treat unless he fawned on her. Steer into the teeth of the storm and trust in me. The bad weather concerns only the sea and sky, not this boat; for I am Caesar. My presence aboard her is an insurance against shipwreck, and will in fact protect the sea from the fury of the winds, which in the circumstances cannot be allowed to blow much longer. No: I forbid you to put her about; use your sail to sweep us clear away from Epirus. As soon as we reach an Italian harbour, you will realize that it was the one possible place where we could have moored in safety. Understand, meanwhile, that this wild tumult of sea and sky merely means that the Goddess Fortune is considering how best to please me.'

He had hardly finished speaking when a hurricane struck the dinghy, stripped off sails and rigging and strained the timbers until they groaned aloud. Winds from every region of the world assembled to destroy her. First a westerly gale, which had already made the Atlantic labour, invaded the Adriatic, and would have driven its waves as high as the cliff-tops had not a chill north wind from Scythia caught them on the flank and prevented this; so that the sea grew confused, not knowing which master to obey. And though the North Wind gained the advantage by twisting the waves about with such force that the sea-bed showed far below, the swell he raised never reached its objective, a line of cliffs to the south, because the westerly wind fended it off. The struggle was so violent that, even if both rivals had simultaneously abandoned it, the waves would have continued to fight as angrily as ever. My belief is that the savage north-easter also took part in this battle-royal, and that the stormy Sirocco also refused to stay quietly in Aeolus's famous cave. All the winds, in fact, from every quarter came rushing towards the same point, each in defence of his own part of the sky; which had the effect of keeping the sea exactly where it was. Yet elsewhere such enormous masses of water were displaced by their hurly-burly, that the Tyrrhenian Sea invaded the Aegean, the Adriatic went roaring into the Ionian Gulf, and the land had to acknowledge defeat by the sea – letting several peaks, against which the waves had always pounded in vain, be temporarily submerged. Such monstrous waves were never known on any shore; they must have been carried from some region lying beyond the vast Ocean Stream which girdles the world. It was as when long ago Juppiter, grown weary of punishing mankind with thunderbolts, borrowed his brother Neptune's trident and allowed water for once to do its worst – the consequent Deluge swept away the whole human race and the sea became limited by sky alone. On the present occasion, it would have risen to the stars, had not Juppiter pushed clouds down to repress it.

The darkness was not like the familiar darkness of night; an infernal blackness, unrelieved even by a ghastly glare, obscured the entire sky. Rain cataracted into the sea from low-flying cloud. Lightning came in dim flickers, not vivid streaks, though the dome of heaven was jarred by rolling thunder. Nature seemed on the verge of chaos; one might have supposed that the elements had already dissolved their harmonious association and left perpetual Night to jumble the shades of the Underworld with the bright Gods of Olympus – the only hope still left to the latter being that they had not yet succumbed to the universal catastrophe.

Caesar and Amyclas found themselves riding on the crest of a wave as tall as the precipice of Leucas, their masthead piercing the clouds: and then again dropping into a trough so deep that the keel grated on the bottom. The sea now consisted of watery peaks towering above sandy valleys.

Amyclas's seamanship was unequal to the frightful task of dealing with the cross-swell. However, the very confusion of the storm proved helpful: since all the winds seemed to be blowing simultaneously, one wave would heel the boat over, the next would right her, and only their violent squabbles kept her afloat. The shoals of Saso, or the rocky coast of Thessaly, or the dangerous coves of Ambracia, would have held no terrors for these two in the dinghy; they seemed far more likely to be dashed on the summits of the Ceraunian range!

At last Caesar convinced himself that the danger was worthy of his destiny. He shouted that the Gods had certainly gone to a deal of trouble by launching such a colossal storm against his small boat. 'If the glory of my death,' he said, 'has been divinely awarded to the sea rather than the battlefield, I am not afraid to find my remarkable career cut short by fate. I have already achieved enough for any one man. I have conquered the Northern tribes; the mere terror of my name has made Pompey's forces surrender to me, and I have supplanted him at Rome. Moreover, my Consulship was awarded me by popular acclamation, despite the opposition of his armies; and I have now held every office available under the Constitution, including that of Dictator. Nobody but the Goddess Fortune, who alone knows my secret ambitions, will realize that I might have gone yet further, by dying as King of Rome, no longer a mere citizen. If the sea keeps my battered body instead of casting it ashore for the pyre and the tomb, I will not care; because everyone will be frightened by my disappearance and half expect me to turn up again somewhere without warning.'

As he spoke, an extraordinary thing happened: a tremendous tenth wave seized the broken dinghy and carried it shoreward with a rush,

depositing it high and dry, between rocks, on a narrow strip of level
ground. Caesar leaped out, and in that moment regained possession of
countless kingdoms and cities, and of his own lucky life.

His return to camp the next morning caused considerably more stir
than his departure. The officers came crowding up with tears and
expostulations which greatly gratified him. They complained that he
should never go to such cruel lengths, however indomitable his
courage. 'What would have happened to us,' they asked, 'if the winds
had been reluctantly forced to tear you in pieces? It was most unkind
thus to hazard your life when the very existence of so many nations
depends on it, and so large a part of the world has chosen you as its
leader. It makes us ashamed to think that we were fast asleep while you
battled with the sea. Did none of us deserve the honour of dying with
you? Imagine your sailing for Italy all alone because you had not the
heart to order any of us out in such a storm! Few men court death
unless they have fallen into utter despair; and to run the risk of drowning when you are the master of the world is to presume on the good-
will of Heaven. Well, now that Fortune has cast you safely back ashore,
allow us to hope that this proof of her favour will satisfy you. It hardly
shows gratitude when you force her to present the sovereign of mankind as a poor shipwrecked sailor who has somehow managed to keep
his head above water.'

They argued until dawn; then the sky cleared, the winds dropped,
and the exhausted waves subsided.

Mark Antony and the other Caesarean generals in Italy observed
this change of weather: the sea had grown calmer and a clear South
Wind[1] would soon take control of it. They launched their fleet, which
the steadiness of the wind and of the steersmen's hands kept well
together; the ships suggested infantry soldiers marching in close order
across a plain. Yet they were unlucky that night: the wind blew fitfully, and some caught more of it than others, which threw them all
out of station. It was as when the first frosts in Thrace force the cranes
to migrate from the mouth of the river Strymon. At the start of their
journey to the Nile, they fly in formation, making what appear to be
letters in the sky; but presently they reach a considerable altitude and

1. Here it is called a North, not a South Wind. Lucan has misread Caesar's
Commentaries and I have therefore called the winds by their right names, to make
at least geographic sense.

find the South Wind blowing strongly up there, whereupon they obliterate the letters by flying in scattered flocks. At dawn, however, the breeze freshened and blew so stiffly that Antony's fleet was carried past Elisso, and had to aim at Nymphaeum, three miles farther along the coast. There a sudden shift of wind to the south-west gave them safe harbourage.[1]

When Pompey saw that Caesar had assembled his main forces and that a clash was imminent, he decided to send his beloved wife Cornelia away to Lesbos where she would be spared the alarms of war. Tender-hearted husbands are like that: anxiety for his wife's safety made even Pompey shrink from an immediate engagement. If there was one thing in existence which he wanted to protect from the catastrophe threatening Rome and the whole world, it was Cornelia's life. He had already come to his decision, but could not bring himself to give the order for her removal, preferring to put off the inevitable and snatch what pleasure he might before fate intervened.

One night, Cornelia awoke in the grey dawn and clasped him to her, searching for his lips; but he turned from her in distress and she was shocked to find that his cheeks were wet with tears. Asked what ailed him, he sighed deeply and explained: 'Darling, I could once tell you that you were dearer to me than life; but life was then still sweet. The sad day which we have postponed too long, or which we should have postponed yet longer, has come at last. Caesar and his entire army are here and we must meet him in battle; I am therefore sending you to Lesbos, where you will be safe. Please do not renew your entreaties; I have already fought with myself to keep you at my side, but the answer is "no"! It will not be a protracted separation. The coming battle is bound to prove decisive – one of two great men must topple to a fall. But I am much mistaken in your love for me if the spectacle of civil war does not horrify you; so please be content to wait until my messengers bring news of the dangers I have faced.

'The truth is that, since fighting may break out at any moment, I am ashamed to sleep peacefully beside you, or to rise from your embraces while trumpets announce the doom of this distracted world. How can I face the horror of civil war unless I share it by voluntary self-denial?

1. Lucan omits to mention that a Rhodian fleet of sixteen warships from Nymphaeum sailed out against Mark Antony, and that the same shift of wind wrecked every one of them, with enormous loss of life.

Now you must go off and conceal yourself where you can be safer than any distant king or remote tribe, and not feel so crushed by the weight of your anxiety as if you had stayed with me. And should Heaven have decided to wreck my army, I want the better part of me to survive; I expect you to prepare a pleasant retreat in which we can hide together from Caesar's vengeance.'

The shock was so overpowering that Cornelia turned quite numb, and some time elapsed before she could find words to frame her reproaches. At last she said: 'Pompey, you leave me no chance of complaining to the Gods that they have cruelly parted us by death, which I would do if the sad task of kindling your funeral pyre fell to me. But I am being vulgarly packed off like any wife of whom her husband has tired! So we are to break up our marriage just because your former father-in-law is on the way and because you want to appease him – are those your intentions? O Pompey! Do you really believe that I am faithless enough to choose a refuge which you do not share? Until to-day we have been inseparable, and you are being exceedingly cruel to send me off and expect me to defy the lightning of disaster all by myself. What do you mean by "safety" – will it be safety for me to die of apprehension on your behalf while you are still alive and offering prayers to the Gods? And even if you were killed, and I were to show myself superior to misfortune by committing suicide as soon as the news arrived, it would not be the same; I should have outlived you by a great many days, because of the slowness with which news travels. And oh, how cruel you are in habituating me to the idea of your defeat by this exercise in fortitude! Forgive me: you will find me a bad pupil, I am afraid . . . If the Gods are kind enough to answer my prayer, I shall be the last person in the world to be informed of your victory – I shall wander about on the cliffs of Lesbos dreading the arrival of the packet-boat. Even good news will hardly improve matters; since I shall be living in a remote island where Caesar might yet capture me, though he were in flight from you. Everyone must soon know that Pompey's wife is now hiding at Mitylene – it will make Lesbos famous. So this is my demand: if beaten and forced to escape by sea, go anywhere else you please except Lesbos; because that is the very first place where the enemy will come to search for you.'

Then Cornelia sprang out of bed in frantic grief, intent on beginning her new life of anguish without the least delay. Though they had been faithful lovers for many years, she deliberately wasted her last chance of hugging him to her breast, or caressing his head. They parted in such haste and sorrow that neither could bear to say 'good-bye'. It was the saddest day that she or he had ever known – or ever would know, because every grief which followed fell upon hearts already dulled by misfortune.

Cornelia swayed, but was caught by her attendants as she collapsed, and carried in their arms down to the shore. There she threw herself at full length on the sand, clutching at it; but they finally got her aboard. She suffered far more than when, as Pompey's loyal companion, she had said good-bye to the shores of her native land with Caesar's men pressing hard on their heels; this second flight had to be made all alone.

She slept fitfully the next night; it was the first that she had spent without him since their marriage. The coldness and silence of his side of the bed frightened her; she felt defenceless and deserted. If ever she drowsed off for a while, she would forget the day's events and stretch out her hands in the darkness; but wake to find them cheated. The fact was that, though burning with love for Pompey, she could not bring herself to curl up and occupy the whole bed, but always kept his place vacant. She feared that she had lost him for ever; and the reality proved to be even worse. It would not be long now before they met again, as miserable shades.

BOOK SIX

THE two rivals, who had now decided to fight it out, brought their armies face to face by camping them on opposite slopes. Caesar might have seized a number of Greek cities had not pride prevented him from putting himself in debt to the Fates by the defeat of anyone except Pompey. He concentrated his ambitions on that disastrous hour when a single throw of the dice would decide which of them must die. Three times he marshalled his cavalry and infantry on the hill-top to show that, if possible, he meant to destroy Rome; but since Pompey clearly did not intend to be lured from his entrenchments by such demonstrations, he abandoned camp and, working under cover of the woods, struck suddenly at the fortified port of Dyrrhachium, a city of Corinthian origin. Pompey headed him off by marching straight along the coast and occupying a rocky hill which the local Taulantians call Petra.[1] His camp served as an additional protection to Dyrrhachium, though this was heavily enough fortified to resist any assault. Its defences did not consist in ancient walls which, however high and massive, are always apt to be destroyed by siege warfare or the mere passage of time; they were natural defences, irreducible by siege-engines – sheer cliffs, their bases hollowed out by the waves, and deep water on every side of the town but one, where a neck of ground joined it to the mainland. Sailors are terrified by these cliffs; when the South Wind churns up the Ionian Sea its breakers thud menacingly against them, shaking the houses and temples built above and scattering spray on their roofs.

Caesar now conceived the unlikely plan of blockading Pompey's scattered armies with a hidden ring of fortifications placed far back on the hills. After a quick survey of the country he decided not to use the ordinary turfed rampart, but huge rocks and blocks cut from the quarry face, and masonry stolen from the houses and walls of Greek

1. On the contary, Caesar reached Dyrrhachium first.

towns. As a result, he built a containing work, protected by a fosse and with turreted forts raised upon it at intervals, which would be proof against any battering-ram or siege-engine. He carried it over the broken ground at a uniform height, taking in a great semi-circle of country: fields, scrubby slopes, and forests where wild beasts still lurked. For awhile Pompey had no need of fodder or grazing; or of water, because several small streams rose near by and ran down to the sea. He could even shift his camp inside the work, which was of such length that when Caesar made a tour of inspection from end to end, he always rested half-way.

Though poets praise the walls of Troy, declaring that they must have been built by gods, and though the Parthians are equally astounded at the walls of Babylon on the Tigris, what about these fortifications, extemporized by Caesar in time of war? They enclosed as much space as the walls of Babylon, or of Antioch on the Orontes, or of Nineveh the capital city of Assyria.[1] Yet, for all this, Caesar's men had laboured to no purpose. Their engineering skill might well have been employed in damming the Hellespont with a causeway from Sestos to Abydos; or in cutting a canal through the Isthmus of Corinth to the Peloponnese, which would have spared ships the need of doubling Cape Malea; or they might have defied Nature by improving almost any other part of the world. Instead, they merely limited the stage on which the drama of civil war was enacted: trying to confine in a narrow coastal strip the men who would presently break out and fight all over the Empire – Pompeians destined to die at Pharsalus and Thapsus.

Pompey did not at first notice what Caesar was about, much as a peasant in central Sicily would not hear the sea roaring off Cape Pelorus; or as a Caledonian Briton would remain unaware of the Kentish surf. But when the wall began to rise, he marched out from Petra at the head of his troops and disposed them on different hills: to immobilize Caesar's forces by threatening every point of his works simultaneously. For the same purpose he built lines of his own within Caesar's, surrounding them with a stockade. The territory which he thus secured against raids was perhaps equal to that separating Rome from the Arician Grove (where Iphigeneia and Orestes brought the

1. The burned-brick walls of Babylon had been seventy feet thick, two hundred and fifty high, and forty-eight miles long. Caesar's work ran for about sixteen miles and was perhaps twenty feet high.

worship of Taurian Diana in ages past); his defences being about as
long as the stretch of the Tiber between Rome and Ostia, if one does
not count the bends. No regular engagement took place for awhile –
that is to say the trumpets never sounded the assault – but the armies
exchanged javelins as they felt inclined,[1] many a soldier being killed
by a practice shot. The fact was that both Pompey and Caesar were
preoccupied by problems of supply.

Pompey's fodder was running short. His cavalry had galloped across
the fields and trampled the young grass; and what remained was now
cropped close. He tried to feed the chargers on sedge, but without
success. They were still neighing for fresh grass as they dropped down
on their haunches – some of them in the middle of a drill-evolution –
and expired. Their carcases gradually decomposed and, since the
weather was unhealthy, a thick and almost visible cloud of putrefaction
rose. (Nesida and Ischia, two islands near Naples, exhale a similarly
poisonous air, which sends those who breathe it into a delirium.) Next,
Pompey's troops began to fall ill, because the drinking water had
absorbed the poison, sooner even than the air, and corrupted their
intestines. The skin of their cheeks tightened until the eyes protruded;
and first erysipelas, the forerunner of plagues, and then plague itself,
burned in their faces, making every head loll on its shoulders. Death
now mowed down his victims in ever-swelling numbers, and with
practically no interval of sickness; he may be said to have outrun the
disease. Rows of unburied corpses increased the mortality; since the
survivors had merely hauled them outside the tent-lines and left them
there to rot. Pompey's losses would have been still heavier if his camp
had not been so close to the sea; and if a North Wind had not sprung
up to freshen the air; and if corn-ships had not arrived from
Egypt.

Caesar's army experienced hardships of a very different kind. Although encamped on healthy hills with spring water in abundance,
and free to move in all directions, they suffered from famine as if in a
beleaguered city. The young wheat had not yet formed ears; Caesar
found his poor fellows stretched out on the ground eating grass like
cattle, or busily stripping leaves from bushes and trees and grubbing up
poisonous-looking roots for food. They snatched at whatever could
be cooked in a pot, or chewed with their teeth, or swallowed, though

1. Pompey's men are reported to have used only slings and arrows.

it rasped their throats – things that nobody before had ever ventured to taste – and still pressed the siege of their well-fed opponents.

At last Pompey decided to regain freedom of movement by a sortie, but scorned to attack at night when the enemy would be resting; he would breach Caesar's defences by daylight on a wide front, throwing down forts and wall, and paying the toll in blood.

The most suitable objective seemed to be the so-called Minician Fort and the adjoining stretch of wall; he could approach under cover of a wood. Trees prevented the dust from betraying his advance; when his Eagles suddenly emerged glittering, and every trumpet sounded the assault, the surprise was complete. It looked as though no fighting would be necessary: the Caesareans, though ordered to stand, had fallen prone like dead men. The cloud of javelins that flew at them was wasted, because nobody dared face it. After the javelins came a shower of torches thrown into the timber fort; then a battering-ram went into action against the wall. Pompey's eagles were on the point of being carried into the open country beyond; and Caesar himself, with the help of Fortune and a thousand squadrons of cavalry, would have been powerless to restore the situation, had not one brave man, armed and still upright, denied Pompey his victory.

He was called Scaeva, and had enlisted even before Caesar's first campaign in Gaul, and been promoted to the rank of centurion in recognition of his many wounds. Not realizing that what would be gallantry on any other occasion was wickedness in a civil war, Scaeva prepared to do his worst. When he saw his fellow-legionaries abandoning their weapons and trying to escape, he shouted: 'Where are you going, cowards? No soldier of Caesar's ever runs away. Shame on you for not adding to the pile of his loyal dead! And if you have lost all sense of discipline, anger at least ought to make you hold the position. Pompey has chosen this as the softest spot to attack; let us force him to pay heavily for the insult. Personally, I should die happier if Caesar were watching me, but since he is not available, Pompey must do instead – I shall compel him to praise me as I fall. Come, comrades, let us rush against the enemies' weapons until we blunt or break them, even though our life blood spurts out. By now, Caesar must have heard the blare of trumpets and seen the column of smoke, so the battle is as good as won; he will come hurrying up and reassert his right to this wall before we die.'

Scaeva's words were like a clarion blast. His comrades rallied to him in eager admiration, wondering whether, although trapped and out-numbered, they could do a little better than merely be killed. Scaeva stood on the battered wall and pelted the Pompeians below, first with the dead bodies of his comrades who had been killed by the collapse of the fort, and then with fallen beams and blocks of masonry. He seized a stake or a stout pole and, charging at the Pompeians as they swarmed over the battlements, sent them hurtling down; he drew his sword and hacked off the hands of others who were clambering up behind; he seized a stone and dashed out an enemy's brains; he thrust a flaming torch into another man's hairy face and seared his eyes.

The pile of corpses rose until it was level with the top of the wall, whereupon Scaeva sprang forward and leaped into the midst of the enemy, as a leopard springs over the points of the hunting-spears. There, as the whole army pressed tightly about him, he killed men both to front and to rear. The edge of his sword was now so blunted, and so clotted with blood, that it served only as a club. Everyone was determined to finish him, and no sword or lance missed its mark. A new sort of battle indeed: one man against an entire army! The boss of his shield rang with blows, his helmet was shattered and its jagged edges galled the sides of his head. His last defence against thrusts delivered below the breast were shafts of spears already lodged deep in his body. How foolish of the Pompeians to waste javelins and arrows on such a man! They could never destroy him. Only Greek fire from a siege catapult, or a boulder from a mangonel, or an iron-headed battering-ram might have disposed of him. He stood like a stone wall in Caesar's defence, keeping Pompey back. In case anyone might blame him for not fighting with both hands, or for being too careful of life, he dropped his shield and exposed his breast, until a forest of spears lodged there as well.

He resembled one of those African elephants, attacked by a swarm of hunters; some missiles bounce off his tough hide; some pierce it, but a twitch of his muscles removes them; others drive in farther, but still draw no blood. The elephant's heart lies too deep inside for those innumerable arrows and javelins to reach. At last Scaeva staggered and gazed about him, as the elephant would also do in extremity, looking for an enemy to crush as he fell. At that moment a Cretan shot at him from some little distance and blinded his left eye – a feat that any archer would have prayed to perform. Scaeva merely plucked out the arrow, which was in his way, threw it down with the eye-ball still clinging to the point, and trod on it.

It was like a fight in the amphitheatre at Rome – Libyan hunter against Pannonian bear. The Libyan throws a javelin, making it spin with the help of a strap, and drives it into the bear's haunch; she whirls madly round and round, trying in vain to attack it. Scaeva's face was one mass of blood, and distorted with rage. The enemy raised a shout of triumph; they would not have been happier if Caesar himself had been wounded, unless he had lost as much blood as this centurion. But Scaeva concealed his rage and soldier's pride, saying gently: 'Spare me, comrades! Lower your weapons, I pray! You need use no more of them now; I will die if you only pull out these spears sticking in my breast. Yet take me up first and carry me into Pompey's camp. He will be gratified if I show a glorious example of desertion from Caesar, rather than of devoted death in his service.'

An unlucky Pompeian named Aulus, deceived by this speech, prepared to lift Scaeva on his shoulders, weapons and all; but he had not noticed the sword held point forward which now darted like lightning at his throat. Scaeva yelled for joy because the sole alleviation for his pain was the death of another enemy. He shouted: 'Any man who thinks I am yet beaten deserves to die! And if Pompey wants me to sheathe this sword, he must bow and lower his standards to Caesar's. Do you think I am as frightened of death as you are? Death is far dearer to me than Pompey's cause, or the Senate's, can be to you!'

As he spoke, a cloud of dust announced the approach of Caesarean reinforcements; whereupon Pompey fell back, thus escaping the obloquy of having had his whole army routed by a single man. Scaeva collapsed as soon as the battle ended, since rage alone had kept him alive. His comrades crowded down to where he lay, hoisted his fainting body proudly upon their shoulders and adored him as the human embodiment of the great God Courage. When he died they competed for the honour of extracting the weapons from his battered corpse; then dedicated his arms to the Gods, and used his armour to adorn a bare-breasted statue of Mars. How fortunate Scaeva would have been had he won this glory fighting in a foreign war against the sturdy Iberians, or the Cantabrians with their small shields, or the Teutons with their long ones! But, this being civil war, he was denied the hope of shouting in a triumphal procession and hanging up his arms in the Temple of Capitoline Juppiter. The unlucky fellow's courage served only to place a tyrant in power![1]

Though repulsed at this point, Pompey did not relax his military efforts, any more than the waves weary of battering against a cliff and eating away its base in the expectation of an eventual land-slide. He attacked one end of Caesar's line by land and sea, disposed of the defenders, and so broke out of the net; to the delight of his men who were now at last able to bivouac in open country. It was as when the swollen Po overflows its banks and floods entire districts. Wherever the dykes give way before the current a whole river passes through the gap and covers land which has never hitherto been under water – so that while some farmers see their fields ruined, others find that the river, by leaving a layer of fertile mud on theirs, has generously increased the arable acreage.

Caesar had been warned of the assault by smoke signal from the top of a fort, but when he arrived it was too late: he found the wall down, the dust settled, and the corpses of his men cold enough for the battle to have taken place on the previous day. The very tranquillity of the scene enraged him, and seeing that the Pompeians dared take their ease after this success, decided at all costs to teach them a lesson. He suddenly attacked the troops commanded by Lucius Torquatus, whom he had spared at the capture of Oricum. Torquatus took immediate counter-measures – as a sailor hurriedly lowers canvas when a squall strikes his boat, off Circeium in Latium, and makes the mast quiver. He withdrew his troops from the outer rampart of the newly constructed camp and defended the inner fort. Caesar was already fighting at its barricades when Pompey launched his main forces from the hills and trapped him.

It is alarming enough for the peasants on the slopes of Etna, if a Sirocco is blowing and at the same time the giant Enceladus struggles to escape from beneath, sending the lava run in a fiery river down the mountainside. It was even worse for the Caesareans when they broke and fled at the sight of the dust clouds raised by Pompey's advance, but then suddenly found their retreat converted into a suicidal charge by

1. Despite Lucan's graphic account, Scaeva neither lost an eye nor succumbed to his wounds; but 230 holes were counted in his shield. Caesar paid him a handsome gratuity and promoted him from eighth to first centurion. His company were also rewarded.

the appearance of further enemy forces in the other direction. This battle might well have been decisive, and a general truce might well have been called, had not Pompey himself restrained the fury of his troops. Rome, in fact, might still be a sovereign people, under the heel of no tyrant, had Pompey been as bloody-minded as Sulla. We must everlastingly regret that Caesar profited by the crime of fighting his son-in-law, because the latter had scruples about killing him.[1]

But for this, the slaughter of Utica in Libya would never have taken place, nor that of Munda in Spain, nor would the Nile have borne along, to its shame, the corpse of one far nobler than King Ptolemy of Egypt – Pompey the Great himself. Moreover, the corpse of King Juba would never have lain stripped of its royal armour on the African sands, nor would the blood of Metellus Scipio have placated the ghosts of the Carthaginians whom his ancestor conquered, nor would the noble Cato have died. Dyrrhachium might, indeed, have seen the end of Rome's agony, by sparing us the tragic drama of Pharsalus.

Caesar now quitted this region, which the Gods had not intended him to occupy, and led his battered army towards Thessaly. Pompey was then urged by his lieutenants to reoccupy Italy, now lying open to him, rather than pursue his father-in-law's retreating army; but in vain. He replied: 'Until I can safely disband my forces, I will not copy Caesar's example by visiting Rome. When this war started I could have held Italy, though at the cost of quartering my troops in the temples and making a battlefield of the Forum. To keep Rome inviolate, I would willingly march to the icy north of Scythia, or to the blistering heat of Equatorial Africa. It was to spare Rome the horrors of war that I evacuated the City; shall I rob her of the blessings of peace now that I am victorious? Better that all Italy should be left under the nominal rule of Caesar than ravaged by this war.'

Then he marched off, following a crooked eastward route across the broken range of Candavia until he reached Thessaly, the destined battleground.

To the north-east of Thessaly Mount Ossa towers; to the east, Mount

---

1. Pompey's infantry advanced cautiously, for fear of being ambushed, and his cavalry were prevented from turning Caesar's retreat into a rout by the ten-foot outer defences of the camp. The retreat had been occasioned by the flight of the Caesarean cavalry. When Pompey failed to follow up his success, Caesar commented: 'He does not know how to use a victory.'

Pelion; to the south Mount Othrys, over which the midsummer Sun stands at noon, after rising in the Lion. To the westward and west-north-westward the Pindus range shortens the day by hiding the afternoon sun, and intercepts the cool evening breezes; and far up the coast on the other side Mount Olympus protects the Thessalians at its foot from northerly gales and never allows them to catch sight of the Great Bear.

The plain ringed in by these mountains once formed a vast lake. There being no outlet for the rivers which ran into it, not even at Tempe, they filled a single basin and the accumulated waters could do nothing else but rise steadily. However, when one day Hercules tore Ossa and Olympus apart, the sea was all at once invaded by a deluge of fresh water. Alas: it would have been better for Thessaly had it remained for ever beneath the lake waters! The land contains the cities of Phylace, whose King Protesilaus was the first Greek to disembark in the Trojan War; and Pteleus, the port from which he sailed; and Dorion, where Thamyris angered the Muses by challenging them to a competition in song; and Trachis, with near-by Meliboea, both of which Philoctetes made glorious by winning Hercules's bow, as a prize for setting alight the dying hero's funeral pyre. And Larisa, celebrated in ancient times as the home of Achilles, son of the Sea-goddess Thetis; and Pelasgian Argos, now under the plow, but once famous for its racehorses; and Phthiotian Thebes, where Echion's wife Agave fled with the head of their son Pentheus, complaining that this was all she would rescue for the funeral pyre from the Bacchantes who had helped her in dismembering him!

Well, when this lake had been drained by Hercules, its bed became dry land cut by numerous rivers. The Aeas, a small clear stream, now runs west through Epirus and debouches into the Ionian Sea; so does the Inachus, an equally small stream whose god was said to have been the father of Io, later the Goddess Isis, Juppiter's bride; and the turbid Acheloüs, whose god would have married Oeneus's daughter Deianeira, had not Hercules worsted him in battle – and which is gradually enlarging the Echinades Islands, at its mouth, with the silt it carries down. There is also the Evenus, whose waters Hercules stained by the killing of Nessus the Centaur, and which runs southward through Calydon, formerly the kingdom of Atalanta's lover Meleager; and the rapid Spercheus, which runs east into the Malean Gulf, just above

Euboea; and the pure stream of Amphrysus, by whose banks Apollo once tended the cattle of King Admetus. The Asopus, the Phoenix, and the Melas also have their sources in Thessaly; and the Araurus, from whose waters neither fog, nor mist, nor light breezes ever rise. And let us not forget those tributaries of the Peneus which lose their name when they flow into it – the Apidanus, the slow-moving Enipeus, and the Titaresus – the last named is the only one which refuses to mix with the Peneus, but glides above its waters as though on dry land; Homer explains that it is somehow connected with the river Styx, and that because the Gods hold the Stygian waters in such awe, it scorns to adulterate them with common water.

Thessaly's fertile soil, revealed when the lake emptied, was first ploughed by the Bebrycans, and next in turn by the Lelegians, the Aeolians, and the Dolopians. Then the Magnesians made a name for themselves as horse-breeders, and the Minyans as sailors – theirs is the part of Thessaly where the Centaurs were born in the caves of Pelethionium; the children of Nephele the cloud-phantom, with whom Ixion lay. These Centaurs were half men and half horses. They included Monychus, who used to trample the rocks of Pholoë until they split under his hooves; and fierce Rhoecus, who did what the North Wind could hardly do – uprooted ash-trees and used them as missiles; and Pholus, Hercules's host; and perverse Nessus, who ferried passengers across the Evenus until Hercules shot him dead; lastly, old Cheiron, who now appears in the winter sky as the Archer and aims his bow at the Scorpion, though it is far larger than himself.

It was in Thessaly that the seeds of warfare first germinated. Neptune struck the rocks with his trident and out sprang the original charger; then the Lapiths invented the bit and bridle by which he was tamed – they obliged him to champ the bit until foam flew from his mouth. Again, it was at Thessalian Pagasae that the first ship was launched – the *Argo* – which suddenly transformed man into an amphibious creature. Also, the Thessalian king Ionus was the first man to hammer molten metal into ingots – silver, stamped gold, and copper smelted in huge furnaces – and thus made it easy for people to reckon wealth, which in turn tempted them to iniquitous wars of conquest. Moreover, Tempe in Thessaly was the home of the immense serpent Python before he went to live at Delphi – which is why the laurels for the Pythian Games are always fetched from there. And it was a Thessalian, the impious Aloeus, who sent his sons Otus and Ephialtes to war against the Gods; these were the giants who, piling Ossa upon Olympus, and Pelion upon Ossa, interfered with the movements of the heavenly bodies.

When Caesar and Pompey encamped on this accursed soil, a general presentiment arose that the decisive hour was at hand. This sense affected people in different ways. Cowards took the gloomiest possible view; a few bolstered their courage, although the issue was extremely doubtful, and expected to be victorious. Among the pessimists was Sextus, Pompey's unworthy son, the one who later went into exile and besmirched the family name by his exploits in Sicilian waters: whereas Pompey had earned a Triumph by the suppression of piracy, Sextus played the pirate himself. Being distracted by fear, he wanted to discover without delay what Fate held in store for him. Yet he did not approach the Delphic Oracle, or that of Dodona, famous for its esculent oaks – their acorns were once the staple food of primitive man – and where the will of Juppiter is deduced from the sound of brass whip-lashes striking copper cauldrons. Nor did he sacrifice a victim and have the omens taken from its entrails; nor consult either a responsible augur, or someone who could have foretold the future by the legitimate, though mysterious, Babylonian arts of geomancy and astrology. No: the wretch was convinced that the infernal powers – Pluto and his ghosts – always told the truth and knew far more than the Olympians. He trusted, that is to say, in the wicked art which Juppiter and his family abominate, namely witchcraft – with all the savage and disgusting offerings that it involves. He was encouraged in this evil delusion by the presence near the camp of certain Thessalian witches, who performed feats that would have seemed impossible even to the most morbid imagination.

Now, Thessaly produces the poisonous plants and magical stones used for incantatory purposes by witches who wish to make the Gods subservient to them. Thus when Medea came here from Colchis and practised her magical arts at Iolcus, she did not need to bring any simples – all were indigenous to Thessaly. Moreover, the impious spells which these infamous women utter do, in fact, force the reluctant Gods to pay heed, even though the vows and prayers of their faithful devotees must go unheeded. The voices of witches alone penetrate to the remotest parts of Heaven and compel the attention of the particular deity invoked, however preoccupied he may be with celestial business. Thus, as soon as the horrid sound of muttering reaches Heaven, the Gods must desert all other petitioners – even if the images of Babylon and the sorcerers of mysterious Egypt happen to be simultaneously invoking them.

Witches compound dreadful love philtres that not even the sternest hearts, apparently fated never to melt, can resist, and that inspire even austere old men with illicit passion. Nor is this effect produced only by philtres and the use of *hippomanes* – a juicy excrescence growing in the head of a new-born foal, the eating of which fills the mare with maternal love. Witches can destroy a man's mind by incantations, and merely by twirling the threads on a magical wheel can induce erotic passion between people who are neither decently married nor have felt the least physical attraction for each other. They can also control natural phenomena: making night fall before the day has ended, forcing the sky to disobey its orders, and surprising Juppiter by their arrest of the heavenly axle-tree as it swings rapidly around. They will suddenly deluge the earth with showers of rain, draw thick veils of moisture around the Sun and create thunderstorms without a 'by your leave' to Juppiter; or, as suddenly, charm away a canopy of weeping rain clouds. At their command the sea boils even when no winds are blowing; or remains calm despite a roaring Sirocco that makes all sails belly out. They can arrest the waterfall in mid-flight down a precipice, or the stream in full course, or Nile in his midsummer flood. It is easy for them to make the winding Maeander run straight, or the sluggish Rhône flow as swiftly as the upper reaches of its tributary, the Saône; or even to reduce the height of mountains, so that Olympus falls below cloud level. Witches have thawed the Scythian snows, in the depth of winter, without the Sun's help; and restrained the tide from washing over a shore, despite the pull of the Moon. More, they have thrown the earth off centre, and made it wobble dangerously; and even split its enormous mass in two, so that the stars could be observed spinning round beneath.

Every deadly and destructive creature lives in horror of these women and at the same time provides them with its lethal properties. The savage tiger, and the lion in his royal rage, will tamely lick a witch's hands; the cold-blooded snake will uncoil for her and stretch out at full length on the frosty ground; vipers twined amorously together will interrupt their ecstasy at her command; and if she breathes on a venomous serpent, her venom will be fatal to it.

How remarkable that the Gods pay such close attention to spells and simples! Why are they so terrified of disobeying? Are they perhaps bound by some undisclosed pact, or can they take real pleasure in doing as they have been asked? I mean: are the witches favoured because of some piety about which we know nothing, or because they secretly threaten the Gods with punishment for not keeping their agreement? And another thing: are they armed with direct power over the Olympians, or do they act indirectly by putting pressure on Demogorgon, creator of all the Gods, who can bind the world with the same bonds of compulsion as hold him everlastingly chained in the lowest hell?

Witches have introduced the art of dragging the stars from the sky; and know how to turn the Moon dim and muddy-coloured, as though she were being eclipsed by the Earth's shadow – after which they pull her close to them and torture her until she secretes poisonous foam on the plants growing underneath. Nevertheless, the deadly arch-witch Erichtho scorned these wicked practices as not nearly wicked enough, and had been making even filthier experiments. Considering it a crime to occupy an ordinary decent house, she avoided the town and kept on good terms with the infernal powers by squatting in tombs out of which she had driven the ghostly tenants. Once there, she could not be prevented either by the Olympian gods, or by the fact that she was still alive, from conversing with the lipless dead, or from learning all the mysteries of their god Pluto.

Her aged face was lean and loathsome, of Stygian pallor, and matted hair hung over it. She never appeared abroad in daylight and quitted the tombs only on wet or cloudy nights, when she went to catch and bottle whatever lightning happened to fall. The cornfield was blighted by her passage across it, and her breath poisoned the pure country air. Instead of invoking the Olympians with the usual hymn offered by suppliants, then giving a priest a sacrificial victim and asking him to read the omens, she would pollute their altars with smoking lumps of incense snatched from a burning pyre. No sooner had she stated her demands than the Gods granted them, for fear of being subjected to a second spell.

Erichtho would confine men's souls in a tomb so that, although their bodies still moved about, they were deprived of the long life due to them; and could reverse the process by bringing the dead back to life after their bodies had been duly buried. She would also steal half-roasted scraps of flesh and bone from children's pyres; snatch the funeral torches from their parents' hands; and when crumbling fragments of pall and grave-clothes and human skin were carried aloft by the black smoke and came fluttering down again, she would be waiting to harvest them. If the corpse was not cremated, but placed in a stone sarcophagus – to dry up its moisture, arrest corruption and harden the marrow in its bones – Erichtho always attacked it with greedy passion. She used her fingers to scoop out the glaring eyeballs, and gnawed the pale nails off its withered hands. Or, if the corpse had been hanged, she would first bite the nose free, and then tear away the other extremities. If it had been crucified, she would strip the cross of its treasures – lumps of weather-beaten flesh, white protruding bones, with the nails pinning the hands to the cross-piece and whatever corrupt and clotted filth had formed on the limbs; and if a tendon resisted her teeth she would hang her whole weight on it. If, however, she found a corpse exposed for the wild beasts and carrion-birds, she would squat down patiently, using neither a knife nor her nails to mutilate it, and wait for the wolves to arrive; whereupon she would snatch the gobbets of flesh from their very jaws.

Erichtho never hesitated to commit murder, should the warm life-blood from a slit throat be needed for her spells, or still quivering human flesh for her hellish repasts. She would perform the unnatural operation called 'Caesarean' on pregnant women, but only to place the child upon an altar-hearth; and whenever she found a bold villain whom she could profitably employ, killed him and kept his ghost in bondage. She turned every death to her advantage – ripped the downy beard from a youth's corpse, or used her left hand to tear away his forelock as he died. If one of her relatives were laid out for burial she would bend over the body, pretending to kiss it, but covertly nip off nose and ears, and then, having prized the mouth open, do the same with the tip of the dry and motionless tongue – mumbling inarticulate words into the dead mouth, which conveyed a wicked secret to the ghosts of the Underworld.

Sextus Pompey had heard of Erichtho from local gossip and one midnight, the time when the Antipodes enjoy the warmth of midday, he set out through the deserted fields to search for this old miscreant. Her agents assisted him by visiting one rifled tomb after another until at last they spied her perched on a steep and distant crag, among the cliffs of Mount Haemus. She was composing a new and special spell, the like of which had never been heard before, whether by wizards or the gods of wizards. In case the war might deprive Thessaly of its expected slaughter by drifting elsewhere, she laid a bond upon the battlefield of Pharsalus, already poisoned with her deadly drugs, and confined the war to that district; thus she won power over dead soldiers from everywhere in the world. Itching to mutilate the corpses of fallen kings and gain control of important ghosts by plundering the pyres of Roman noblemen, she spent hours wondering on what part of the elder Pompey's corpse she could pounce or, if that failed, what she could steal from Caesar's.

Sextus, who disgraced his pious father by this consultation, spoke first. He said to Erichtho: 'Because you are famous in Thessaly not only for revealing the future but also for altering the course of destiny, I am here for exact information about the expected battle. I am by no means an undistinguished Roman; you see in me the well-known son of Pompey, from whom I shall inherit either sovereignty of the world, or else a most distressing fate. The uncertainty of the future is affecting my nerves; but I know that, if all doubt were removed, I should be able to face any particular danger that confronted me. I want to be saved from the fear of a sudden unforeseen disaster. It is none of my business whether you extract the truth from the Gods under torture, or whether you let them alone and torture the dead. I should of course prefer you to unlatch the gates of Hell, summon the Queen of Death in person and compel her to name the destined victims of to-morrow's battle. This is no slight request, I am aware; but you certainly ought to inquire, in your own interest, which of the two armies will gain the day.'

Erichtho felt flattered that her wicked arts had become so notorious. 'Young man,' she replied, 'if you wanted me to alter some unimportant decree of fate, I could readily compel the Gods' obedience. When the planetary influences condemn any particular soul to death, we Thessalian witches are always able to secure a reprieve; or when they promise him long life, we can yet cut him off in his prime by the use of magical drugs. But some events have been predetermined since the beginning of time; where that is so, we cannot save or kill a single individual without confusing the destinies of all mankind, and have to admit that Fortune is more powerful than all of us working together. However, if you will be content to hear in advance about the approaching fight, there are many simple means of discovering the truth. We can force the earth, the sky, the Pit, the seas and the cliffs of Rhodope to address us. And so many soldiers have been killed of late in this neighbourhood that it should be easy to find a clear-voiced recent corpse, instead of having to employ one of those dismal fellows whose limbs are dried up by the sun and who only squeak incoherently.'

Thickening the darkness of the night by some act of witchcraft and, wrapping a turbid cloud about her gruesome head by way of added security, Erichtho wandered among the unburied bodies fallen in that day's skirmish. She drove off the wolves and forced the carrion-birds to unhook their claws before they had quite finished their meal; poking each corpse in turn to find one whose lungs were still sound enough to make him a suitable mouthpiece of the required prophecy. The destinies of numerous war victims now hung in the balance – which would she select for resuscitation? She was so powerful that had she decided to raise every dead man there, the dark Pit would doubtless have been forced to disgorge their souls, and the wicked creature would thus have set the antagonists at one another's throats again.

Presently she found a corpse that suited her purpose; catching his neck in a noose, through which she put a hook to prevent it from slipping, she dragged him away over rocks and stones. Soon she reached the dell selected as the scene of her ghastly miracle; this lay sheltered by a beetling precipice at the bottom of a steep slope, almost as far down as the Underworld itself, and vaguely seen yew plantations, too thick for the sun's rays to penetrate, leaned forward to screen it.

All was dank here and perpetually dark, except for the weird light created by sorcery. Even the chasm of Taenarus in Laconia – a gloomy no-man's-land between our world and the world of the dead to which Pluto and Persephone do not much mind their subjects straying – has a livelier air.

Erichtho could certainly make the Fates obey her, but it is doubtful whether she drew ghosts up to this cave or whether she harrowed Hell and dragged them after her. At any rate, she now wore a motley robe of the sort that the Furies affect and revealed her face by tossing back her hair, which bristled as she wreathed it with a garland of vipers. Observing that young Pompey's attendants were terrified and that he too was trembling and dropping his eyes in horror, she said reassuringly: 'Nothing here need alarm you: I am merely about to revive a corpse, so that he can become an ordinary man again and speak intelligibly. But though I showed you the waters of Styx, Phlegethon's fiery banks, the Furies, Cerberus with his mane of serpents, and the giants languishing in their chains, why should you be afraid? Cowards, it is the dead who have reason to fear *me!*'

Then she made several cuts in the corpse's breast, and after washing out the contents of his veins, poured in warm menstrual blood mixed with every kind of unnatural poison – the froth of dogs suffering from hydrophobia, a lynx's guts, the hump of a corpse-eating hyaena, the marrow of a snake-fattened stag, one of those remora fish that can keep a ship motionless on the high seas, though the east wind howls through her rigging; also dragon's eyes, eagle-stones which when warmed by the she-eagle explode with a loud noise, an Arabian seraph of the sort that pounces on travellers, a few of those Red Sea vipers that guard the pearl-oyster beds, the sloughed skin of a Libyan horned snake, and the ashes of the Phoenix stolen from the altar at Heliopolis. To these commoner ingredients she added the bewitched leaves of plants that she had spat upon when they first appeared, thereby steeping them in the venom of her own body.

This done, Erichtho began to use her voice, which had more power over the rulers of the Underworld than any drug. For awhile the sounds she uttered were discordant and altogether inhuman. The bark of a dog, the howl of a wolf, the quavering hoot of one variety of owl, the screech of another, the shriek and roar of wild beasts, a serpent's hiss, crash of waves upon rocks, murmur of forests, thunder escaping from a cloud – all these noises could be recognized in Erichtho's voice. But presently she spoke plainly enough, employing a Thessalian spell which would drive straight down to Hell; and said as follows:

'I invoke you, Kindly Ones, who torture the damned; I invoke Chaos, always anxious to tumble worlds into ruin; I invoke the true Ruler of the Earth, who suffers endless agony below, since the gods are so long a-dying. I invoke Styx, and the Elysian Fields where no witch will ever attain. I invoke you, Proserpina, as one who prefers life with Pluto in the Underworld to life with your detested mother Ceres in

Heaven; and as the infernal aspect of triple Hecate who allows ghosts to enjoy secret intercourse with me. I invoke you, Thrice Great Hermes, janitor of the lordly halls of Death, whose task is to feed hungry Cerberus on the flesh of men; and you, the three spinning Fates; and you, old Charon, ferryman of Hell, wearied by rowing ghosts back to me across the fiery stream.

'You must all listen, because these charms proceed from a mouth accursed and defiled by an unvaried diet of human flesh; and because I have chopped off many a woman's breast and mixed it with warm brains as an offering to your divinity; and because I have sacrificed many a healthy infant to you, laying its head and tripes upon a paten.

'My demand is not for any old worn-out ghost who has long become habituated to the gloom of Tartarus, but for one now in descent from the Upper World, and still hesitating at the entrance to the tunnel – so that, if he obeys my spells, he need not go down twice. Let me be plain: I want a Pompeian soldier, who has just died, to tell Pompey's son what will be the result of the Civil War, which has proved of such advantage to you all.'

There was foam on her lips as she raised her head and stared at the ghost beside her; but it shrank from re-entering the punctured breast. Why should it be confined in a prison so hateful as a body dead of a deep belly-wound? Poor ghost, cruelly robbed of death's final gift – absolution from the fate of ever dying again!

Erichtho was astounded and furious that the Fates allowed the ghost to vacillate. First she took live serpents and beat the rigid body with them; then she magically opened the vents that led to the Underworld, and barked down angrily into the silence below: 'Hey there, you, Tisiphone and Megaera, what are you about? Did you not hear? I have been expecting you to hurry with your ruthless whips across the empty floor of Erebus and make this ghost obey me. Observe that I no longer call you Kindly Ones. I am using your proper names, you Stygian bitches! Be careful or you will find yourselves hounded relentlessly by me from tomb to tomb, and from pyre to pyre in broad daylight without escape . . . And you pale, dirty creature, Proserpina Hecate; before paying your annual visit to the Olympians, you undergo a little beauty treatment, eh? But I shall prevent that in future, and force you to display your real complexion. I shall tell everyone exactly what food is served to you down there beneath the earth, and what guilty

secret attaches you to that gloomy royal husband of yours! When
Mother Ceres hears of your defilement, she will never want to see you
again. As for you, Pluto, who got far the worst share of the world
when it was divided at your father's dethronement, unless you are
prudent I shall crack the roof of your den and let the sunlight in to
strike you blind!

'Now will you all obey me, or must I appeal to your Superior, at the
sound of whose name the earth trembles, who alone can look directly
at the Gorgon's head, who can make the very Furies cringe and lash
them with their own scourges? Yes: I mean the God who dwells in an
underworld beneath your underworld, and therefore ranks you con-
temptuously with the Olympians – the God who is not afraid to swear
by your Styx and then break his oath!'

The corpse's frozen blood grew warm; it coursed into the blackened
wounds and through each artery until it reached the fingers and toes.
Both lungs began to work and new life invaded the marrow of his
bones, so that every joint throbbed, every muscle tightened, and then,
instead of slowly raising himself limb by limb from the ground, he
leaped up suddenly and stood erect. Granted, his jaw still hung down
and his eyes glared; indeed, he looked more like a dying man than one
restored to life, because he remained pale and stiff and seemed stupefied by his return to the upper air. Nor did a sound come from his
mouth; Erichtho's charm allowed him to reply only, not to volunteer
information.

She told him: 'If you answer my questions truthfully, your reward
will be great: perpetual insurance against witchcraft. I will burn your
body upon a special pyre and sing a charm that will make you deaf to
the incantations of all other sorcerers in the world. Surely this second
life is worth undergoing at such a price? When I end it, you will fall
into a sleep of oblivion which neither drugs nor spells can possibly
disturb. Now, pay attention: though it may be well enough for the
oracles and prophets who serve the Olympians to give riddling
responses, a man who dares consult the dead deserves to be told the
truth. I must therefore ask you not to grudge him the particulars he
demands, but to specify exact names and places; the Fates will use
your voice for whatever communication they have to make.'

She then recited a spell which enabled him to understand exactly
what she meant.

Tears filled his eyes as he answered: 'I had hardly reached the tall dyke of the silent river Lethe, before you fetched me back; I never even came to where the unkind Fates sit spinning. However, each ghost whom I met told me that the peace of the Underworld is shattered by the bitterness with which the dead of both factions are still carrying on this Civil War. And I heard from the confabulations of famous ghosts – some from the Elysian Fields, some from murky Tartarus – what the future threatens. Nearly all the former, those who had been lucky enough to escape punishment, seemed melancholy. The two Decii, father and son, both of whom sacrificed their lives in defence of Rome, were weeping at the cruelty of Fortune; with Camillus and Curius[1] – and Sulla, too! Scipio Africanus was grieving for the fate of his descendant Metellus Scipio, who is due to fall in Libya; Cato the Elder, the implacable foe of Carthage, was grieving for his great-grandson, Porcius Cato, who will prefer suicide to slavery. The only honourable ghost whom I saw looking in the least cheerful was that of Lucius Junius Brutus, who drove out the tyrannical Tarquins and became the first Consul; apparently some member of his family is destined to emulate him. On the other hand, the dishonourable ghosts from Tartarus were in ecstasies: I recognized Catiline the conspirator, who had broken his manacles and come to celebrate the news, along with that brutal Marius and bare-armed Cethegus. In fact, all the darlings of the popular party were delighted to hear how the war is to end, including Marcus Livius Drusus,[2] and the Gracchi whose extravagant programme and intemperate acts he copied. Even the hands which had been fettered with eternal gyves in Pluto's dungeon clapped applause, and a mob of the damned tried to force their way into Elysium.

'Pluto has now left his dim quarters and gone to put a sharper edge on the punishment-rocks and adamantine chains which he is making ready for the victor of the war. But, Sextus Pompey, you may console yourself by the knowledge that when your father dies, a safe place will be reserved for him and his family in the brighter part of the Infernal Kingdom. Moreover, all glory is short-lived; it will not be long before death reduces the rivals to an equality. Tell your family not to shrink from death. And be proud of your courage; however

1. See notes on Book II, 308; XI, 545, and I, 169.
2. Tribune of the people in 91 B.C., a famous demagogue.

meagre your funeral may be, you will come down where I am going and presently trample in contempt on ghosts whom Rome has raised to godhead.[1] Meanwhile, the coming battle will declare which of the rivals shall die beside the Tiber, and which beside the Nile; yet does that matter much?

'Never mind about your own fate, which will be prophesied in detail by your father when you go to Sicily. You will, of course, pay more attention to him than to me, but even he will find it hard to advise which cities you should visit and which should be avoided. Yours is an unlucky family: neither Europe, Asia, nor Africa can provide it with a refuge. Each of you will be buried in a different continent, and all in countries over which your father has triumphed.[2] The truth is that nowhere in the world will be much safer than Pharsalus.'

Erichtho ceased. The soldier stood in gloomy silence as if demanding death again. This called for more spells and more drugs, because Pluto could not re-assert his claim to a life once forfeited; so she heaped a great pyre of logs, towards which the soldier walked. He climbed to the top, lay down, and Erichtho, producing a lighted torch, conceded him death at last.

Afterwards she escorted Sextus back to his quarters. Dawn was about to break, but she commanded Night to continue as black as before, until they had safely passed by the sentries and entered the camp.

1. Caesar and his descendants.
2. Pompey had celebrated triumphs over Numidia, Spain, and Asia. He was killed in Egypt; Sextus at Miletus in Asia; his elder brother Gnaeus in Spain.

BOOK SEVEN

Never had the Sun been more reluctant to fulfil his eternal duty of rising from the eastern waves and driving his chariot across the sky. He dragged at his horses' mouths, pulling them back so that only the speed of the heavens themselves, revolving in the same direction, kept him on his course. He even longed to have his light dimmed by an eclipse; and, if he attracted the clouds, this was not because he needed them to feed his flames (as Heraclitus and the Stoics would have said) but because he had no desire to shine serenely on the Thessalian plains.

On the night before the battle, the last happy hours that Pompey was fated to spend, he dreamed a pleasant but deceitful dream. He was at Rome, seated in the theatre which he had himself built, and heard his name enthusiastically shouted from every tier by an immense throng of fellow-citizens. It must have been the time of his last Triumph,[1] many years previously, when he was still young and fresh from conquering the Spanish tribes on the Ebro: he had defeated in turn all the guerilla forces which Sertorius, the Marian leader, brought against him. Order was now restored throughout the West and, though only a knight, he sat listening to the plaudits of Roman senators. His white peace-time robe exacted no less reverence than the embroidered robe of purple had done when he rode in the triumphal chariot.

It makes no odds whether this dream came as an escape from the anxious apprehension that his run of victories had ended; or whether it was one more example of dream-contraries, the foretelling of sorrows under the guise of joys; or whether the Goddess Fortune, knowing that he would never again see Italy in waking life, granted him this delightful vision of home as a last favour. The sentries and trumpeters did well not to disturb him; his next night would be haunted by

1. A most delusive dream. Pompey's first Triumph was over the Numidians in 81 B.C., not over the Spaniards in 71 B.C.

unhappy recollections of the day's fighting – nothing but war and war. Alas, that every Roman did not sleep so sound and was not granted so happy a dream as Pompey! Heaven should certainly have allowed all his fellow-citizens the chance of seeing him once more in a vision of the night, for a brief realization of the great love that bound them to him, and him to them – though fully aware of his approaching defeat.

Pompey went out to fight that day in the conviction that he was destined to die at Rome; and the Romans, whose prayers for his safety had never gone unanswered, could not have believed that cruel fate was to deny them even the satisfaction of having their beloved leader buried in the City. Everyone would have welcomed him spontaneously, young and old, including little children. Women would have crowded together, dishevelling their hair and beating their breasts – as in the year-long mourning for Lucius Junius Brutus who expelled the Tarquins. And though Caesar had brought the news himself and overawed them by his tyrannical power, and forced them to offer incense and laurel crowns to Capitoline Juppiter in celebration of his victory, they would still have wept. Poor Romans, gently moaning for grief, but unable to assemble in Pompey's theatre and there make common lamentation!

The stars had fled at the sun's approach, and a confused roar spread through Pompey's camp: his men were demanding the signal for battle. Fortune had dragged the world to ruin at last. Most of the soldiers would never see that sun set, yet they came crowding excitedly around general headquarters trying to hasten the swiftly approaching hour of slaughter. What a horrible form of insanity – this eagerness to precipitate their own doom and their country's as well! They called Pompey cowardly and obstinate and altogether too tender-hearted towards his father-in-law; accused him of being so dazzled by the sense of power which the command of troops from all over the world gave him, that he was protracting the war unnecessarily. Much the same complaint was made by the Eastern monarchs and their men, who said that they had not bargained for so long a war and wished to go home. Ah, why do the Gods, once they have decided on a nation's ruin, force it to be wicked as well as stupid? Pompey's men were actually pleading for permission to fight the battle which would destroy them. Marcus Tullius Cicero, the finest orator of his day, came forward as their spokesman. This was the same Cicero who, when Catiline was plotting his rebellion, had awed the villain into flight merely by a firm insistence on peaceful consular authority. Since Cicero hated war, felt muzzled by military convention, and yearned for the Law Courts and Forum from which he had been so long absent, his eloquence lent some authority to a foolish petition.[1]

'Pompey,' he said, 'Fortune demands only a single acknowledgement from you of all her favours: namely, that you will make use of her. I am speaking for every Roman nobleman and foreign king under your command. Mankind has fallen on its knees before you, and now prostrates itself, pleading that you will consent to overthrow your former father-in-law. Why should he be permitted to keep the whole world in arms? I cannot blame the nations which you once conquered by a mere rush through their territory, for being now disappointed at your slowness in leading them to victory. Have you lost courage or belief in your destiny? Do you fear that the Gods will forsake you? That would be ingratitude. Nevertheless, be warned: if you hesitate to trust them with the furtherance of the senatorial cause, your troops will not wait for orders, but wrench up the standards and rush leaderless to arms. You should be ashamed to have victory forced upon you. We chose you as commander-in-chief, did we not? Those who are fighting their own wars have every right to do battle when and where they will. The united nations have drawn sword to cut Caesar's throat, and are brandishing their weapons – why restrain them? Every man here is impatient for the trumpets to sound the charge. You must hurry, otherwise you will be left behind in the rear. What we Senators want to know is: are we being led to battle or are we merely attending an idle military parade?'

Pompey groaned. He realized that fate was against him and that the Gods were tricking him.

'Since you are all intent on offering battle,' he replied, 'and since not strategy but straightforward fighting is required of me, let us go ahead with it. It will be no fault of mine if Fortune brings the whole allied army to ruin, making this the last day on earth for a great part of mankind; I call Rome to witness that battle has been forced upon me. Were it not for your insistence, I should manoeuvre the enemy into so hopeless a position that the war would end, without fighting in Caesar's

1. Cicero was not present on this occasion.

surrender to justice for his flagrant breach of the peace. You are wilfully and wickedly blind. This is a civil war, yet you shrink from a bloodless victory. We have driven the enemy from their strongholds and denied them retreat to the sea; we have forced them in desperation to eat unripe corn and pray that they may rather fall in battle, after killing as many of us as possible, than die of hunger. This campaign is already half won; my strategy has ensured that even the recruits have nothing to fear from it. But though the approach of danger may frighten some men into violent action, true courage consists not only in resolute hand-to-hand fighting once this danger is upon them, but also in patient avoidance of a battle. Are you asking me to sacrifice the solid tactical advantages we have gained, and let a mere contest in swordsmanship decide the fate of the world? Soldiers would always prefer a leader who fights to one who wins the war by strategy. Fortune has entrusted me with the safety of the State, which I have secured and increased; but now the responsibility for preserving it in the blind clash of armies must rest on you. I refuse to accept either the odium or the glory of the coming ordeal. It seems as though, when my righteous prayers and Caesar's iniquitous ones reached the ears of the Gods simultaneously, they decided against me and called for a battle. But what a dreadful day this will prove – how much crime and distress it must cause everywhere, how many thrones must topple, what torrents of Roman blood must darken the river Enipeus!

'I should be willing to have my head pierced by the very first javelin hurled, if that did not damage our cause; and personally I shall be no happier if we win the battle than if we lose it. Once the slaughter is over I cannot avoid being an object of either universal hate or universal pity; because whoever gains the day must necessarily inflict utter ruin on his defeated rival.'

Pompey then gave orders to fall in under arms, letting his own troops and those of his allies indulge their war-like passions. It was as when a helmsman, surprised by a southerly gale, makes no use of his seamanship but ignominiously abandons the tiller, allowing the winds to sweep the ship where they please, and becoming a useless passenger. A confused and anxious buzz pervaded the camp, and even brave soldiers felt their hearts beat irregularly. Many faces were pale with the presage of approaching death, and the realization that the day had come which would set a perpetual seal upon human affairs, by deciding what form of government Rome must now enjoy. Individual fears yielded to larger fears for humankind.

Who could consider his own danger if he witnessed a general catastrophe – the sea licking the mountain tops, the Sun tumbled down to earth in the collapse of the sky? It was much the same on this occasion: nobody could afford to wonder whether he would save his own skin, but only what the fate of Pompey and, therefore, the fate of Rome, would be.

The troops felt no confidence in their swords until showers of sparks had leaped from the grindstones on which they whetted them; they also sharpened their lances, fitted new strings to their bows and carefully chose the arrows for their quivers. Cavalrymen lengthened their riding goads and shortened their bridles. If I may compare things human with divine, this scene must have recalled the preparations for battle against the furious giants on the Phlegraean plain – when the Cyclops of Etna reforged Mars' sword and Neptune's trident; when Apollo repointed the arrows with which he had forced the Serpent Python to unwind his coils in death; when Athene rearranged the Gorgon tresses on her Aegis; and when fresh thunderbolts were forged for Juppiter by the same Cyclopes.

Portents of many different kinds had not been wanting. At Pompey's first entry into Thessaly all Heaven opposed him. Meteors came flying down in huge columns of fire, land water-spouts[1] were also seen alternating with fireballs which nearly blinded the troops – striking the crests from their helmets, melting swords in their scabbards, tearing javelins from their hands, and making all of them smoke with celestial sulphur. Next, swarms of bees covered the standards, which were pulled out of their sockets only with great effort and became so heavy that they bent the standard-bearers double; and the brazen Eagles wept tears, because after the imminent battle they would no longer be the property of the Roman Senate and people. Finally, a bull was brought to the sacrificial altar, which it knocked over before escaping at a run into the plain; and this loss of the destined victim was unlucky in the extreme.

But what evil powers of air, or of the Pit, what Furies, what Stygian gods, what monsters steeped in night, did Caesar invoke – and without

---

1. A rare phenomenon. One is said to have passed down a canal between the British and German armies, during the Battle of Mons in August 1914.

being called to account for his infamy? Though he was about to fight a ruthless and impious battle, his prayer for victory was answered.

It is a moot point whether the Pompeians were then granted actual visions by the Gods, or whether they merely suffered a hysterical hallucination. At all events, many believed that they saw Pindus collide with Olympus and the Haemus range subside into an immense chasm; that they also heard the plain of Pharsalus ringing all night with the sound of battle, and saw blood rush down the side of Mount Ossa, to stain the waters of Lake Boebeis. When it suddenly grew dark at midday, men cast looks of wonder at one another, at the clouds of night wreathing their helmets, at the vague shapes that flitted about before their eyes – the ghosts of dead parents and relatives. But because everyone had the same guilty desire, to drive their weapons through a father's throat or a brother's breast, they were not abashed by these visitations and even took pride and solace in them as promises that their wicked hopes would be fulfilled.

Since this premonition of disaster had now become general, it was not remarkable that individuals who were destined to die felt panic-stricken. Moreover, every Roman citizen, whether he lived at Cadiz – an ancient colony of Tyre – or by the river Araxes in Armenia, or in whatever other quarter of the globe, felt a sudden nameless and inexplicable grief, and took himself to task for it. Yet how could he know what was being lost that day on the plains of Thessaly? It is even said, I do not know how truly, that Gaius Cornelius the Augur was sitting on the hills above Padua (a city founded by Antenor and the Euganeians) near where the volcanic spring of Aponus bubbles up and the main stream of the Timavo divides into rivulets. Suddenly he exclaimed: 'This unnatural war is being decided to-day. As I speak, a great battle is taking place between the armies of Caesar and Pompey.' Perhaps this knowledge came to him from observation of a thunderstorm; perhaps he observed a certain antagonism between the opposite poles of the sky; or perhaps Apollo sadly notified him of the battle by dimming the sun. It is certain, however, that Nature made the day of Pharsalus unlike any other, and that if skilled augurs had been posted all over the world to observe the unusual celestial phenomena they would have unanimously reached the same conclusion. The greatness of the two rivals could be deduced from the attention which Heaven paid them by thus advertising their fates. Whether the fame that they earned will be enough, by itself, to immortalize them for distant posterity, or whether the pains I have here taken to celebrate them may be of assistance in this respect, is not of much consequence. But we may be sure that no account of that battle will ever fail to excite alternate hope and dread in men yet unborn; that all will read the tragic tale with deep emotion, as if it were something still due to happen, and not ancient history; and that all will consistently side with Pompey.

When the doomed Pompeian soldiers descended from their position on the hills and faced the rising sun, the whole landscape shone with the glitter of their weapons; and Pompey had seen to it that this was no mere mob of men – they were carefully marshalled. Lentulus Spinther commanded the left wing which included the redoubtable First Legion, and the Fourth;[1] while unlucky Domitius Ahenobarbus commanded the right wing. In the centre stood Pompey's steadiest troops, the Cilician legions,[2] under Metellus Scipio, Pompey's present father-in-law – later to lead the Senatorial forces in Libya. The Enipeus and its irrigation channels protected Pompey's right flank and beside it he stationed certain allied contingents, the Cappadocian mountaineers and his loose-reined Pontic cavalry.[3]

Away on the left, where the plain was dry, kings, petty kings, and various other subject allies took up their positions – Numidians from Libya, Cydonians from Crete, Iturean archers from Palestine, Galatians eager to fight the man who had conquered their Gallic kinsfolk, Spaniards brandishing their targes. Thus Pompey denied Caesar the opportunity of celebrating separate triumphs over these nations later on, by grouping them together and allowing him to squander the blood of all mankind in a single battle.[4]

Caesar had struck camp that day and was about to forage in the cornlands when he saw with surprise that the enemy had at last come out against him. This was the sight for which he had prayed a thousand

1. No: Pompey commanded the critical left wing in person.
2. No: they were on the right wing, with Africanus's Spanish levies. Metellus Scipio, in the centre, commanded the eight Syrian legions which Caesar had hoped to defeat before they could join forces with Pompey.
3. No: they were stationed between the centre and right wing.
4. Pompey commanded 45,000 infantry and 10,000 cavalry, against Caesar's total force of 22,000. They formed a front of two and a half miles between the Enipeus and the town of Pharsalus.

times; it would let him stake his whole fortune on a single cast. Sick of waiting for the fulfilment of his fiery ambitions to be sole ruler, he had begun to loathe the war as a crime which took over-long to perpetrate. But now realizing that battle must soon be joined, that everything was nodding to a crash and that either he or Pompey would be buried under the ruins, he felt even this desire for immediate slaughter failing in him. He had always counted on victory, but could he be sure of it to-day? Granted, he had no need to feel apprehension after reviewing his own military career; yet could he feel hope after reviewing Pompey's? However, he mustered the necessary bravado before he addressed his troops.

'Men,' he said, 'my destiny depends on your steadiness to-day. You have conquered the world, and this is the opportunity for which you have prayed these many months. But prayers are no longer called for; the time has come to settle the fate of mankind with your swords, and prove how great a man Caesar is. I remember the promise that you made me beside the Rubicon: the promise which encouraged me to invade Italy. You undertook to fight until we had assured ourselves of the triumph which Pompey and the Senate denied us. This is the day that must finally decide which of us two had the greater justice on his side; the loser will be the one who had least. In my support, you have taken fire and sword into your native land, but you must fight fiercely to-day in justification of your illegal acts. What, after all, is an illegal act? The answer depends on who judges it when the battle is over. Never mind what happens to me; my sole prayer is that you will remain free to rule the world. I want no more than to re-enter private life, wear civilian clothes, be an ordinary citizen again. So long as you win the sovereignty, I will accept whatever odium your victory entails, and serve you in any capacity demanded of me.

'Do not think that you have a serious task ahead of you. Pompey's army consists largely of levies from the Greek gymnasia, trained in wrestling and athletics but hardly able to carry a full weight of arms and equipment, let alone use them; and of undisciplined barbarians, shouting gibberish at each other, who hate fighting and even marching. Few of you will be required to face fellow-Romans; for the most part your task will be to rid the earth of surplus population. I expect you to hack your way straight through those enemies of Rome, those infamous and cowardly foreigners, sweeping a whole world away with one vigorous sword-stroke, and trampling it underfoot. I expect you to prove that the nations over whom Pompey celebrated so many triumphs at Rome were not worth a single one. Besides, what concern is it of the Armenians whether he or I rule Rome? What barbarian would shed a drop of his blood to win Italy back from Pompey? They are united only in their hatred of us Romans and resent our national superiority. This makes me luckier than Pompey: Fate has ruled that none but my own soldiers will be serving under me, and the numerous campaigns which we fought together have assured me of your courage. I know you all: when it comes to action, I shall recognize every flashing sword or flying javelin and be able to name its owner correctly. And when I see you battling with set faces and fiery eyes, that will be a sure portent of victory – I have never yet been mistaken in the sight.

'You must forgive me if I detain you, and my own glorious destiny, by this speech, when we are so furiously eager for battle. I tremble at the vistas of glory now opening before me. Never have I felt the Gods so close at hand and ready to grant so much – a narrow verge alone separates us from the goal of our ambitions. When the battle is won, I shall have power to give away whole kingdoms. This is indeed an extraordinary celestial change. To think that the Gods can grant any man so much, in Thessaly of all places!

'To-day will decide whether we are to be rewarded or punished for going to war. Picture to yourselves what will happen if Pompey beats us: Caesar dragged away in chains, Caesar crucified, Caesar's head cut off and displayed on the Rostrum, Caesar's body left unburied! And do not forget how Sulla behaved, the Sulla against whose pupil Pompey we are fighting this second civil war. He promised to spare six thousand Marian prisoners, yet butchered them in the voting pens [1] of the Campus Martius. My chief anxiety is on your account. I shall commit suicide if you are routed; and whoever turns his back to the enemy will see me stabbing myself to death. Yet that cannot happen if, as I suppose, the Gods have ceased to interest themselves in celestial affairs and are engrossed with the troubles that have overtaken Rome. They will surely grant me victory. They know that I shall never behave as Pompey did when you were bottled up inside his camp near Dyrrhachium and unable to fight him on equal terms: shamelessly glutting

1. See Book II, 197.

my sword with blood by a massacre of defenceless men, whose only crime is that they have marched against me.[1]

'Soldiers, I beg you not to stab any fugitive between the shoulders as he runs; even if he is no Roman let him rank as such. But while the sun still glitters on the enemies' breastplates, forget all ties of affection or reverence, though you see your own fathers in the opposing ranks; strike fearlessly at their faces! And whoever finds himself driving his sword through a kinsman's heart or throat must take credit for this act, which in any other circumstances would be a crime; the credit will be the same whether your opponent is a stranger or not, because no difference can be made between one enemy soldier and another.

'Now, before joining battle, you must level the rampart with the trench; for I intend to march out in full strength without leaving a rearguard to defend this camp. You need not pause to consider where you will sleep to-night; Pompey's doomed troops have comfortable quarters, which you will take over from them.'[2]

His speech had hardly ended when the assembly broke up. The troops dispersed hurriedly to their stations, where they armed, breakfasted and, in foretaste of victory, joined in the work of kicking down the ramparts. Then they charged ahead in mass with no further orders from Caesar, leaving all to Fate. If every man had been a father-in-law of Pompey's, and intent on becoming sole master of Rome, they could not have made a wilder rush.[3]

Pompey, watching their headlong advance, realized that battle was being forced upon him and that this was indeed the day appointed by the Gods. His blood chilled, and to a general of his experience such

1. Lucan does not mention Pompey's threat to treat all neutrals as enemies; or Caesar's promise to treat them as friends.

2. Caesar, as a matter of fact, spoke chiefly about his constant offers to make peace with Pompey, all of which were refused, and of his reluctance to fight even now; and while the battle was in progress he cried out: 'Spare your fellow-citizens,' and allowed each of his men to save any one life he pleased in the opposing forces.

3. The truth is that Caesar made careful tactical dispositions. Mark Antony commanded on the right, Gnaeus Domitius in the centre, Publius Sulla on the left. Caesar also posted himself on the left, opposite Pompey. He detached six hundred men to guard the camp (which he had not dismantled), and then drafted a picked force of six battalions to act as a reserve on the right wing, should Pompey's cavalry attempt an enveloping movement. Finally, he gave orders that no battalion must advance until he gave the signal.

a qualm before battle seemed an extremely ominous sign. Yet he smothered his apprehensions and rode down the line on his tall charger.

'Brave men,' he shouted, 'the long awaited day is here – the welcome day which will end this civil war. Fight as you have never yet fought! You need only make one supreme effort, because all the nations of the world are at your side; but any man who pines for wife and children cannot buy the right to rejoin them except with his sword. The prizes of war are laid out on this level plain. Moreover, justice is with us, and we can count upon the Gods' support: they will surely guide our weapons into Caesar's heart, thus sealing with his blood their approval of our ancient Republican laws. If they intended to make him ruler of the world, they would doubtless have hurried my grey hairs to the tomb long ago. The proof that they still love Rome, and the allies of Rome, is that I am still alive and in command of this army. Every possible step has been taken to insure victory. Famous men have consented to serve in the ranks, and thus maintain the tradition of times gone by. Were heroes like Curius and Camillus alive now, and the two Decii, who deliberately died for Rome – they too would be found in our ranks. Contingents from the extreme East and from numerous cities, near and far, have also rallied to my standards. Never before was so huge and various an army gathered together under one commander. We have serving with us representatives of every nation in the entire northern hemisphere, from the Tropic of Cancer to the Arctic Circle. Caesar's force is contemptibly small; we shall outflank and surround it so completely that only a handful of our troops will see any fighting. Most of you will not be called upon to do more than shout!

'Think of Rome! Imagine the mothers of families leaning over the walls with dishevelled hair, and white-headed senators who would be among us if their old bones permitted, falling as suppliants at your feet! Imagine the Goddess of Rome coming in person and pleading with you to save her from Caesar's tyranny. Imagine that every Roman alive to-day, and every one who shall be born hereafter, is joining in her prayer – the former begging to die free; the latter, to be born free. And if I may now be allowed to mention myself, my wife and my sons, I assure you that we feel as our compatriots do. Were it consonant with the dignity of a commander-in-chief, I would grovel at your feet and implore you to preserve Roman freedom; for if you lose this battle you will pass the sentence of exile on me, Pompey the Great –

you will make me the butt of my kinsmen and a disgrace to yourselves. My one hope would then be to escape the humiliation of being captured and learning at my age, for the first time, how to act as a slave.'

This touching speech roused their courage, and they all resolved, as a last resort, not to survive the battle.

Thus it happened that both armies entered the combat with equal enthusiasm: Pompey's intent on escaping tyranny, Caesar's on imposing it. And as a direct result of their engagement it can be said that, whatever our present century – the ninth from the foundation of Rome – may have in store for us, it will not be large-scale warfare.[1] Nations yet unborn were condemned to die at Pharsalus. The Latin race has since become a mere memory and nothing survives to mark the sites of such famous cities as Gabii, Veii, Cora, Alba Longa, and Laurentum but crumbling ruins: Latium is now a deserted region where nobody ever comes to live, except the Senate when, once a year, they are reluctantly obliged by King Numa's Law[2] to spend a night at Alba celebrating the Latin Holiday. This destruction of national memorials is not due simply to the tooth of time; the cities I have mentioned became emptied as a direct result of civil war. And the population of the whole world has also declined steeply: sufficient inhabitants cannot be found for the towns and villages of rural Italy, and the city of Rome would be large enough to house our entire native race. Our Italian cornlands are tilled by slave-labour; ancient farmhouses stand empty and their rotten roofs are in danger of collapse.[3]

The City population is no longer native Roman, but the refuse of humanity: such a hodge-podge of races that we could not fight a

1. Lucan is trying to explain the military weakness of Nero's Rome as due to the losses suffered a hundred years before. But the Empire had been greatly extended and strengthened since then; Britain had been added in Lucan's own day. The fact was that Nero's reign of terror had undermined Army morale; the garrison in Armenia had been ignominiously defeated and obliged to pass beneath the yoke, Syria nearly lost, eighty thousand Romans massacred in the storm of Camulodunum [Meldon] and Verulamium [St Albans].

2. Really Tullus Hostilius's Law.

3. The Latin peasants who survived Sulla's massacre had abandoned their holdings and flocked to a more congenial life at Rome. Agricultural land was bought up by capitalists and turned into big estates worked by slaves; and no use could be found for the farm houses because the slaves were locked in barracks every night to prevent them from raising a revolt.

civil war, even if we wished. And for all this the Battle of Pharsalus is to blame. The Roman Calendar marks the anniversaries of our defeats at Cannae and the Allia as unlucky days; yet the day of Pharsalus, which passes unrecorded, was still unluckier. It is painful to think how easily Fate might have used other means to destroy the men who fell then: unhealthy marsh air, epidemics, pangs of famine, destruction of cities by fire or earthquake. But no, they were drawn from every quarter of the earth to premature death on the battlefield; marshalled there by scions of ancient dynasties, in proof of the grandeur that must now pass from Rome.

What city had ever made so many conquests, or extended its empire so widely? Every new war pushed back her frontiers north and south, and apart from a small section of the Orient, the stars in their courses looked down on no land that was not under her control.[1] But thanks to that bloody fight, the Indians lost their fear of Roman jurisdiction; nor has any Consul looped up his toga and marked out with a plough the course of a new city on the Scythian steppe, for Sarmatian or Dahaean nomads to build and inhabit.

It is owing to the Battle of Pharsalus that vengeance has never been taken on the Parthians for our defeat at Carrhae; and that the Goddess of Freedom, banished from Italy by the Civil War, has long since fled beyond the Tigris and the Rhine and refuses to return, though we may cut our throats in wooing her! Germans and Scythians bask in her blessed presence, but she does not deign to glance back at this country – if only Rome had never known who she was! We Romans, in fact, deserve to be slaves: we deserved it when Romulus killed his brother Remus after the twelve vultures appeared on his left hand,[2] then built his city and peopled it with criminals who had taken refuge in the Asylum. And we deserved slavery ever afterwards until the fratricidal Battle of Pharsalus.

I even regret that Brutus drove out the Tarquins! What advantage is it to us now that we enjoyed a few centuries of constitutional government and learned to let consuls rather than kings name the years?

1. Lucan must have been aware that the Far East, from which it took so many months to import silks and spices, was immensely larger than the Western world, and that the African coast extended far south of the Red Sea.
2. A side-reference to Nero's murder of his adoptive brother Britannicus with whom he should have shared the Empire.

The Arabians, Medians, and other orientals who have lived continuously under tyrants are far more fortunate than we; they need not feel
ashamed of being slaves, as we must. It is most false to say that Gods
rule this world, and that Juppiter rules the Gods; nothing but blind
chance makes the world go round. How ridiculous to pretend that if
Juppiter were really lord of our destinies, he could have looked idly
down on the massacre at Pharsalus, wasting his thunderbolts on Pholoë,
Oeta, the pines of Mimas, and the forest of Rhodope (none of which
had offended him) and leaving Caesar's assassination to Gaius Cassius
Longinus! If it is true that he darkened the day when Atreus set that
horrid banquet before his brother Thyestes at Argos – the roast flesh
of his own sons – why was the Sun permitted to shine on Thessaly,
where so many fathers and sons were fighting one another? No: the
Gods have never been interested in man's fate. Yet we are revenged
on them now, if I may put it that way, by the consequences of the war
which they failed to prevent: here in Rome we deify our dead Caesars,
we dress their images in divine style, furnishing them with thunderbolts, haloes, stars and all, worshipping their ghosts as though they
were Olympian gods and swearing oaths by their names!

The space that Fate had interposed between the advancing armies
shrank rapidly, and every soldier singled out a particular adversary at
whom to aim his javelin – the one who seemed destined to return the
compliment. Although some recognized the faces of fathers and of
brothers and realized the full horror of the situation, they had no desire
to change sides. Yet all felt their hearts turn suddenly numb and cold,
as natural affection froze within them, and whole companies stood for
awhile like statues, their weapons poised.

Crastinus was the man who deserved the full wrath of Heaven to
fall upon him, and not in the form of ordinary death, because everyone
must die some day; but of a death that would preserve the sensibilities.
For this Crastinus hurled the first javelin to draw Roman blood. How
mad a fellow he must have been to anticipate even Caesar's order for
letting fly![1] Immediately afterwards, strident blasts from clarion,
cornet, and trumpet sounded the assault, and the armies clashed in

---

1. Crastinus was a discharged centurion of the Tenth Legion who had
volunteered for further service, and told Caesar before the battle: 'You will be
grateful to me whether I live or die.' He headed the charge on the wing and died
from a sword thrust through the mouth.

battle. An immense roar arose and burst on the remote dome which rises above cloud level and has never experienced a thunderstorm – the summit of Mount Olympus. The same sound travelled across the valleys of Mount Haemus, to the caves of Pelion; it struck Pindus, Pangaeum, and the crags of Oeta – terrifying the armies with the echoes of their own madness.

Innumerable javelins flew, but not every soldier hoped that his would find its mark; some prayed that the point would lodge harmlessly in the ground and thus save them from blood-guilt. Chance and haste between them guided every aim, and Fortune chose who should be the guilty ones.

Ituraeans, Medes, and Arabians, though all formidable archers, poured their arrows indiscriminately into the thick of the enemy; and for this they cannot be censured – the true criminals were our Roman legionaries. A cloud of javelins from both armies darkened the sky, but inflicted lesss damage than the sword, which alone could fully satisfy their fratricidal bloodlust.

The Pompeians locked shields and fought in close order; but this prevented them from using their weapons to full advantage – indeed, they found it difficult to avoid wounding one another with their swords. Against that barrier of shields and bodies the Caesareans charged furiously, forcing a passage. There is no surer way of piercing a heart than to break through the protecting cuirass of chain mail; which was what every soldier attempted to do. But the armies differed in this: that while Caesar's men were actively waging civil war, Pompey's were uninspired by the same guilty passion and merely defending themselves.

Fortune did not lose much time in overthrowing and sweeping away the ruins of Pompey's host. His cavalry had enveloped Caesar's right flank in a wide encircling movement while the light-armed irregulars made a mass attack. Each contingent fought with its own native weapons but all had the same object: to spill Roman blood. They discharged volleys of arrows, firebrands, and stones, also leaden sling-shots which flew so fast that they melted in the air. Caesar, fearing that the leading companies might give way, moved forward his six reserve battalions from the right rear, and hurled them against the disorderly mass of allied cavalry – who were driven off the field in shameless panic; thus proving that one can never trust barbarian hordes to

participate in a Roman civil war. As soon as the first charger, stabbed
in the chest, had thrown and trampled its rider, whole squadrons
whirled about and galloped wildly back. The light-armed Pompeian
foot were left unprotected for Caesar's legionaries to slaughter. What
followed was less a battle than a continuous massacre; and even so the
Caesareans were too small a force to complete it. Alas, that the blood
of foreigners was not all that crimsoned the Pharsalian plains and
streams, and that their corpses were not the only ones scattered over
the cornfields! And that so many Galatians, Syrians, Cappadocians,
Gauls, Iberians, Armenians, and Cilicians had to fall; because, when
the Civil War ended, these would have been included in the Roman
Empire.

Panic spread, and Caesar's prospects visibly brightened. Pompey's
centre, the strongest part of his army, now became involved; and the
confused fighting which had been taking place in other quarters was
concentrated here in a bitter engagement. The Caesareans had met
worthy opponents at last: their own brothers and fathers, not foreign
auxiliaries from distant kingdoms. This phase of the battle epitomised
the evil fury sponsored by Caesar. I would rather not write about it;
I refuse to acquaint posterity with the full horrors unchained by this
civil war. Let my tears and complaints perish without record: I cannot
bring myself to describe a clash between Roman legions.[1] Caesar
could be seen rushing from point to point, whipping up the frenzy
which already possessed his men and inciting them to yet more desperate acts of wickedness. His eye was quick to notice which men had
reddened their swords to the hilt, and which only to the point; which
were merely obeying the order to fight and holding their weapons
irresolutely, and which were enjoying the work so much that they
never blanched at the murder of their fellow-citizens. He also stooped
over the sprawled corpses and, if he found one of his men bleeding to
death, staunched the flow by the pressure of his own fingers.

Caesar's progress resembled that of Bellona, Goddess of War, when
she brandishes her bloody scourge; or Mars when he inspires the
Bistonians of Thrace by lashing on his chariot horses – the same team
which Athene once terrified by displaying her Aegis.[2] Wherever he

1. But he does so in the next hundred lines.
2. Athene had assisted Hercules in a chariot fight against Mars and his son
Cycnus. Cycnus was killed and Mars wounded, by her help.

moved, a dark cloud of crime and slaughter accompanied him, and a concerted groan was heard, mixed with the clang of men's breast-plates as they struck the ground, and of swords being shattered against swords. He was always there to hand his men new swords or weapons salvaged from the field: 'Hack at their faces!' he shouted.[1] He led the front ranks to the attack in person, but then took a javelin and slipped back to the rear where he beat malingerers forward with the butt end. 'Never mind the private soldiers,' he cried. 'Kill the Senators!' For Caesar had his finger on the pulse of free Rome, now making her last stand on earth; he knew exactly how the blood flowed in her veins, and where she was most vulnerable. His men obeyed this new order and began hacking down all senators and knights: members of the Lepidan, Metellan, Corvinian, and Torquatan families, who had often commanded Roman armies and were the most distinguished men in the state, Pompey alone excepted.[2]

But what was Brutus doing on this occasion, sword in hand and disguised as a private soldier – Brutus, glory of Rome, last survivor of a house famous in our history? He was rashly trying to cut his way through the enemy ranks and kill Caesar; careless of his life, but doomed to die later at Philippi in another battle as decisive as that of Pharsalus.[3] Brutus's attempt proved idle, because Caesar had not yet risen above the decent limit of human greatness by tyrannizing over a prostrate world, and had not yet therefore earned the right to be assassinated. He would continue to live until Brutus won immortal fame by stabbing him with a dagger.

The flower of our nobility perished in that battle; a mound of patrician corpses afterwards found lying there contained not one plebeian. One death must be noted for attention: that of Domitius Ahenobarbus whom fate had led from defeat to defeat; whenever Pompey lost a battle he was always present – yet he died free. He fell cheerfully, wounded in a thousand places, and glad to escape the shame of being pardoned by Caesar a second time. Caesar found him

1. He advised them to go for the young patricians' faces, because they would be more afraid of having their good looks spoiled than of being wounded in some less obvious place.

2. No members of these old families are elsewhere recorded to have fallen at Pharsalus.

3. 44 B.C., when he was defeated by Mark Antony. This account of Brutus at Pharsalus seems to be a dramatic invention of Lucan's.

weltering in his blood and remarked ironically: 'Ah, it is you, Domitius, the man whom the Senate chose as Governor-General of Gaul
instead of me! Are you deserting the Pompeian cause and retiring from
the war?' The dying Domitius just managed to gasp out: 'Caesar, you
do not realize what a fearful price you will have to pay for your
treason. And you are still no match for your son-in-law; you cannot
yet count on victory. I go freely and happily to join the ghosts beside
the river Styx, in the resolute hope that you will be crushed in battle
and forced to indemnify Pompey and myself for the great mischief
you have done us.' Then the darkness of death closed his eyes.

It would be wrong to pick on any further victims, among all these
thousands, for particular lament, or to describe individual deaths –
telling who was stabbed in the belly; whose intestines burst out and
dangled to the ground where he trod on them; who faced the enemy
and died with a sword piercing his throat . . . Some wounded men
collapsed; some continued to stand upright, though their arms were
lopped off; others had their breasts transfixed by a javelin, or were
pinned to the earth with a spear-thrust. Often the blood spouted like
a fountain and wetted the enemy's arms. One man drove his sword
through his own brother's breast and, having decapitated him, threw
away the head to avoid the disgrace of despoiling a near relative's
corpse. Another mutilated his father's face, in a furious attempt to
convince those who saw him that he had not committed parricide.
No, this is hardly an occasion for mourning the fate of individuals.
Pharsalus differed from all other Roman defeats in so much as whole
armies died there – the allied forces of Greece, Pontus, and Assyria –
and yet the torrent of Roman blood was enough to sweep theirs
from the field. The world suffered an irreparable disaster, because what
we lost at Pharsalus was more than life and property; Roman liberty
lay prostrate and Caesar's swords sufficed thereafter to cow generation
after generation. But do we great-grandchildren of the combatants
really deserve to be born slaves? Are we cowards that we fear to die?
No, this is a punishment for our fathers' fears: Fortune who gave us
tyranny should have also given us a chance to take the field against
our tyrants.

Though Pompey understood that the Gods had deserted Rome and
himself, even a beaten army was not too terrible a sight to make him
despair of final success. He stood on a knoll above the plain from which,

now that the fighting was over, he could see corpses scattered every-where and estimate the full extent of the losses. While feeling as if he were bleeding to death, he did not do what other ruined commanders have done in similar circumstances: rejoice to drag the entire world down with him. He persuaded himself that the Gods were worth invoking, and considered how to win their favour, despite the present calamity, consoling himself with the hope that the greater part of the Roman army might be rescued from destruction. 'Gods of Heaven!' he prayed. 'Hold your hands! Spare what yet remains of the world! Rome may still survive, even though I am doomed. Do you wish to chastise me still further? Then I have a wife and two sons left as hostages in Fortune's hands. Tell me: if I and they are destroyed, will that put an end to the Civil War? Will that sacrifice content you, or is it Fortune's whim to mangle and ruin the entire human race? I willingly yield her all that remains mine.'

Then he rounded up his dwindling army and had the retreat blown, to prevent them from throwing away their lives in a now hopeless cause. He did not, of course, shrink from offering his throat or breast to the enemy swordsmen; but feared that, if he did so, his men would continue to stand their ground and allow themselves to be slaughtered in heaps above his corpse. Or perhaps he wished to die where Caesar would not be there to see? If so, it was a vain hope: if Caesar chose to demand Pompey's severed head, no land would grudge it him. And Pompey had another reason for flight: the beloved face of his wife, without whom he could not die, because she was a part of him.

He spurred his horse from the field, fearless of the javelins flying behind him, and moved dauntlessly to his doom. He neither groaned nor wept, but looked serenely on the plain of Pharsalus, displaying the dignified sorrow which one might have expected from so great a man when faced by the misfortunes of Rome. Victory had never elated him, nor had defeat ever depressed him; and faithless Fortune who owned him her superior in the time of his three Triumphs, found that he was her superior still. After surrendering the heavy burden entrusted to him by Fate, he rode off with a light heart; and now found leisure to dwell upon the happy past and, since hope was vanished beyond recall, dwell contentedly upon what he once had been. How right to quit the stricken field and make the Gods witnesses that any soldiers who cared to fight on were no longer dying for his sake!

As in the lamentable battles of Thapsus and Munda, as in the slaughter on the banks of the Nile, so at Pharsalus, when Pompey had fled, the struggle ceased to be between those who loved him and those who loved fighting. Rather, it was the struggle, which continues to-day, between Freedom and Caesardom; and the senators proved by their willingness to die that a constitutional, not a personal, dispute underlay it.

Pompey must, I think, have felt relieved to ride off, without staying to watch the final scene of the disaster; but as he glanced back at the fountains of blood that spurted from the dying and darkened the streams of the Enipeus, he might well have pitied Caesar. How would Caesar feel when he entered Rome again after such a victory? Whatever sufferings might lie ahead of Pompey, as a solitary exile in strange lands or as a prisoner of King Ptolemy, his former patrons the Olympian Gods and Fortune could give him one certain consolation: that victory would have been worse than defeat. And the universal grief, mourning and tears for Pompey's fall were inappropriate; he deserved as much adoration in his present abasement as in his past Triumphs. Calmly and with none of the self-abasement that suppliants affect, he considered all the cities which he had taken, all the kingdoms which he had bestowed on his allies in Egypt and Africa; and chose from among them one where he might end his life.

The first city to greet Pompey as he rode by, noble and uncrushed, was Larisa in Phthiotis. Her citizens came streaming out to meet him, as if he were returning triumphant. They wept, they brought gifts, they threw open their temples and houses in welcome, they offered to share his defeat. And, indeed, Pompey's immense fame was hardly dimmed. No general could equal him, except his younger self, and he might yet have roused the nations of the world to fight under him and so continued his interrupted course of victory. But all that he would say was: 'Be wise and pledge your loyalty to the victor. Though he may be trampling on a heap of Roman corpses, his feet entangled in their guts, I nevertheless make him a present of the cities and nations of the world, for which a beaten man like myself has no further use.'

He rode off, followed by the groans and lamentations of the people. The numerous reproaches which they hurled at the Gods proved that they loved him for himself, not for his success; until now he could not have been sure of this, and the realization made him happy.

When the fields were sufficiently drenched with Roman blood for Caesar's taste, and the Pompeians still on their feet seemed hardly worth slaughtering, he called off the attack. But lest the panic-stricken fugitives might rally in their camp and be ready to fight again after a night's rest, he decided to seize it at once. It seemed unlikely that his veterans would resent this order, however wearied they might be; soldiers need little encouragement when plunder is in prospect. 'Our victory is complete, men,' he shouted, 'and now comes the recompense for our exertions and losses. It is not my business to present you with what each can take for himself; let me merely point out that the Pompeian camp lies before you, its tents well stocked with bullion – gold robbed from the western nations and abundant treasures from the East – not only Pompey's hoard but the hoards of his royal allies, all waiting for someone to claim them. Hurry ahead of those beaten fugitives, or they will deprive you of your battle earnings.'[1]

No trench or rampart could have withstood the attack of men so intent on winning the reward for so evil a victory; they were frantic to discover just how large it would be. In the event, they found several tempting heaps of coin collected from different nations to pay for the war, but not enough to satisfy their excessive greed; even if they had been able to lay their hands on all the gold mined in Spain, or washed from the river Tagus, or gathered from the sands of India by wealthy Arimaspians, they would still have considered themselves cheated. Since what had led them to promise Caesar their support was the hope of sacking Rome – including the Public Treasury and the Temple of Capitoline Juppiter – this pillage of a mere camp disappointed them. That night, however, turf beds prepared for patricians were occupied by bloodstained plebeians; couches spread for kings, by roughs from the ranks; and some men lay down where their murdered fathers or brothers had last slept.[2]

Frantic nightmares haunted their sleep: all were obsessed with the wicked and cruel fighting in which they had taken part, their hands twitched ceaselessly as though still grasping swords. I am ready to

---

1. Caesar, on the contrary, begged his men not to let the plunder distract them from consolidating their victory.

2. The unnecessarily luxurious furnishings of the patrician tents surprised the Caesareans, who had been short for months of the commonest necessities.

believe that groans arose from the battlefield, that a miasma of death choked them, and that the ghosts of their enemies assembled to corrupt and darken the night air with Stygian terrors. Victory had demanded divine retribution; no one could sleep soundly for the torches swung by the Furies and the hissing of snakes upon their heads. Each man was haunted by a different ghost, sometimes old, sometimes young, perhaps his brother, perhaps his father – but a whole spirit army crowded around Caesar's bed. He suffered as Orestes the Argive suffered from his mother's Furies (until purified by his sister Iphigeneia, priestess of Taurian Artemis), and his mind was no less disturbed than that of Pentheus king of Thebes, when Bacchus drove him mad, or than his mother Agave, when she came to her senses and found that she had torn him in pieces. All the swords drawn at Pharsalus, all the daggers that would be drawn in the Senate House when the day of vengeance dawned, were pointed that night at Caesar's heart, and the monstrous Furies scourged him without remorse. Yet he escaped the full punishment because, while this horde of ghosts was invading his sleep, Pompey continued alive.

When Caesar awoke, nothing pleased him better than to review the battlefield. The streams were still running red, the mounds of corpses were settling down into corruption, and it was easy to see where the various foreign contingents had been engaged. He chose a spot from which he could study and recognize the features of the dead, and told his men to serve him a luxurious breakfast there; glad that the soil was hidden by corpses and overjoyed that the Gods had so far approved of his cause as to grant him victory. Yet he was bloody-minded enough not to spoil the spectacle on which he now feasted his eyes by building pyres for the wretched dead; and left the Gods an uninterrupted view of what they had cruelly sanctioned.[1]

Hannibal burned the body of his enemy Paulus Aemilius, the Consul who fell at Cannae, with the funeral honours due to his rank; Caesar should have taken lessons in humane behaviour from him, but obsessed with thoughts of further vengeance he could not forget that these were Romans and his private foes. Individual funerals would, perhaps, have been too much to expect of him, but he might at least have built a common pyre for all the fallen. And it would have been a

1. The plain was treeless, and the task of cremating twenty thousand corpses would have baffled even the pious Pompey.

pleasant act of vengeance on the departing Pompey to have collected
an enormous quantity of timber in the forests of Pindus and Oeta and
set it ablaze for him as his farewell salute from Thessaly.

Nevertheless, Caesar's fury was in vain. It did not much matter
whether the corpses were cremated or allowed to contrive their own
gradual dissolution; Nature would take them back into her own gentle
bosom. And if fire did not burn them now it would do so eventually,
when the universal conflagration destroys everything in existence –
the sea, the stars, and the Earth with all the dead men's bones she houses.
And wherever Caesar's spirit might go after death, he would not elude
the vengeful ghosts of his victims – if he soared to Heaven, they would
out-soar him; indeed, no refuge could be much safer than the darkness
of the Underworld.

Dead men are free from the vicissitudes of Fortune, Mother Earth
has room for every one of her children, and a corpse to whom an urn
is denied has the whole sky to cover it. But why did Caesar punish his
numerous enemies by denying them decent burial? Was this not
foolish? He could no longer drink the water or breathe the pestilential
air of Pharsalus; he was routed by the corpses of the defeated, who
now claimed possession of the field.

Not only Thessalian wolves gathered to the gruesome feast, but the
packs of distant Thrace scented the blood and came crowding down;
and so did the mountain lions of Pholoë, with bears, and wild dogs,
and other keen-nosed carrion-eaters. In flew the birds that had acted
as camp-followers to the armies throughout the Civil War; and the
cranes, which normally migrated to the Nile when winter came to
Thrace, postponed their visit, because here were better pickings.[1] The
flock of vultures was the largest ever seen, and every wood in Thessaly
sent out its quota of birds to gorge on the dead; when they flew back
with bloody feathers the branches where they roosted dripped a red
dew. Often the weary birds flying overhead let fall fragments of
clotted gore or corrupt flesh which struck the victor's accursed standards, or his very head. But even so the beasts and birds did not strip
those skeletons clean; they found plenty of solid flesh to batten on,
without needing to pluck at the intestines or crack the marrow-bones.
In fact, they left most of the Roman dead lying untasted; but sun and

1. This rhetorical thought is more than usually far-fetched. It was now
Spring; and cranes (like bears) are not carnivorous.

rain did their gradual work and at last the corpses became integrated with the soil of Thessaly.

Ah, wretched Thessaly! How did you offend the Gods so deeply that they chose you out of all the other countries in the world as the scene of this unprecedented and wicked slaughter? Posterity will never forget or forgive what happened on your soil. Every cornfield must sprout for awhile with red-tipped blades, every plough-share disturb the ghost of some dead Roman. And long before the memory of Pharsalus can begin to fade, a second equally criminal battle must bathe your fields with blood.[1]

Though we were to ransack the tombs of our ancestors, both recent ones and those which have been split open by the burrowing roots of trees and had their urns overturned – yet the ploughs and harrows of Thessaly still turn up more Roman bones than we could ever collect. No Roman sailor would now willingly moor his ship to the shore, no Roman farmer would willingly till a soil haunted by the ghosts of his countrymen, no Roman shepherd would dare let his sheep crop the grass, in thicket or field, that might spring from the bones of some unburied legionary: Thessaly would, in fact, be as deserted as those regions of the icy North or the burning South which the climate renders uninhabitable – had it been the sole country, not merely the first,[2] to be the scene of civil war.

If only the almighty Gods had allowed us to lay a curse on a single country! Instead, they spread it across the entire world: they arranged for the Senate's defeat at Munda and Mutina by land, and by sea at Naulochus, Mylae, and Actium – thus acquitting Thessaly of peculiar guilt.

1. Lucan means the Battle of Philippi, which he once more pretends to have taken place at the Philippi near Pharsalus, not at the Macedonian Philippi.
2. Lucan is forgetting Caesar's campaigns in Spain, Italy, Gaul and Epirus already described; and the civil war fought between Sulla and Marius.

BOOK EIGHT

POMPEY urged on his flagging charger, which no longer answered to the spur, past the forest slopes of Tempe and down the valley created (as I have already mentioned) by Hercules; his frequent changes of direction baffled Caesar's pursuit. But the soughing of wind in the trees, and the shouts of his staff as they laboured after him were terrifying; he thought every time: 'The enemy is upon me.' Although fallen from power, he knew that his life was still of extreme value; and believed that Caesar would be prepared to offer as much for his head, as he for Caesar's.

His noble face was too well known to pass unrecognized. While following the rough country tracks he met several Greek contingents on their way to join his camp at Pharsalus. Not having yet heard the news of the battle, all were so astounded at the sudden change in his fortunes that they could hardly believe him when he acknowledged himself ruined. Such encounters were extremely painful. Pompey would have liked to pass through the world incognito; but Fortune, who had loaded him with favours in the past, now made these an instrument of punishment. His universal fame became an embarrassing burden, and he realized at last that he should never have opposed Sulla's wishes by insisting on his Numidian Triumph at the age of only twenty-five. He even regretted his Triumphs over the Cilician pirates and the armies of Mithridates. The truth is that the greatest souls feel abased when their lives outlast the power which they once enjoyed; unless a man can die at the moment that his fortunes begin to ebb, and so escape the sorrow of failure, recollection of past successes must be a bitter mockery. No one should consent to accept glory who is not prepared to kill himself as soon as it leaves him.

Pompey reached the coast at the point where the river Peneus, now dyed with Roman blood, debouches into the Aegean Sea, and went, with some disquiet, aboard a craft which would hardly have looked safe on a river, let alone a gusty sea. Just imagine what this meant: Pompey the Great, whose fleet was still master of Corfu and manned by hardy sailors of Leucas, Cilicia, and the Liburnian coast, slinking away in such a cockleshell of a boat! The thought of his beloved wife Cornelia drew him towards her hiding-place in Lesbos, where she was now feeling even more sorrowful than if she had stood on the battle-field of Pharsalus. Forebodings of defeat gave her broken sleep. At night she brooded anxiously on the war and, as soon as dawn came, would hurry to the edge of a cliff and gaze across the sea. Cornelia was always the first to see the top-sails of ships bobbing above the horizon, yet when they approached she dared not ask after Pompey.

One morning, as she kept watch, a ship made straight for the harbour, but she could not be sure what news it would bring.[1] Hitherto, her worst fear had been to hear reports that the war was going badly. This ship, however brought news of actual disaster, and the messenger was her husband in person. What a pity that she could not immediately mourn and weep, but still felt only apprehension, not sorrow! As the ship drew nearer she sprang up from her seat and learned how treacherous and unkind the Gods had been: on the deck stood Pompey in grimy clothes, and with his white hair straggling over a haggard face. Cornelia gasped for grief and fainted dead away; her heart ceased to throb, and she lay for awhile in what she hoped was death. Presently the sailors moored the vessel and Pompey disembarked on the empty beach. When Cornelia's faithful maids saw him coming towards her along the cliff-top, they choked back their complaints against the cruelty of Heaven, moaning softly instead, and tried in vain to lift their senseless mistress from the ground. It was Pompey who restored those rigid limbs to life by enfolding them in a warm embrace. The blood coursed through her veins again: she grew aware that she lay in his arms, and faced the sadness of his eyes.

He reproved her for sinking beneath the blow that fate had struck. 'A descendant of such noble ancestors as the Scipios,' he said, 'should not allow her courage to wilt at the first breath of ill fortune. Here is your chance of perpetual fame, which a woman can earn only by her husband's reverses, not by her personal successes in war or politics. Be high-minded, let your love for me wrestle with destiny and find

1. This was a merchantman commanded by one Petilius, who had since taken Pompey aboard.

strength in defeat! Your glory will be the greater now that I have forfeited my insignia of office and am no more attended by the victorious
Senate or a long trail of allied kings. I want you to be my sole companion in distress; yet since it would be indecorous for you to show
excessive grief while I am still alive, you must take pains to control
yourself. The final proof of fidelity will not come until I die. So far
my defeat has caused you little loss: Pompey the Great (though Great
no longer) lives yet, and to grieve for my vanished reputation would
show that you loved it better than me.'

At this rebuke Cornelia rose feebly from the ground, and began to
sob: 'If only I had married that hateful Caesar! The dowry which I
brought to both my husbands was disaster. When I married you, a
Fury must have acted as bridesmaid, and the ghosts of Crassus and his
son as bridemen. I should have remained true to their memory and
never married again. The disaster of Carrhae has repeated itself, and I
am to blame for scaring away the Gods from what is the better cause,
and so bringing ruin on the world. Glorious husband, no match for me,
how could Fortune have dared to overcome you? Oh, why did I consent to a marriage bound to bring ill-luck? I am ready to die for your
sake: kill me, if you like, and throw my body into the sea. The sacrifice
would placate the Gods, persuading them to smoothe the waves, confirm the allied kings in their loyalty, and strengthen the whole world
in its devotion to you. I should have preferred to buy you victory with
my life; but now let me expiate your defeat in the same way. Wherever
my rival, the ruthless Julia, may have been buried, her ghost is free to
visit Lesbos and exact the penalty she demands. It was Julia who
punished our marriage with a civil war; perhaps she will be appeased
by my death – perhaps she will stop her mischief-making when you are
hers once more!'

Cornelia sank back into Pompey's arms, and everyone present wept,
including the stern-hearted Pompey himself – whose eyes had been
dry even when he surveyed the battlefield of Pharsalus.

The inhabitants of Mytilene flocked up and told him: 'We shall
always remember with pride that so great a man as you entrusted us
with the care of your wife: and to-day please be good enough to
honour this city, with which you are linked by sacred ties of affection.
Accept our hospitality for one night at least – we should like Mytilene
to become a place of pilgrimage for Romans on your account. No city

is so worthy to welcome you in defeat; because, though others may rely on Caesar's clemency, we have already incurred the guilt of sheltering Cornelia. Besides, Lesbos is an island, and Caesar has no fleet; we can expect most of the surviving senators to come here in search of you. Why not rally your fortunes on this famous shore? Lesbos is wholly at your disposal. Strip our temples of their treasures, enlist our fighting men for service, either on land or sea, wherever you think they will be more useful. Though beaten, you are free to harvest the island's resources and thus deny them to your rapacious enemy. All we ask is never to be accused of having shown disloyalty in your hour of adversity, after following you while Fortune was still kind.'

This loyal address restored Pompey's faith in humanity and caused him great satisfaction. He replied: 'By committing my wife to your charge I proved that no corner of the earth is dearer to me than Lesbos; during her stay with you, Lesbos became my own beloved island, and even replaced Rome in my affections. When I escaped from Thessaly, it was to Lesbos that I first sailed; and though aware that you had already earned Caesar's resentment by caring for my wife, I did not fear to come here in person and offer you a golden opportunity of earning his pardon by my arrest. Now I cannot incriminate you further; I must follow wherever destiny guides me. How fortunate is Lesbos, how famous she will always be, whether other nations or kingdoms learn from her example to grant me asylum, or whether she prove to be the only faithful ally I possess. I am resolved to search the world and discover where good lies, and where evil. Immortal Gods – if any god still supports my cause – this is the last prayer I shall address to you: "Grant me to find elsewhere as noble-hearted a people as the Lesbians, who have allowed a beaten man, in flight from Caesar, not only to land on their shores but to sail away again." '[1]

Then he re-embarked with his sorrowing wife; and the sight provoked so loud an outcry of grief ashore, and so many fists were shaken in reproach to Heaven, that it looked as though the entire population of the island had been banished overseas! It was not so much that Pompey had wished them good-bye, though his ill-luck saddened them; but that they had come to regard Cornelia as one of themselves. When she stepped aboard the vessel a great groan went up. Even if she

1. What Pompey really told the people of Mytilene was that they should take courage and trust in Caesar's well-known clemency.

had been returning to her husband's camp after a victory, the ladies of Lesbos could hardly have let her go without tears; because she had won all hearts by her gentleness, modesty, and purity, which made her a welcome guest in every home. Indeed, she had shown so little pride while Pompey's star was still in the ascendant that anyone might have thought him already beaten.

By this time half of the Sun's fiery disk had dipped into the sea; a position in which it was wholly visible neither to the people of Greece nor to the people of Atlantis, if such there be.[1]

Pompey now anxiously considered whether he should take refuge in one of his allied cities, or venture to some kingdom of doubtful allegiance, or perhaps travel far to the South beyond the burning deserts of the Upper Nile until he reached the untracked wilderness. So gloomy were his thoughts, so deep his loathing of the future, that he tried to distract himself by questioning the master of the ship about the stars. He wanted to know what astronomical principles should be observed when steering for the Syrian coast, and which star in the Great Bear should be chosen when making for Libya. The knowledge-able master informed him that the stars in the sky were most mislead-ing: all of them except one moved slowly around the heavens. 'I refer to the Pole Star,' he said, 'which never sinks beneath the horizon; it is the brightest star in either the Great or the Little Bear, and we steer by it. When we see the Little Bear rising towards the zenith until it stands above the main-top, this means that we are heading for the Bosphorus and the Black Sea, along whose curved shore the Scythians live; when, on the other hand, Boötes and the Pole Star begin to drop towards sea level, then we are heading south for Syria. After passing Syria we pick up Canopus, a star which is afraid of the North Wind and prefers to cruise about in the Southern sky; and if we keep Canopus to port and coast on past Egypt, we reach the Gulf of Sirte, half-way down the Mediterranean. But where do you want me to shape my course? You have not yet given me sailing orders.'

All that Pompey cared to answer was: 'I want you to keep as far away as possible from the coast of Thessaly and from the Western world in general; let the winds blow you where they will. When you first took me aboard I knew exactly what orders to give you, because I

1. It did not occur to Lucan that the sun would still be clearly visible in Western Greece and Italy, as well as in Atlantis.

had left a hostage with Fortune. Now that she is safely by my side, let Fortune herself choose a port for us.'

So the master hauled at the sails on the level sailyards and put the helm hard a-port; yet to negotiate the rough seas off Chios and the rocks of Asina, he slackened her bowsheets and tautened the stern-sheets. The ship's prow cut the water with a different sound as the result of this manoeuvre, which was executed even more skilfully than when a charioteer wheels his car sharply to the left around the turning-post without fouling it. Presently the sun rose, the stars faded, and land was revealed.

Many survivors of Pharsalus had gone to search for Pompey. His son Sextus, who had also been in Lesbos[1] with a band of faithful nobles, overtook him first. Though an exile, Pompey still had a retinue of Eastern princes, and sent Deiotarus, the aged King of Galatia, who had followed his tracks, to apply for help in a very distant region.[2] These were his instructions: 'Since the Roman Empire, as we knew it, has been destroyed at Pharsalus, it remains, noble Deiotarus, most faithful of my kings, to test the loyalty of the Eastern nations who live in Mesopotamia between the Euphrates and Tigris – rivers as yet untroubled by Caesar's armies. I wish you to visit the lands of Scythia and Parthia, where you may give the proud Arsacid king this message from me: "If our treaty stands, the treaty which I swore to observe in the name of Capitoline Juppiter, and which you also swore in the presence of your mages, then it is your duty to marshal your horse-archers and your Armenian and Getan allies, as well, in my defence. You will recall that when I marched through the Caspian Gates against the bellicose Alans I left Parthia in peace; your horsemen were free to scour the plains instead of taking refuge behind the walls of Seleucia. I passed far beyond your kingdom towards the rising sun until I reached the land where the rapid Ganges and the Jhelum flow.[3] Thence

1. Yes: Sextus Pompey had not really been in Thessaly consulting Erichtho, but in Lesbos, though apparently he avoided Mytilene; he may have resented Pompey's marriage with Cornelia, since he was the son of Mucia, her divorced predecessor.

2. Deiotarus had been with him in the small boat mentioned above.

3. This message, invented by Lucan, would have been patently untrue. Pompey never went farther than Albania, on the shores of the Caspian Sea, which lay considerably west of Persia. To reach India he would have had to march some two thousand miles through Parthian territory.

I continued my victorious progress, but refrained from adding Parthia to the long list of my Triumphs – which leaves you as the only king with whom I can now treat on equal terms. Nor was this the sole occasion when I protected the Arsacid dynasty. Who but I restrained the Romans from taking just vengeance on you for Crassus's defeat at Carrhae?[1]

' "In fact, you are under so deep an obligation to me that you must feel obliged to cross the river Euphrates, the boundary between West and East fixed by Alexander the Great, using the bridge which he built at Zeugma. If you invade the Roman Empire in Pompey's name, Rome will welcome her conquerors." '

It was a difficult commission, yet Deiotarus accepted it. He hastily borrowed a servant's clothes, discarded his badges of royalty and prepared to disembark at once. How much safer a poor man can be than a king was proved by Deiotarus's assumption of this disguise! Pompey put him ashore and sailed on past the rocky coasts of Icaria and the island of Samos; avoided the sheltered waters of Ephesus and Colophon; met with stiff breezes off Cos; gave a wide berth to Cnidos and Rhodes, the famous home of the Sun-god; cut across the mouth of the Telmessian Gulf; and finally approached Pamphylia. So far he had not ventured to touch at any port, but now entered the Lycian town of Phaselis which was not sufficiently large to be dangerous, the more so since most of its inhabitants were away at the war. Thence he coasted past Pamphylia until Mount Taurus came in sight with the river Dipsus cataracting down its side.

Hitherto Pompey had perhaps never considered that he might one day benefit personally by his suppression of the local pirates; but here he was sailing along in a small vessel with no fear of being attacked. Numerous senators who had rallied to him were now also aboard, and presently they made the modest port of Syhedra, at the mouth of the Cilician river Selinus. There he called a meeting which he sadly addressed as follows:

'Friends, who fought with me and have fled with me, you are as dear to my heart as our own native land. Here in Cilicia, unaccompanied by any troops, I pause to decide what steps I should take for beginning my military career afresh; and I call on you to support me

1. Pompey persuaded the Senate not to proceed with the Parthian War while Caesar was still actively engaged in Gaul.

courageously. The Thessalian campaign has not altogether ruined me; I can yet raise my head from the dust. You will remember how Marius was forced to lodge in the ruins of Carthage, but contrived to fight his way back to power and win his seventh consulship, a feat which had never before been noted in the Roman Annals. Fortune, which has treated me far less cruelly than Marius, can hardly keep me from rising again. I have a thousand ships in the Adriatic and a thousand loyal captains; the result of Pharsalus has been to scatter my forces, but they have not deserted to the enemy.

'The name of Pompey will protect me wherever I go; the whole world has witnessed my exploits and learned to respect me. I should now like you to consider which is the strongest and most reliable nation that I can decently call to the aid of Rome – Libya, Parthia, or Egypt? But first I shall tell you what I have decided, after anxious thought. I do not trust King Ptolemy of Egypt: he is too young, at thirteen years, to understand his obligations under the treaty that he signed with me. Still less do I trust King Juba who is double-faced like all Moors and, being descended from Hannibal's sister, has inherited the Carthaginian ambition of invading Italy no less ruthlessly than Hannibal himself. His lineal ancestors were Numidians, but he remembers his collateral ones; and that Varus recently visited him, pleading for help against Curio, has made him despise us Romans as people of little account.

'Our wisest course, in the circumstances, will be to make for the river Euphrates, which divides the Eastern World from ours, or for the Caspian Gates which lead to huge tracts of country where we could live undisturbed. The Parthians occupy a totally different hemisphere. Their kingdom is bordered by a quite different ocean from ours, and the sea which separates the two continents has a distinct colour – it is called the Red Sea. Their chief delight is in conquest. They possess the strongest chargers and the strongest bows of any nation on earth; and every horse-archer has a deadly aim, including boys and old men. These were the first troops to check the progress of Alexander the Great's phalanx. They also captured Bactra, the Median capital, and Assyrian Babylon with its immense fortifications. Nor do they stand in awe of Roman javelins; they will face our legions boldly, because they have proved the value of their own arrows at the defeat of Crassus's army. Furthermore, those arrows are poisoned; a mere scratch from the point can prove fatal. I heartily wish, of course, that we did not need to rely on the pitiless Arsacids, whose ascendancy in the East closely parallels ours in the West; but Heaven has been very kind to them. It is my ambition to uproot the oriental nations and hurl them in mass against our enemy. And if the King of Parthia dishonours my solemn treaty with him, I shall not appeal to the mercy of the kings whom I made; I propose instead to repair my shattered fortunes in the untrodden regions of the rising sun wherever chance may take me. And if I die at the world's end, it will be with the consoling thought that Caesar has had the opportunity neither of outraging my corpse, nor – the crowning insult – of burying it with the piety expected of a father-in-law.

'When I review my life, it occurs to me that I was always respected in the East even by the tribes beyond the Caspian Sea and beside the River Don; everyone followed my career. The name of Pompey was famous throughout the Orient even before I invaded those foreign lands, and more famous still when I returned in triumph. I trust that Rome will bless my enterprise; the Gods could grant us nothing better than that we should involve the Parthian King in our civil wars and by destroying his armies make him share our calamity. When Caesar comes up against the Parthians, either he will avenge Crassus or the Parthians will avenge me.'

The low muttering of Pompey's associates soon informed him that they condemned the project. Lentulus Spinther, the ex-Consul, who had a greater sense of honour than any of them, asked Pompey with noble indignation: 'Why has the defeat at Pharsalus broken your spirit? Do you truly believe that the fate of all nations was decided in a single day? Your heart is bleeding – can nothing staunch the flow? It is absurd to think that you have no alternative except to prostrate yourself before the Parthian king. Why try to escape from our world to a wholly different climate, to an alien sky and alien stars? Would you adopt the religion of the barbarous Parthian fire-worshippers? And why pretend that love of liberty has prompted you to ask them for military aid? If Pompey can bring himself to be any man's slave, then the suffering Empire has been much mistaken. It is true that the Parthian king trembled to hear your name when you were the virtual ruler of Rome and brought captive kings from the Hyrcanian forests and the frontiers of India to grace your Triumph. But why present yourself to him broken and defeated, the victim of fate, and so inspire him with greedy ambition – by persuading him that if so celebrated a man as you can come suing for assistance, then Rome is as good as conquered? Whatever you tell him will be unworthy of yourself; he knows no Latin and will expect you to convey your appeal in dumb-show with streaming eyes.

'And why should our honour be tarnished by such an anomaly as that Parthia, of all countries, should forestall us in vengeance of the wrong done to Rome? You were elected commander-in-chief only for the duration of the civil war, is that not so? And why advertise our internal differences and disasters to uncouth orientals who so far know nothing about them? Imagine, too, inviting the Parthians across the Euphrates! To do so would be to deprive Rome of her one solace in this great defeat: that she has, at least, been conquered by a son of her own. Surely you would not enjoy marching through the western world at the head of a foreign horde, with the standards captured at Carrhae paraded in the van? While the issue was still in doubt at Pharsalus the King of Parthia, alone among important Eastern monarchs, failed to present himself at your camp; when he hears who won the battle will he now favour your cause and challenge the all-powerful Caesar? I hardly think that, as a Parthian, he would have sufficient confidence.

'Every Northerner is a born fighter and scorns death, because of the harsh climate: the farther one proceeds to the South or the East, the softer the people, until one meets men dressed in flowing robes just like women. In the pleasant land of Media, on the level plains of Mesopotamia and beyond, the Parthians are invincible since they always manage to escape pursuit. But in mountainous country they are useless: you cannot make them scale steep ranges, or fight in dark ravines, or swim across swollen rivers, or sweat all day under a stifling sun on a dusty battlefield. They keep no battering-rams nor any other form of siege engine; and are incapable even of bridging a fosse by filling it with earth. And when they attack, any arrow-proof shelter will keep them out as easily as a solid city wall. Parthians never give battle; they merely skirmish, wheeling here and there, fighting as they flee; and are always readier to yield ground than to capture an enemy position. Their arrows are winged with guile; they avoid hand-to-hand combat by shooting from a distance and trusting the wind to direct their arrows. The only weapon fit for brave men is the sword; but the Parthians retire from a battle as soon as their quivers are empty; they put their trust in poison, not in cold steel. Tell me, Pompey, can anyone call the Parthians soldiers when they fear to become involved in a regular battle? Is this shameful alliance worth considering? Do you really intend to die a world away from your native country and be buried beneath alien soil – probably in a mean and undignified tomb which will, nevertheless, excite the envious notice of Crassus's ghost? For his body was merely thrown into a river.

'Besides, it is all very well for you to talk in this strain; any brave man can face death, the ultimate penalty, without flinching. But what of Cornelia? If she falls into the power of that evil-hearted king she has worse than death to fear. Surely you have no illusions about his marital habits? Love among the barbarians implies a bestial and degrading polygamy; a thousand wives are always present in the harem to witness his sexual prowess. The King, flushed with wine and gorged with food, undertakes frolics too monstrous even to figure in the laws against unnatural vice; he passes from one woman to another all night – not sparing even his sisters or his own mother. Thebes has earned an evil reputation because of the crime which Oedipus committed by marrying Jocasta, though he did not know that he was her son; yet many Arsacids are born from deliberate acts of Oedipean incest and afterwards ascend to the throne! What sort of behaviour can be expected of a man who begets children on his own mother? And though Cornelia, the noble daughter of Cornelius Metellus, will be merely one of a thousand concubines waiting beside the King's bed, you may be sure that he will feel hotter and more savage lust for her than for any other of them. When he remembers that she was young Crassus's wife before she was yours, he will treat her as though she were one of the captives taken long ago at Carrhae.

'Does not the memory of that disaster still rankle in your heart? You ought to blush not only at appealing for the Parthian King's help but at having made war on your fellow-Romans instead of on him. The world can bring no greater reproach against Caesar and yourself than this: that you forgot your duty of avenging Crassus and his son. Every general in the Army should have hurried towards Bactra, and brought the expeditionary force to full strength by denuding the whole northern frontier of troops; leaving the Dacians and Germans

to their own devices until Susa and Seleucia had been destroyed and
their buildings sent crashing down upon the tombs of their treacherous
monarchs.

'It is my prayer that the truce with Parthia will be broken and that,
if this Civil War proves to have been decided at Pharsalus, the conqueror will elect to invade her. Parthia is the one nation over which I
could rejoice to see Caesar triumph. Pompey, if you persist in your
plan of crossing the cold Araxes, you must expect to meet the mourn-
ful ghost of Crassus, riddled with Scythian arrows, and to hear his
words of reproach: "My comrades and I were denied decent funeral
rites, and have long counted on you to avenge us. Surely you are not
arranging a peace treaty with our enemies?"[1]

'You will then be confronted by many memorials of our disgrace:
the walls around which the headless trunks of our generals were
dragged, the spot where they were thrown into the Euphrates – or into
the Tigris which carried them through subterranean lakes and then
belched them out again. A man who can bring himself to face sights
like these, must also be capable of appealing for clemency to the victor
of Pharsalus. My advice, therefore, is to review the Roman Empire –
first considering Egypt, and the great kingdom of Libya stretching
far to the South. If you cannot trust King Juba, then you must trust the
boy-King Ptolemy who, after all, owes his throne to your kindness,
and whose guardian you are. Egypt is a rich, self-sufficient country,
extending from the Libyan Gulf of Sirte to the Delta – the region
enclosed by seven rushing branches of the famous River Nile, which
makes rain in Egypt unnecessary. Why be afraid of one who is king
in name only and has not yet emerged from the age of innocence?
Were you visiting an aged monarch, the case might be different: you
could expect neither justice nor honour from him, nor reverence for
the Gods. Subjects are happiest while their king is still inexperienced
and preserves his youthful sense of shame.'

Lentulus convinced the assembly. When things grow desperate,
extraordinary freedom of speech is allowed; and the meeting duly

1. The Parthians did not emulate Hannibal's chivalrous burning of a defeated
general's body, if only because they regarded fire as too sacred an element for
funeral purposes. Lucan's fulminations against the Parthian king must be read
as really written against Nero, who had invited King Tiridates to Rome and
made much of him, and who also had committed incest with his own mother,
and other unnatural crimes.

voted against Pompey's proposal. As a result they all hastily sailed from Cilicia to Cyprus – the island which the Goddess Venus apparently prefers to any other, because it was at Paphos that she settled after her birth from sea-foam. (It may, of course, be inconsistent with true religion to believe that any of the gods or goddesses was born, rather than being co-eval with time.) Pompey did not stay long in Cyprus but sailed past the unbroken line of cliffs to the south and headed for Egypt across the open sea.[1] Waves came rolling down from the west and carried him beyond the lighthouse of Pharos, which guides ships to Alexandria and is blessed by so many sailors on dark nights. After a hard struggle, the captain reached the largest and most easterly of the Nile's seven mouths; it debouches at Pelusium into shallow waters.

The Sun rose in the Scales at this season – the Scales that balance Night and Day at the Autumnal Equinox, before the Sun begins to repay Night the hours robbed from her during the Spring. On hearing that King Ptolemy now resided on Mount Casius,[2] to the east of Pelusium, Pompey sailed off to visit him; the wind had turned favourable and the day was still young. But meanwhile scouts had galloped along the shore to inform the Court of his unexpected arrival. This news terrified the wicked Royal Councillors, who hardly had time to decide on their policy; however, they all assembled, and were first addressed by Achoreus, a grave old man, grown mild-mannered with the years. He had been born at Memphis, where they frivolously worship domestic animals and where the famous Nilometer measures the annual floods; yet he respected the Olympian Gods and, as priest of the Moon-goddess, had seen the induction and ritual drowning of more than one sacred Apis bull. Achoreus enlarged on the loyalty which the King owed both to Pompey, who had deserved well of him, and to the terms of his own father's will. Nevertheless, Pothinus, the eunuch chamberlain, who knew better than Achoreus how to manage evil-hearted kings, presumed to sign Pompey's death warrant.

'Over-scrupulous attention to divine law, my lord Ptolemy,' he said, 'leads many a man into trouble. Loyalty is by no means praiseworthy when Fortune has deserted the man who exacts it. My advice is to keep a watchful eye on the Gods and follow their examples: pay

1. He now had collected 2000 troops.
2. Ptolemy's troops were faced by those of his sister Cleopatra, co-heiress to the kingdom, whom he had driven out.

court to those whom they favour, and avoid those whom they chasten.
There is as much difference between the stars and the earth, or between
fire and sea, as there is between what is expedient and what is equitable.
Once kings begin to think in terms of abstract justice their power
wanes, and down go their fortresses. If a king is disliked, he can protect
himself only by ruthless and unlimited massacre; and when he begins
to be cruel, he must so continue. The palace is no place for an upright
man; nor is virtue consonant with monarchy. A king who fears to be
pitiless must live in constant terror of his life.

'Pompey ought to be punished if he despises you because of your
youth; he seems to think that you are too weak to beat off the attack of
an already beaten man. We do not want a foreigner to rule us; and
should you prefer to abdicate, remember that Egypt was left by the
late king jointly to you and your sister Cleopatra. Let her return from
banishment and reign in your place. Whatever happens, we must keep
the Roman army out of Egypt, and not give Caesar more power over
us than we recently gave Pompey.

'Look at Pompey, rejected by the whole world and haunted by the
ghosts of those who died in the civil war! He has lost his self-reliance
and wanders around in search of some nation prepared to share his
downfall. It is not merely Caesar's sword that he fears; he cannot face
the Senate either, so many of whose members are now feeding the
Thessalian vultures; or his foreign contingents, whom he deserted on
the battlefield and left to be massacred; or his ruined allied kings. The
guilt of Pharsalus weighs so heavily upon him that he cannot find
asylum in any land; but here he comes to do us Egyptians mischief –
the one people whom he has not yet succeeded in destroying.

'My lord Ptolemy, we have greater cause to complain of Pompey
than he of us; why should he involve our remote and tranquil country
in Caesar's displeasure? Already we have been compromised to such
an extent that our only hope of escape is by assassinating him. Granted,
we prayed for the success of Pompey's arms. That was because he had
persuaded the Senate to recognize Egyptian sovereignty. Granted,
also, the fatal sword which he compels us to draw was intended for use
against whoever lost the war, not particularly against him. I should,
indeed, have preferred to kill Caesar; but we cannot defy the current
which is carrying the whole world away, and Pompey is therefore fated
to be the victim. Surely he must realize that we will try to kill him?

What reliance can the wretch possibly place on Egypt? He knows that ours is an unwarlike nation, which has enough difficulty in making ends meet even with the help of the Nile floods. It is best to take stock of the resources at your command, my lord Ptolemy, and admit their inadequacy. Do you feel strong enough to shore up the ruins of Pompey's fall – the ruins beneath which Rome herself lies prostrate? Dare you presume to disinter the ghost of battle from the field of Pharsalus, and let it stalk along the Nile valley? We sent troops to neither side while the war was in progress; are we now to declare in favour of Pompey, when everyone else deserts him, and challenge his conqueror Caesar? It is all very well for allies who have shared a general's prosperity to stand by him when Fortune has forsaken his arms; but nobody in his senses chooses the already unfortunate as objects of his loyal friendship.'

The Royal Council voted unanimously for murder, and young Ptolemy beamed when his servants obligingly permitted him to give the effective orders. Achillas, Captain of the Royal Guard, was the assassin selected. With a group of armed confederates he took a dinghy and rowed out from the Casian Promontory into a region of quicksands and shallows, where he awaited Pompey's ship. Ye Gods! How disgraceful that the civil war was not fought cleanly! How incredible that it should have come to this: that the barbarians of Memphis and the sybarites of Canopus should presume to intervene in our affairs and settle an outstanding political problem – in a word, that a pack of disgusting foreigners, rather than fellow-Romans, should kill Pompey the Great!

'The Great' was a title that had tempted Caesar to the crime of invading Italy; yet Ptolemy did not hesitate to deal the stroke which laid Pompey low for ever. That dirty little imp, how dared he to meddle profanely in a conflict that let loose all the thunders of heaven? Even if Pompey had not been a world-conqueror who celebrated three Triumphs, even if he had not been a king-maker, the champion of senatorial government, and Caesar's son-in-law, he was at least a Roman. Any Egyptian king should think twice before thrusting his sword into a Roman heart. The impudent boy did not realize how insecure his own position was: he now possessed no valid title to the Egyptian throne, because Pompey, who bestowed it on him, had lost the war.

Contrary winds would not allow Pompey's ship to enter under sail, so she was rowed towards that accursed shore, and presently the dinghy went to meet her. Achillas invited Pompey to step aboard and be ferried ashore, explaining that the shoals would endanger a vessel of any burden, since the Casian Promontory was exposed to heavy seas from both quarters. None of Pompey's attendants failed to notice an ominous sign. Were King Ptolemy acting in good faith he would have sailed out at the head of his fleet in gratitude to the man who had placed the sceptre in his hand. But Pompey, being fated to die miserably here, walked like a blind man into the trap; he seemed delighted to fall in with Achillas's suggestion, thereby proving that he would rather die than show any signs of fear. When Cornelia wished to follow him into the dinghy, all the more anxious not to be left behind because she anticipated treachery, he waved her back brusquely, saying: 'Why be so rash, my dearest? Why be so rash, Sextus, my son? Stay here, both of you and watch what happens. If they fail to behead me, it will be a proof that King Ptolemy can be trusted.'

Cornelia stretched her hands in supplication. 'Oh, how cruel you are!' she cried. 'This is exactly the way you treated me once before, when you packed me off to Lesbos! Such partings always bring bad luck. After your escape from Thessaly, you might just as well have made for some other port than Mytilene, instead of taking me from my secure retreat and then forbidding me to land elsewhere. Am I to serve only as your perpetual sailing companion?'

Pompey paid no attention to this outburst, and Cornelia continued to lean anxiously over the stern-rail, in such distress of mind that she could fix her eyes neither on his departing figure, nor on anything else. The Roman vessels lay at anchor, their crews feeling a certain disquiet. It never occurred to them that there would be foul play; but they feared that Pompey might disgrace himself by making too humble a pleas to a king of his own creation.

A Roman soldier in the dinghy had greeted Pompey by name as he prepared to step aboard. This was Lucius Septimius, a former military tribune, who had deserted the Roman army to take service under treacherous King Ptolemy; a man as savage, violent, and ruthless as a wild beast. After Fortune had carefully prevented this wretch from taking part in the Battle of Pharsalus, she might have been expected to continue merciful. But no, she had posted hired assassins in every quarter of the world, so that a Roman would always be at hand to murder a Roman. Even Caesar was disgraced (not to mention the Gods) when young King Ptolemy gave orders for Pompey's decapitation, and one of Pompey's own veterans obeyed him.[1] How infamous the name of Septimius will be in after ages! If Brutus's assassination of Caesar was called a crime, what should his deed be called?

Pompey's last hour had come. When the Egyptian boat bore him off, he lost the power of independent action. Suddenly the wicked murderers drew their swords. Pompey, seeing what they were about, covered his head with a cloak, to conceal the death agony. Then he pressed one hand against his eyes and another against his mouth, so as not to spoil his heroic reputation by tears or groans. Even when Achillas had stabbed him through the side, he did not acknowledge the wound by any cry or gesture; he sat quite motionless, testing his own valour in that moment of doom. The following thoughts doubtless engrossed his mind as he died: 'Rome's tragic story can never be forgotten, and posterity will dwell with tears on the tale of this treacherous Egyptian boat. Let me, rather, recall my own fame. Mine has been a long, continuously successful career; and nobody will ever know whether I was able to face adversity with fortitude, unless I prove it now. I must not allow myself to feel ashamed that death has come in this sordid style; whoever has stabbed me, did so in Caesar's name. My body may be mutilated, my limbs scattered; but I swear by all the Gods that I am a fortunate being, and none will contradict me. Though life may rob a man of prosperity, death cannot. Cornelia and Sextus are watching the assassination; therefore I must be the more steadfast in abstaining from groans. If their admiration for my courage outweighs their grief for my death, that will be true affection.'

Pompey, we may be certain, exercised this stubborn control over his mind, as he died.

Cornelia, however, found it far harder to witness that cruel murder than to have suffered it herself. The miserable woman shrieked wildly: 'Oh, dearest one, it is all my fault! After you escaped from Greece you came far out of your way to pick me up at Mytilene; meanwhile Caesar must have sent word to Egypt. He alone could have given orders for this crime. But whoever the divinely appointed assassin

1. Septimius had commanded a company under Pompey in the war against the Cilician pirates.

may be, and whether he has been acting on Caesar's orders or prompted by some personal grudge, he cannot know where my husband's heart lies. Poor defeated Pompey is only too pleased to die before I do! And that is most unjust: he deserves to see me being killed – and why should I not be killed? I am as guilty in Caesar's eyes as anyone else, having been the sole woman who marched with Pompey's army or sailed in his fleet. No disasters ever crushed my spirit: I stood by Pompey when he was defeated, as none of his royal allies did. Yet I am rewarded by being left behind in the safety of this ship! Pompey broke faith as though I deserved to survive him. So I must die alone, and without King Ptolemy's assistance.

'Hands off, sailors!' she cried to the crew. 'Let me leap overboard and drown, or hang myself on one of your ropes! Or get some friend who loved Pompey well enough to transfix me with a sword – he can do it for Pompey's sake and then go to Caesar and claim the credit. Oh, you cruel fellows, why try to save me? My husband is still just alive, yet I have already lost the power to dispose of my own body – you should not restrain me from suicide. I suppose I am to be reserved for Caesar?'

She fell fainting into the arms of her companions; and the ship sheered off hastily, as soon as ringing blows on Pompey's breast and back had disposed of him. Those who saw his lifeless head declare that the noble and indomitable features had lost nothing in majesty; no assassin could alter their expression. Septimius, however, improved on the crime. Before Pompey could breathe his last, he slit open the protecting cloak; laid the drooping head across a thwart, severed the neck sinews and hacked clumsily at the bones; for Imperial executioners had not yet learned the knack of whipping off a head at a single blow. When the decapitation was completed, Achillas claimed the privilege of carrying the trophy for recognition to the sacrilegious young King. Septimius had sunk so low that he played second fiddle to Achillas; he had removed Pompey's glorious head merely to let another man have the glory of carrying it away – that surely was the very depth of infamy attainable by a Roman!

Achillas now grasped Pompey's hair – those splendid locks falling over a brow which had struck fear into the hearts of kings – and though the features still worked, the lips still moved, and the open eyes were still unglazed, he impaled the head on an Egyptian javelin. Pompey's

head, which had so often led his armies to a truceless war – which had
so long dominated the Senate, the voters in the Campus Martius, the
magistrates on the Rostrum – the head which typified the Fortune of
Rome! But Ptolemy needed lasting proof of his crime and therefore
entrusted the head to the embalmers. This disgusting fraternity drained
it of blood, removed the brain, drew out through the nostrils all the
internal moisture which might have hastened the process of corruption, and pickled the skin by the infusion of drugs.

Fate ruled that this degenerate young king would be the last male
descendant of the Lagus line and yield the throne to his adulterous
sister Cleopatra; none the less, was that sufficient punishment for what
he had done? Though Alexander the Great, who had bestowed the
kingdom on his ancestor, lay buried at Alexandria in a consecrated
vault, and though huge pyramids and mausoleums had been built
above the unworthy bones of Ptolemy after Ptolemy, yet Pompey's
headless trunk was thrown into the shallow sea and battered against
the reefs. Would it have been so very difficult to embalm the whole
body for Caesar's edification?

Fortune showed great fidelity in her dealings with Pompey: she
brought him exclusively good luck throughout his life, then, when
death fell due, haled him from the summit of worldly power and
savagely concentrated into a single day all the calamities which he had
so far been spared. He was one who never experienced a mixture of
joy and sorrows: no god modified his prosperity, none mitigated the
final disaster. Fortune, in fact, withheld her hand until the last, and
then struck him down at one blow. To-day his body drifted hither
and thither at the sea's whim, tossed now on sands, now on sharp rocks,
and the salt water seeped into his wounds until there was no means of
recognizing it as Pompey's except by its lack of a head.

Nevertheless, before Caesar could arrive in Egypt, it occurred to
Fortune that she would give Pompey a funeral, thus making sure that
he would neither avoid burial altogether nor be awarded too splendid
a tomb. One of Pompey's servants, by name Cordus, a native of
Idalus in Cyprus, where King Cinyras once reigned, had escaped from
the dinghy and gone into hiding ashore; but when night fell loyalty
conquered his fears, and he waded trembling into the water, searching
for his master's corpse. A sad, dim moon shone through a covering of
clouds, yet Cordus could distinguish a dark object among the foaming

VIII. 720-60]   *Cordus Cremates the Trunk*

waves, of which he took firm hold to prevent the sea from snatching
it away again. But his prize was too heavy for lifting, so he waited for
the next wave, which helped him to push it shoreward. As soon as he
had hauled the body above the waterline, he cast himself upon it,
weeping over every wound. Presently he gazed up at the dusky sky,
and prayed: 'O Goddess Fortune, I am speaking on behalf of your
favourite, Pompey! He does not demand any of your expensive pyres,
heaped with incense to give off a rich smoke when he is burned.
Neither does he demand that noble Romans should carry on their
shoulders the bier of one who was truly the father of his country, or
that the trophies won in his Triumphs should be displayed in his
funeral procession; or that dirges should rise from every City square;
or that a whole army should march, with arms reversed, around his
pyre. He asks no more than a poor man's funeral: enough fuel to burn
his body, no spices to feed the flames, and a mean fellow like myself to
kindle them. The vengeful Gods should be satisfied that Cornelia,
though close at hand, is unable to pay Pompey her last respects – to
tear her hair, grovel on the sand, embrace the corpse, and give orders
for the torch to be applied.'

As he spoke, Cordus noticed the feeble glare of a pyre, some distance
away, on which another corpse happened to have been laid. He ran
there hastily and pulled the charred wood from under it. 'I do not
know who you are,' he told the corpse, 'but though you seem to be
neglected by your family, yours is a happier fate than Pompey's. So
pray forgive a stranger who robs you of your fire. If any sensibilities
survive death, you will, I am sure, be honoured to lend Pompey a few
logs; if you were cremated yourself and allowed Pompey's mutilated
body to rot, that would be a public scandal.'

Cordus filled the lap of his robe with burning embers and rushed
back to the beloved corpse, against which the waves were once more
lapping greedily. He scraped a shallow trench in the sand, filled this
with the embers, and laid upon them planks from a wrecked vessel,
which he collected along the shore. Here were no solid oaken beams
carefully stacked on one another, with a platform at the summit for
Pompey to rest upon; the fire had, indeed, been placed beside not
underneath, the corpse. Cordus, crouching over the flames, invoked
Pompey's ghost:

'Greatest of commanders, sole glory of Italy, if you would prefer to be tossed by the waves than cremated in such miserable style, pray absent your mighty presence from my officious rites. But though fate is unkind you will, I think, accept a Roman funeral, however poor, to the alternative of being gnawed by some sea-monster, wild beast, or carrion bird, or falling into Caesar's hands! Besides, if Destiny ever grants me a safe return to Italy, your splendid ashes shall not remain here: I will collect them in an urn and take them to Cornelia myself. Meanwhile, let me mark the spot with a small headstone, so that if anyone wishes to appease you by adding the ashes of your head to those of your trunk and limbs, he will know where to come.'

With that, Cordus heaped more driftwood on the fire, and made it blaze high. The corpse slowly disappeared, its fat serving to feed the flames. By now daylight had quenched the dawn stars. Cordus, growing nervous, decided to cut short the funeral and retire to his hiding place again. Yet the poor fellow need not have feared punishment for this crime, which has made him famous for ever;[1] because even Pompey's unnatural father-in-law would have approved of the burial. Cordus had only to approach Caesar, confess that he had cremated the body, and demand the head; he would have earned a full pardon.

Loyalty, however, compelled him to finish his self-appointed task. The bones were not quite burned and still attached to their tendons; but he snatched them from the fire with the marrow bubbling inside, and threw salt water over them. Next, he laid them above the other remains, and to keep the wind from blowing away the mound of sand which he heaped around them, crowned it with a stone. Then fearing that some sailor might disturb Pompey's rest by using the stone as a mooring block, he wrote on it in charcoal: 'Here lies Pompey the Great.' I suppose that one might call this 'Pompey's tomb'. It would have satisfied Caesar, at least, because proving that his son-in-law lay safely underground.

Cordus, of course, showed great presumption in his decision to saddle Pompey with a tomb, and thus imprison his free spirit. The world was Pompey's tomb: not only the Roman Empire but every land to which the name of Rome had spread, even those islands that

1. His name was not Cordus, but Philippus, and an aged Roman who had once served under Pompey came up and helped him to build the pyre with wreckage. The story of the other corpse has apparently been invented to explain how 'Cordus' started a fire without flint, steel or tinder.

lie in the circling Ocean Stream. The headstone, a silent reproach to
the Gods, had no right to be there. Since the whole of Mount Oeta is
sacred to Hercules, and the whole range of Nysa to Bacchus, why
should Egypt honour Pompey's memory with a mere stone? If this
formality had been omitted, all Egypt would have become his sepulchre, which would have discouraged travellers from visiting the Nile
for fear of accidentally trampling on his ashes.

And if a stone worthy of Pompey's venerated name had been found,
it should surely have been inscribed with a full record of the feats he
performed. His execution of bold Lepidus who led the rising in Cisalpine Gaul;[1] his victories over Sertorius after Metellus the Consul had
been recalled to Rome;[2] the Triumph he celebrated while still a
knight; his suppression of the Cilician pirates, which made international commerce safe again. His conquests of the oriental barbarians,
of the nomads, and of all the monarchs in the East and North; his faithful return to civilian life after his victories. Those three Triumphs satisfied him: he did not ask his country to grant others which he had earned.

What monument could be large enough to carry so huge a roll of
honours? And now consider that wretched headstone, bearing Pompey's mere name – the name which once appeared on the dedicatory
tablets of temples, and on triumphal arches – sunk so low in the sand
that one must stoop to read it. A traveller from Rome would pass
heedlessly by unless it were pointed out to him.

The Cumaean Sibyl was right to warn us that 'no Roman should
visit the Nile, whose many mouths flood their banks in summertime.'
Oh, what curse can I call down upon that cruel land of Egypt, which
criminally interfered in our civil wars? I will say this: 'May the Nile
flow backwards and stay in the region where he rises! May the fields of
Egypt be parched for lack of winter rains, may they be lost in the loose
sands of the Ethiopian wilderness!' We Romans have accepted the
Egyptian Goddess Isis, and the dog-headed God Anubis, and the
sistrum with which dead Osiris is mourned – proving him to have been
human – yet Egypt allows Pompey's ghost to dwell in the dust!

1. Pompey did not, however, defeat Lepidus; that was done by Metellus.
Lepidus fled to Gozo, where Pompey's men caught him and brought him in
chains to Sicily, for execution at Lilybaeum.

2. Untrue: Metellus was not Consul at the time, nor was he recalled from
Spain; but Sertorius gave so much trouble that Metellus had to borrow troops
from neighbouring provinces. Pompey went to assist him as pro-Consul.

Rome, however, is no less guilty for having passed senatorial decrees deifying Julius Caesar and granting him temples, while failing to recover Pompey's ashes; his ghost continues in exile to this day. Our ancestors did not bring Pompey home, for fear of offending Caesar; but what prevents us from doing so now, unless the sea has washed them away? Nobody, in a case like this, would be restrained by a superstitious dread of disturbing the ghost of Pompey, who deserves to be worshipped as a god. For my part, I should be happy, almost too happy, were I delegated to land on that hated shore, dig up the bones and carry them back to Italy. To violate a grave so unworthy of its contents would be a privilege! Perhaps one day when drought, plague, excessive heat, or earthquakes trouble our country and Heaven is invited to reveal the cure, we will send for Pompey's remains, on the Gods' instructions, and the Chief Pontiff himself will bear the casket.

Meanwhile, if any sightseer visits the Nile, on his way to heat-ridden Syene and Thebes, where no rain falls even in the Spring; or if any merchant makes for the quiet waters of the Red Sea and the ports of Arabia, to buy oriental trade-goods; then he will turn aside to revere that headstone and those bones – lying uncovered, maybe, on the surface of the sand – and placate Pompey's ghost, which must inspire him with greater awe than the God of Mount Casius. No, the grave can never destroy Pompey's fame; temples of silver and gold do less than nothing to recommend the dead whom they house. There lies Pompey, Fortune incarnate; and his sea-washed headstone on the Egyptian shore is holier than all the altars raised in honour of the divine Julius.

Many Romans, while refusing incense to certain gods in the Capitol,[1] nevertheless worship places which lightning has struck and which the College of Augurs has duly surrounded with a fence. Pompey's grave is similarly consecrated by the divine thunderbolt. And one day it will be a good thing that no enormous marble tomb was raised to stand there for ever; because the present grave will soon disappear and all proof of Pompey's death vanish with it. And in a more fortunate age, Egyptians who point to the stone and say: 'This once marked Pompey's grave,' will meet as little belief from our posterity as do the Cretans when they point out the alleged tomb of Juppiter on Mount Juktas.

1. The deified Caesars.

BOOK NINE

THE truth is that Pompey's ghost did not remain long confined to the Egyptian grave. It came out with a rush, deserting its half-burned bones and wretched pyre, and soared up to the sky. Those frontier regions of air between the earth and the moon's orbit, where our dark atmosphere impinges on the starry brightness of the empyrean, are where the souls of heroes from all over the world collect after death – such, at least, as are fitted by the flame-like quality of their virtue to survive in the lower tracts of heaven among the eternal spheres. This is, however, a refuge denied to men who lie buried in frankincense and gold.

Pompey basked for awhile in the pure light, admiring the busy planets and the steadfast stars, and as he glanced below him saw what a thick veil of darkness obscures our day; the thought of his headless body made him chuckle. Then he swooped down to hover above the Thessalian plains, the standards of butcherly Caesar, and the fleets scattered across the Mediterranean. Finally, as avenger of the crimes committed against Rome, he seated himself first in Cato's dauntless heart, and later in that of noble Brutus.

While the issue of the civil war was still doubtful, Cato hated Pompey, though serving under him – Pompey had, of course, been appointed Commander-in-Chief by the Senate – and became a convinced Pompeian only after the disaster at Pharsalus. Rome having now lost her protector, Cato assumed the part: he re-armed and encouraged those who had cast away their swords in terror, and kept the Civil War alive without either desire for supreme power or fear of slavery. No selfish ambition prompted his new military career; Pompey's death made the cause of liberty still dearer to his heart. With a speed that equalled Caesar's he set about rescuing the survivors of Pharsalus who had streamed back to Dyrrhachium, and ferried them over to Corfu aboard a thousand ships. Nobody would have guessed that this huge fleet, which crowded the narrow straits, was conveying a beaten army.[1]

From Corfu this fleet made south for Cape Malea, near Laconian Taenarus (which provides an exit from the Underworld), and the island of Cythera. The wind blew northerly, so he left Greece behind and sailed past Crete, where the seas were calmer, until he reached the town of Phycus in Cyrenaica. When the Phycians resisted his landing, he sacked their town, as they richly deserved. Thence he sailed pleasantly west and disembarked near Cape Palinurus – Italy is not the only country to have a Cape Palinurus named in honour of Aeneas's Trojan pilot, who evidently appreciated these quiet African ports.[2] Cato sighted a flotilla far out to sea; and felt a moment's anxiety: were they friends or foes? Caesar's movements were so quick that almost any ship might be his. But, on approaching, they proved to be the vessels in which Pompey had reached Egypt; and the news they brought was lamentable enough to make even the stern Cato shed tears.

It appears that Cornelia had persuaded her stepson Sextus Pompey not to sail off at once – in the vain hope that the headless body might drift out to sea again for her to retrieve. She saw in the distance the miserable blaze at which it was being cremated, and cried: 'O Goddess Fortune, you have found me unworthy to save my husband's corpse from the sea, to fling myself upon it in despair, to weep into the wounds, to set a torch to the pyre, to tear out and burn my hair; finally, when all was over, to fill my lap with the bones and ashes, which I should have scattered reproachfully in the temples of the Gods. Has that pyre been kindled without the customary rites? If an Egyptian did that, the ghost will be infuriated. Crassus and his father were luckier, in that the enemy left their bodies to rot; the Gods have shown their spite by burning Pompey's. It is the same story again: will I never be allowed to conduct a funeral decently, a widow weeping over a full urn? ... Yet, after all, what need is there for a grave? Why should grief express itself so formally? I should be undutiful were Pompey's living image not always present in my heart. A wife who intends to survive her husband ought to recover his ashes; but though

1. He used three hundred, not a thousand, ships.
2. Lucan has misread 'Cape Paliurus' for Cape Palinurus; the Italian promontory of that name is near Naples.

yonder distant, malign-looking fire on the shore still shows me something of Pompey, the flame is sinking, and the smoke which carries his mortal part away has grown weaker . . . Dawn approaches, and the hateful winds fill our sails. Listen! I loathe leaving this coast; I love it better now than any of the countries over which my husband triumphed, better even than the painted chariot in which he drove to the Capitol. This is because I have forgotten the Pompey of happier days; the Pompey for whom I long is the one who rests beside the Nile. If I complain about leaving this guilty land, you must understand that its very guilt has endeared it to me . . .

'Sextus, I command you to carry on your father's war courageously throughout the world. Pompey left a message for your brother and yourself, which I treasure in my heart. He said: "When the destined hour of death overtakes me, my sons, I charge you to continue this civil war while Caesar yet lives. Never let any member of his family reign in peace while a single one of ours survives. Use the magic of my name to draw kings and free cities to the Senate's cause. I appoint you my political and military heirs. Take to the sea and fleets will always be found for your service. Remain indomitable, conscious of the power I confer, and all nations will support you as my successors. The only man from whom you can deign to take orders is Cato, should Cato form a party in defence of Roman liberty."

'Well: I have fulfilled my promise to Pompey, and his device has been effective. He must have given me this commission just to restrain me from suicide, knowing that I would keep faith and not die before delivering it; and here I am, still alive. But soon I shall pursue him through empty space and through the dark Underworld – if there is any such place. Who knows how long I am fated to live? I shall, however, continue to punish myself for outliving Pompey. I should, really, have committed suicide when he was murdered in my sight; now I shall forgo such violent forms of death as the sword, the noose, or the jump from a cliff – ashamed if I cannot die of pure sorrow, weeping, and beating my breast.' Cornelia then drew a mourning veil over her head and descended into the gloomy hold, where she indulged in a luxury of grief, hugging the cruel loss to her heart as though it had been Pompey himself. She paid no attention to the pitching of the ship, to the East Wind that howled in the shrouds, or to the yells of the frightened sailors as the sea grew more and more threatening. What they prayed to escape, she prayed to suffer; and lay there resigned to death, encouraging the storm to do its worst.

First, they made Cyprus, where surf beat white against the coast; then the gale abated somewhat and they ran for Cato's camp in Libya. Gnaeus Pompey was waiting on the shore, and watched the ship's arrival with an intense apprehension, because he recognized his brother Sextus and his father's staff grouped on the deck, but not his father. He waded out into the sea, shouting: 'Where is Pompey? Is the world's crowning glory alive, or are we all ruined? Has he died and taken with him to perdition everything that was best in Rome?'

'Brother,' Sextus answered, 'you are fortunate to have been driven to another shore than we were, and only to hear of the crime that I witnessed without daring to avenge it. Our father did not die in battle against Caesar, nor by any worthy hand. He fell into the power of that infamous King of Egypt from whom he had expected both hospitality and thanks for the great honour conferred on the Ptolemaic dynasty; but who murdered him, to atone in Caesar's eyes for the crime of having accepted the throne. I myself saw the assassins slashing our father's noble breast, and therefore concluded that Caesar must already have reached the Nile. This makes me guilty in a sense. Yet could I have suspected that the Egyptians would otherwise dare to commit so foul a murder? However, the sight moved me less than when later I watched the grey head, impaled on a javelin, being carried through the city – I daresay King Ptolemy has kept it for Caesar's heartless inspection. As for the body, we do not know whether Egyptian dogs and vultures tore it in pieces, or whether it was cremated on a furtively built pyre which we noticed. Whatever outrage the Gods planned against the trunk and limbs, I can forgive; but not the outrage against our father's head.'

Gnaeus neither groaned nor wept as he heard the news, but filial love sent him mad with rage. 'All aboard, my men!' he shouted. 'I am taking the fleet out, under oars, into the teeth of the wind. Come, you officers, here's your chance to do something nobler than anyone has yet done in this war. We shall rescue my father's corpse, give it worthy burial, and appease his shade with the blood of that little manikin Ptolemy. What is more, I shall haul King Alexander's body from his shrine and fling it into Lake Mareotis, together with the entire city of Alexandria. And why should I not also rifle the Pyramids of the

Pharaohs' mummies – King Amasis and the rest – and send them floating down the Nile? They have no right to tombs when my father has
none. I am prepared even to desecrate the tomb of Isis herself, whose
worship extends through the world, and unwrapping Osiris's limbs
from their linen bandages, scatter them in the streets; I will use every
godling in Egypt as fuel to cremate my father's head. Nor shall I spare
the land: I will kill every labourer in the fields and expel every Egyptian from his country, whether god or man, leaving Pompey the Great
to possess the wilderness alone.'

Cato admired Gnaeus's spirit, but persuaded him not to implement
this furious plan. Now from all along the coast came the loud echoing
boom of Roman bosoms being pummelled; nothing like it had ever
been heard before. What other great man had ever been so sincerely
mourned by the common people? And when Cornelia tottered ashore,
having wept until she could weep no longer, with her disordered hair
hanging over her face, everyone drubbed on his chest with re-
doubled zeal.

As soon as Cornelia found herself on dry land and among friends, she
collected her unhappy husband's garments, his badges of honour, his
weapons, the gold-embroidered purple gown, which he had three
times worn when he drove in triumph to the temple of Capitoline
Juppiter, and laid them together on a funeral pyre. 'These are my husband's ashes,' she thought sorrowfully. All loyal hearts followed her
example, and soon a great line of pyres marked the curve of the shore,
in honour of those who lay unburied at Pharsalus. It was as when
Apulian farmers set fire to the rank dead grass and thus ensure new
pasture when the winter rains fall; Mount Garganus, Vultur, and sunny
Matinus combine in a single blaze.

Everyone dared reproach the Gods for Pompey's death, yet his
ghost must have felt peculiar satisfaction when Cato pronounced this
short and truthful obituary speech:

'My lamented friend Pompey, albeit far inferior to our ancestors as
regards his sense of what the Roman Constitution sanctions, was a
model to the present age, which displays no sense of justice whatever.
He grew powerful, but proved no enemy to freedom; and when all
Rome clamoured to be enslaved he persisted in remaining a private
citizen – a trait which makes him unique. While controlling the Senate,
he did not infringe their sovereignty. He never embraced the doctrine

that might is right; and always desired that others should have the liberty to refuse what he demanded of them. Though he won immense wealth, he paid far more into the Public Treasury than he kept for himself; though quick to draw the sword, he also knew when to sheathe it; though preferring war to peace, he showed his pacific intentions even when he fought. Pompey enjoyed taking office, but he also enjoyed resigning it; and his family never presumed on the enormous fame he had earned, by scandalous behaviour or wasteful living.

'All nations revered his name, to the great benefit of our country. It is true that any sincere belief in Roman liberty died years ago, when Sulla and Marius were permitted to bring armies into the City; but even the pretence of such belief has died with Pompey. Henceforth a tyrant need no longer blush to exercise supreme power, pleading that an unlimited dictatorship has legally been made his, and using the Senate as his screen. Pompey was fortunate in that the Egyptian assassins forced on him, so soon after his defeat, a death which he should have courted. Who knows whether he might not have consented to live under Caesar's tyranny? The happiest men are those who choose to die at the right time; the next happiest are those compelled to die at the right time.

'My own prayer is that, if I am fated to fall into the power of an enemy – King Juba, for example – he will play the part that young Ptolemy played. I should not even mind his cutting off my head and keeping it as a gift for Caesar; to be spared is what I fear most.'

This eulogy conferred greater honour on Pompey than if the Forum had rung with his praises. Nevertheless, the troops began to complain that Pompey's death had ended the war so far as they were concerned; and King Tarchondimatus of Cilicia gave them a lead by preparing to sail. Cato followed Tarchondimatus to the place of embarkation, reproaching him as he went. 'O you Cilicians,' he cried, 'will you never be persuaded to keep the peace? No sooner has Pompey died, than off you go again to your life of piracy!'

Then he gazed around him at the malcontents, who were gathered in knots and talking excitedly. One of them, their spokesman, said to Cato: 'Pray, forgive us, my lord. It was our affection for Pompey, not our love of civil war, that made us take up arms and join his party. The world indeed preferred fighting under Pompey to living in peace;

but since he is dead, his cause is dead too. Let us go home, to our wives and children who are missing us so sadly. If this war has not ended with the Battle of Pharsalus and Pompey's death, when can it ever end? We have spent our lives in the camp. Let us close them peacefully and look forward to decent burial in our old age – a gift which, it seems, civil war denies even to commanders-in-chief. We have been beaten – what of that? The misfortune of being subjected to Armenian or Parthian rule does not threaten us; when we return, none but native magistrates will keep order in our towns. Lately, Caesar was the second most important Roman alive; and now, I suppose, he takes the first place. Nevertheless, I hold Pompey's memory in such honour that, though defeat may impose a new master on me, I shall refuse to fight for him. It was Pompey whom I served; and now he is gone let fate guide my steps. I cannot expect things to go well; nor would I be allowed to do so. Caesar's fortune is supreme; our army that fought at Pharsalus has been scattered to the winds; and although we beaten soldiers have little hope left, he remains the only man on earth with the power, if he pleases, to spare our lives. While Pompey lived it was a proof of good citizenship to take part in this war; now it would be a crime. You declare yourself a supporter of the Roman Constitution, Cato? Then, come with us and rally to the standards which Caesar has raised, as one of the two new Consuls.' With this parting taunt, the soldier sprang aboard a Cilician ship, followed by a disorderly mob of his comrades.

The cause of Roman liberty seemed lost, and the troops came swarming down to the shore like a masterless rabble; but Cato was inspired to address them in these words:

'I see the case clearly, men. You were fighting in the same spirit as the Caesareans: to defend tyranny. By this I mean that you were Pompeians, rather than Romans. However, Pompey was defeated, which spared you the need of suffering in the cause of a tyrant. You are at last free to live or die, as you wish: able at last to fight your own battles, instead of being engaged to win world sovereignty for any single leader. And this is the time you choose to desert the ranks! You are like old oxen who, freed of the yoke, feel lost without it; you cannot live except under a stern master. Yet now you have a cause worthy of brave men. Since you were ready to shed your blood for Pompey, how can you refuse to fight and die for the freedom of Rome?

Fortune has allowed only one of the tyrannous Triumvirate to survive. You ought to be ashamed of yourselves. The King of Egypt's body-guard and the King of Parthia's archers have done far more than any of you to uphold our Constitution. Be off then, degenerate rascals, if you are neither grateful for Ptolemy's gift, nor dare use your own swords! Who would have believed that you ever fleshed them in combat? Caesar will, I am sure, take your word for it that you were the first to turn and run at Pharsalus. You need have no anxiety about his verdict: since he was not obliged to make prisoners of you in battle, or starve you out in a siege, you will certainly earn his pardon.

'Miserable slaves! Your master has died and you crowd around to congratulate his successor. But I cannot understand why you have no ambition to earn a better reward than merely pardon. Why not, for instance, seize Pompey's unfortunate widow, daughter of the great Metellus, and present her as a gift to Caesar; why not improve on the favour which King Ptolemy has done him by arresting Pompey's sons and bringing them along too? And while you are about it, what of me? The man who cuts off my head and takes it to Caesar will be hand-somely paid, I have no doubt – a lesson to you all that it was well worth while to follow my standards. Come on now, do your worst, and earn the money! Only cowards go away emptyhanded while there is still something worth robbing.'

Cato's reproaches struck home, and the men decided against launch-ing their ships and sailing away. It was as when bees on Mount Hybla desert the cells in the honeycomb where their young have hatched, and each bee, instead of joining the swarm, abandons his task of rifling the bitter thyme and flies off independently. Yet if the bee-keeper clashes his cymbals in rebuke, all at once take fright and resume their task of collecting bee-bread and honey–to his great relief; he knows that the hive has been saved. Similarly, Cato's speech persuaded the troops to stand firm and continue the war.

He decided to keep them fully employed on works of military importance; because they were not accustomed to be idle. First, he set them to fortify the coast, digging in the sand until they were exhausted. Next, he led them against the walled city of Cyrene; the inhabitants refused to admit the army, but Cato did not punish them except by the simple act of conquest. Then he prepared to march into Juba's kingdom of Numidia, which lay east of Mauretania; and though Mother Nature had interposed the Gulf of Sirte, his resolution defeated her.

Two theories are offered to explain the physical peculiarities of the double Gulf of Sirte. Some say that when Nature created the world she purposely left this to be a debatable land between earth and sea: it neither sank low enough to be covered by the water, nor rose high enough to expel it altogether. 'The wilderness of reefs and shallows therefore equally discourages those who try to sail across it, and those who try to walk. Waves as they roll in break on a long succession of beaches before expending their force. Here is a geographical region which the Creatrix has herself abandoned and of which she demands no useful service.'

Others take a different view. They hold that long ago these shoals lay deep beneath the sea, but that the hot Southern Sun, who stokes his fires by sucking up water for fuel, gradually exposed them. Therefore, although the sea still resists this persistent process of absorption, the time must come at last when the Sun's heat proves too strong; then the Gulf will turn into dry land, as it is now well on the way to doing.[1]

When the fleet rowed out from Cyrene, the fierce South Wind, dark with rain clouds, came suddenly roaring up behind, defending his realm which these Roman ships had invaded, troubling the sea over a great area and making waves break in fury on distant shores. Any sails already spread carried away; and though ropes and sheets did their best, the canvas streamed flapping far beyond the bows. Even the cautious captains who had brailed up their sails to the yard-top could not keep their course, but scudded before the gale with bare poles, and were fortunate if they contrived to reach the open sea. Whenever a captain hacked down the mast to prevent his vessel from capsizing, the current caught her and she was driven back against the wind into the shallows, half afloat and half aground. The farther she drifted the more inextricably she was caught among the sand banks – sand banks as solid as those on the coast itself, and occasionally forming a dry rampart above the level of the waves. Thus, by a paradox, some crews found themselves ashore on the high seas.

1. Another theory is that in neolithic times a submarine earthquake caused a chain of coastal islands to subside until they were awash with the sea; and also flooded the interior of Libya, creating Lake Tritonis (see below).

Though several ships were lost in this storm, the greater part of the fleet managed to escape; pilots familiar with the Gulf steered safely up the channel to tranquil Lake Tritonis – traditionally sacred to Triton, whose conch music sounds from end to end of the shore, and to Pallas Athene as well. After being born from Zeus's head, this is where she first chose to alight – doubtless because Libya, as its heat proves, is the land nearest to Heaven – and where, on seeing her face mirrored in the calm waters, she called herself 'Tritonis', to commemorate the event. The river Lethon is said to glide near by, bringing up from its source in the Underworld the gift of forgetfulness, and this is also the legendary site of the Garden of the Hesperides – once hung with fruit and guarded by an unsleeping dragon. It would be churlish to challenge the veracity of legend and ask poets to tell the truth. So let me describe a glittering orchard, the trees of which bent beneath their rich load of heavy golden apples. A group of girls acted as gardeners, and a huge serpent whose eyes were fated never to close in sleep coiled around the laden trees. But Hercules shot the serpent dead and lightened the branches by stealing the apples, which he carried back to his Argive taskmaster, King Eurystheus.

Here, then, the fleet remained. Blown off his course and narrowly escaping the shoals, Gnaeus Pompey, now the commander-in-chief, decided not to continue his voyage along the coast. He stayed in the more fertile part of Libya; while the active and dauntless Cato prepared to lead his troops through unknown tribes inhabiting the shores of the Gulf.[1] Though winter made sailing unsafe, Cato counted on its rain showers to relieve the excessive heat; a march across Libya at that time of year should not, he argued, be either too hot or too cold. But before facing the barren sands he addressed his troops as follows:

'Men, you have linked your fortunes with mine because, like me, you believe that true safety consists in remaining free. Yet be prepared to face an extremely arduous adventure. We must tramp over a scorched and sterile waste, where the sun beats cruelly down, where

1. The true Lake Tritonis, which then covered a few hundred square miles, has since shrunk to the salt lakes of Marith on the extreme west of the Gulf of Sirte; but Strabo calls this Lake Zuchis and gives the name of Tritonis to a small lake near Berenice (Benghazi). Lucan follows his example. Cato's march began at Berenice and ended at Leptis, half-way across the Gulf. He had 10,000 men under him; but broke them up into several divisions, each a day's march ahead of the next.

springs of water are scarce, and where deadly serpents swarm every-where. The path of righteousness is a hard one to tread, and now that our country has been all but ruined we shall find it difficult to secure her approval of our adventures. Those of you who are not merely bent on saving your skins, but dare go obstinately forward, will be privi-leged to follow me through trackless Africa. I have no intention of deceiving you; I will not pretend that this enterprise is anything but dangerous. The sort of men whom I need as my comrades are those who love running risks, men who think it a glorious thing to be Romans and to endure the utmost privations under my eye. If any of you wish to play for safety, thinking life too sweet to gamble with, tell me so at once, and go away into the slavery you have chosen. You may be certain that I will lead this march across the shifting sands, careless though the sun strike my head or serpents block my path, and enjoy the first taste of every danger that confronts us. Whoever catches me drinking, or sneaking off into the shade of trees, or riding a horse when everyone else goes on foot, may complain, if he pleases, of his own thirst or heat or fatigue. But you will find no distinction in this journey between the legionary and his general. True soldiers welcome serpents, thirst, burning sands, and every other hardship as justifying their existence; and you can prove that the retreat at Pharsalus was not, after all, a cowardly rout, only by braving the dangers of Africa.'

They had been a demoralized rabble, but he inspired them with courage and resolution to set out through the desert on a march from which there would be no return; great-hearted Cato was himself fated to die in Africa and be buried in a modest grave – which did not, however, trouble him in the least.

Though Africa is popularly regarded as a third continent, careful consideration of the climate and the prevailing winds show it to be an integral part of Europe. After all, the Nile and the Scythian river Don are at about the same distance from Cadiz, where Europe and Africa divide to make room for the Mediterranean; but a far larger portion of the world is employed in forming Asia. And whereas the West Wind blows from the combined coasts of Europe and Africa, Asia extends from the north of Europe to the south of Africa and is the sole breeding-ground of the East Wind.

The most fertile region of Africa faces Spain, yet even this lacks sufficient streams to encourage colonizing; occasionally rain comes from the North of Europe to water its fields. No miners dig for either copper or gold; deep as one tunnels, nothing can be found but simple earth. The one source of wealth is the valuable citrus-tree, which the natives used merely for its shade until Roman foresters arrived with axes to turn it into furniture; we were, in fact, not only ransacking distant countries of delicacies for our tables, but of tables for our delicacies. The Gulf of Sirte is very different from this: the coast land lies so close to the burning sky that the corn withers in the field, the vine is caked with dust, and no vegetation keeps the soil from being blown about. Such cool airs as most creatures need for comfort do not blow there. Juppiter sends no thunderstorms and Nature's listlessness makes one unaware of the seasons; no plough ever stirs that great dead plain. On the coastal strip alone occasional patches of grass appear, of which the naked Nasamonians take advantage. These hardy fellows also snatch a living from the shoals in the Gulf: they watch for shipwrecks, and grow rich on the plunder – as it were trading with all nations, although no vessel ever enters their harbours.

Cato's men had not expected the same sort of anxieties as trouble sailors; but found the South Wind even more dangerous on the dry shores of the Gulf than at sea. One fault of this part of Africa is that it has no mountains or cliffs to break the force of a gale and dissipate it into random breezes; and no ancient oak forests, with which it can wrestle. The extreme flatness of the land, in fact, allows winds to rage unopposed, wreaking much the same wanton havoc as they did when Ulysses's sailors opened King Aeolus's bag. Eddies of wind travel in aimless circles, sucking up more and more dust as they go, until half the desert seems suspended in the air. The miserable Nasamonian sees one of these columns of dust strike his hut, tear it to pieces and send first the roof, then the walls, then his poor possessions flying overhead. It would be idle to compare such a storm to a fire: smoke can mount a great distance into the sky, but when dust does the same, the very sun is darkened.

A fiercer storm than usual struck the Roman army on the march; the troops staggered and lost their footing, because even the earth on which they trod was dragged from underneath their feet. Were Africa built all of a piece, with solid cliffs confining the South Wind in a prison, the world would doubtless be wrenched from its foundations by his struggle to escape. But since the earth is everywhere so loose and drifts about so easily, he meets no opposition and therefore does little effective damage; the sandy top soil is whirled hither and thither, but the sub-soil remains unmoved. The furious whirlwind snatched helmets, shields, and javelins up into the air and swept off with them. Perhaps they finally dropped down again in some distant country, where they were regarded as a portent: the inhabitants imagining that they had been sent by the Gods, rather than stolen from men. Perhaps, also, a similar phenomenon accounts for the rain of shields which fell while King Numa was sacrificing and which the patrician priests of Mars now carry on state occasions;[1] I am convinced that they were robbed from a company of soldiers, either by the South Wind or the North. At all events, the wind I have been describing was so powerful that Cato's men flung themselves on their faces, wrapping their cloaks tightly around them and clutching at the ground to avoid a flight through the air.

Even so they were nearly beaten by the storm. It hurled dust at them until they were buried under huge drifts and could hardly rise to their feet, and continued to blow until they stood rooted in an ever rising mound of loose soil. Walls were torn apart and the stones carried a great distance, so that the soldiers saw no houses but only falling fragments of houses. When the storm ended, the path which they were following had vanished, and so had all landmarks. They now steered by the stars, which was difficult because, owing to the curvature of the earth, many of the familiar constellations lie far below the African horizon.

The atmosphere had been contracted by the storm and now expanded again; the day grew scorching hot, sweat poured from every limb, and mouths were parched. A small, nasty trickle of water was sighted and a soldier, breaking ranks, scooped up a little muddy liquid with his helmet, which he thrust into Cato's hands. No throat but was coated with dust, and Cato became the object of general envy. 'Do you call yourself a soldier?' he cried in a rage. 'How dare you insult me as the only weakling of this entire army? So I am one of those effeminate creatures who cannot stand a trifle of heat, am I? I have a good mind to make you drink this water yourself, as a punishment, while

1. According to the legend, only one fell, but nineteen exactly similar shields were made to discourage its being stolen.

your comrades go thirsty.' With these words he dashed it to the ground; so that nobody got more than his share.

Presently they reached the one shrine in the interior of Africa – the so-called Oracle of Juppiter, guarded by the fierce Garamantians. But this Juppiter Ammon is unlike our own supreme god: instead of wielding the thunderbolt, he wears ram's horns. Cato's men found no great temple here with treasuries full of glittering gems; for though the wealthy people of Ethiopia, Arabia, and India worship none but Ammon, he has for centuries made a point of living in virtuous frugality and resisted the temptation of overlaying his house with gold.[1] His divine immanence is proved by the presence of green trees. No others grow in the whole of Libya between hot Berenice and the somewhat cooler city of Leptis in Morocco; what enables them to survive is a spring of water that binds the loose soil together. Here, too, the Sun finds little hindrance when he stands directly above the grove at midday; the trees can then scarcely shelter their own trunks, because (as has been ascertained) the circle of the upper solstice cuts the Zodiac exactly half-way between the poles. And if any people live beyond this point, their shadows must fall south at midday, rather than north like ours;[2] and the Little Bear must rise slowly to view; and they must absurdly suppose that the Great Bear sinks into the sea – indeed, none of their stars can fail to create such an impression, since both poles are at the same distance from this equatorial region and the Zodiac forms an arch across its sky.[3] Moreover, the constellations of the Zodiac do not appear to move sideways, as here; when the Scorpion swims up over the horizon it is no more upright than the Bull; the Ram does not rise any faster than the Scales; and the Virgin sets no slower than the Fish. The Archer mounts as high as the Twins; and the He-goat (which, with us, brings rain) as high as the scorching Crab; and the Water-carrier no lower than the Lion.

Ammon's shrine was besieged that day by emissaries of Eastern

1. A reference to the Golden House, Nero's new palace. Lucan here confuses the Oasis of Siwwa, where Ammon had his oracle, with that of Fezzan, where the Garamantians lived; and both oases lie hundreds of miles off the route taken by Cato.

2. Lucan errs: the Oracle of Ammon did not lie in the Tropic of Cancer, but five degrees to the north.

3. This is all nonsense, and was so even in Lucan's day. See A. E. Housman's *Astronomical Appendix* to Lucan, pp. 330–333, for the whole passage.

powers, all asking for advice about the future; but as soon as a Roman general approached everyone politely made way for him. Cato's officers pressed him to test and report on the veracity of this Oracle, which had been famous throughout Africa for many centuries. Labienus was particularly urgent. He told Cato: 'It so happens that our march has taken us to the Oracle of this mighty god; let us use his divine guidance for our passage along the Gulf of Sirte and discover how this war is fated to end. I cannot think of any man for whom Heaven would be readier to reveal the hidden truth than your pure and virtuous self. It is clear that you have always lived in accordance with divine principle, and are a follower of God. And, look, here is an opportunity for a conference with Juppiter Ammon himself. Why not ask him what the fate of that criminal Caesar will be and what will happen to Rome? Why not find out whether constitutional liberty will be restored or whether we are fighting this war in vain? Take a deep breath and utter the holy prayer required. As an austere lover of virtue, you should at least ask Ammon in what virtue consists, and demand a directive for the future.'

But Cato carried a god in his own heart and replied in words worthy of the Oracle itself. 'Come, Labienus!' he said. 'Precisely what question do you want me to put? Whether I should prefer to die in battle, still a free man, or live under tyranny? Or whether it does not matter if life be long or short? Or whether honest men can be harmed by the violence of fortune? Or whether it is enough to be virtuous without troubling to be successful? I could answer each of these questions, and need no oracle to confirm my opinion. Men cannot, logically, be separated from gods, because whatever we do has been predestined. And there is no necessity for the Gods to give responses; the author of the Universe told us at our birth, once and for all, as much as we are allowed to know. Do you really think that he has chosen this desert for his shrine in order to limit the number of visitants and so, as it were, bury the divine truth in drifting sand? What other dwelling place has God but earth, sea, air, and righteous hearts? Why should we need more gods than God? Whatever we see and do must be manifestations of God. Whoever feels anxiety about the future may pray for prophecies; but I can tell exactly where my duty lies, and not because any oracle has given me advice, but because I know that I must die. One may be brave or one may be cowardly; nevertheless, death is certain. That was what God told me at birth, and it is enough for me.'

So saying, Cato moved away from the shrine, without either testing the Oracle or disparaging it, and left the orientals to pay their devotions in peace. Then on he went at the head of his column, not riding in a litter or a chariot, as some generals do, but on foot, javelin in hand; and made his panting troops endure their ordeal by example, rather than compulsion. He slept little and was always the last to drink: whenever after a long day's march, a spring had been discovered and a queue formed at the drinking hole, Cato waited for the humblest camp-follower to quench his thirst. It occurs to me that if fame be the reward of true and unadorned virtue, whether successful or not, then we should call most of our ancestors less famous than fortunate. None of them, by the slaughter of foreign armies, ever won such fame as Cato. Myself, I should much prefer to be remembered as a Cato who led his army around the Gulf of Sirte and through distant parts of Libya, than as a Pompey who celebrated three Triumphs at Rome; or as a Marius who defeated Jugurtha and then had him strangled in prison. Cato was a true father of his country, and far worthier than others who have since been granted this title, to have altars raised in his memory. One day when we are finally freed from slavery, if that ever happens, Cato will be deified; and Rome will then have a god by whose name it need not be ashamed to swear.

The march became even hotter as they approached the most southerly region in creation, where water grew still scarcer. In the very middle of the desert they discovered a spring, solitary and abundant, but beset by so numerous an army of serpents that they practically hid the ground; thirsty asps crowded around the lip of the pool, and dipsads wriggled about on the bottom. Cato was aware that his men would die if they shrank from drinking, so he reassured them at once. 'Men,' he cried, 'do not be deceived! The pool may look deadly, but have no hesitation in filling your cups! Snakes are poisonous only when they sink their fangs into a man and thus infect his blood with their venom; this water is quite harmless.' He took a gulp of the supposed poison; and it was the sole occasion when he asked to drink before anyone else.

Having been unable to ascertain why the soil of Libya is mysteriously plagued with such myriads of venomous reptiles, I can do no better than record the delusive but widespread legend of Medusa, daughter of Phorcys. Medusa is said to have lived in the far west of Africa, at the point where the Ocean laps against the hot earth, in a wide, untilled, treeless region which she had turned entirely to stone merely by gazing around her. The story is that, when her head was cut off, serpents were bred from the fallen blood and came hissing out to display their forked tongues.

Medusa loved to feel the serpents which served her for hair curled close to her neck and dangling down her back, but with their heads raised to form an impressive bang over the forehead – in what has since become the fashionable female style at Rome.[1] And when she used a comb, their poison would flow freely.

Those serpents were the only part of the luckless Medusa which one could study without being turned to stone. Nobody ever felt fear as he gazed at that monster's grinning face, because he had no time to feel any emotion whatsoever. One could not even describe what happened to him as death, for being prevented from gasping out his spirit, this became petrified with his body. A sight of the Furies' serpent locks causes simple madness, and when Orpheus played his lyre in the Underworld he glanced unharmed at the serpents of Cerberus's mane, which presently ceased hissing; Hercules, too, was able to decapitate, without danger, the serpent heads which sprouted from the Hydra's neck. But Medusa was dreaded by her own father Phorcys, Neptune's second-in-command, by her mother Ceto, and even by her sister-Gorgons; she had the extraordinary power of paralysing everything in sea, in sky, or on earth by turning it to stone. Birds suddenly grew heavy and crashed to the ground; beasts stood frozen on their rocks; entire tribes of neighbouring Ethiopians were transformed to statues. No living creature, in fact, could bear to look at that face, not even the serpents on her head; which explains why they curled back from her forehead. Moreover, Medusa's head made Titan, the giant who supports the western pillars, turn to stone; and eventually saved the day for the Olympian Gods, when Pallas Athene wore it in the centre of her aegis at the terrible Battle of Phlegra, and converted the snake-legged Giants into mountains. It was to Medusa's lair that Perseus, son of that Danaë whom Jupiter had wooed in a shower of gold, went flying with the winged sandals given him by the Arcadian god Hermes. When

1. Nero also affected it.

Pallas Athene saw him heading west, and recognized the sandals and the falchion in his hand as belonging to her half-brother (inventor of the lyre and the oil which wrestlers use), she decided to help him. The falchion, by the way, was already stained with the blood of Hundred-eyed Argus, the giant ordered by Juppiter to guard Io, daughter of Inachus, whom Juno had metamorphosed into a heifer. Athene offered Perseus a bargain: if he promised her Medusa's head she would show him how to cut it off. Then she placed a polished bronze shield in his left hand, and told him that when he reached the Libyan frontier he must fly backwards through Gorgon territory and employ the shield as a mirror, thus avoiding petrifaction.

Perseus found Medusa asleep – it was to be her last sleep – but some of the serpents on her head kept watch and darted out to protect her, while the rest lay draped like a curtain over her face and closed eyes. He felt somewhat nervous and the falchion trembled in his hand; but Athene guided the blow, which he struck while looking at the shield, and it fell clean at the junction of head and body. Medusa's features must have worn a ghastly grimace in the moment of her decapitation – I have no doubt that the mouth belched poison and the eyes flashed instant death. Athene herself could not look at those eyes, and though Perseus had averted his face he would nevertheless have been petrified, had she not ruffled Medusa's hair and made the dead serpents serve as a veil. Then he seized the head and soared safely away.

Perseus had planned to take the quickest route across Europe, but Athene forbade this; asking him to consider the damage he would do if he passed over cities and cultivated lands. On seeing such a large object flying aloft, everyone would look up, and be turned to stone; the corn would also be ruined. So he wheeled about and with the West Wind behind him sailed across Libya, because that was an un-tilled region, viewed only by the Sun and the stars. In Libya, as I have already explained, the Sun travels straight overhead, burning up the soil; another effect being that, when the Sun passes exactly underneath, the conical shadow of the Earth rises higher here than anywhere else – so that if the Moon were to forget her usual slanting orbit and run along the Zodiac, without troubling to pass either north or south of the Earth's shadow, she would find herself eclipsed.

Thus, though the Libyan soil was sterile and the fields unproductive, they drank the poisonous blood, dripping from Medusa's head, which became more poisonous still by contact with the loose burning earth. The first snake to spring from the ground after this rain of Gorgon's blood was the deadly asp with its puffed neck; and since the blood happened to be particularly abundant at this point, and mixed with clotted venom, it proved to be the most deadly of all the Libyan varieties. The asp loves heat and therefore never visits cold regions, always keeping to the desert west of the Nile; so we should be ashamed to have let our mercantile instincts get the better of us by importing this African poison into Italy.

Among other snakes are the enormous coiling haemorrhois, whose victims die from loss of blood; the chersydros, especially designed to live in the shoals of Sirte; the cenchris, distinguished both by its minutely chequered and spotted belly (which suggests the Theban serpentine stone), and by its inveterate habit of travelling in a straight line; the ammodytes, which has adopted the protective colouring of Libyan sand; the cerastes, wriggling its broken backbone – Helen trod on its ancestor while she was eloping with Paris; the scytale, unique in its habit of sloughing a skin while hoarfrost still covers the ground; the withered dipsas; the dangerous two-headed amphisbaena; the water-polluting natrix; the flying javelin-snake; the parias, which ploughs a furrow as it goes; the gluttonous, foaming-jawed prester; the seps, whose venom dissolves bone as well as flesh; but above all the basilisk, which scares away all lesser snakes by its terrifying hiss, and reigns alone over the empty desert – for it can kill without biting. Even the golden-scaled sacred serpent, which everywhere else in the world is worshipped as a benignant deity, becomes a terror in the scorching climate of Libya. It takes wing and flies through the air; or pursues large herds of cattle and, winding its coils around full-grown bulls, flogs them to death with its tail; the very elephant is unprotected by his enormous bulk, for though not venomous, the sacred serpent can crush every living creature to death.

Cato led his hardy troops forward across the burning desert, and many strange and extraordinary deaths resulted from the slightest of wounds. One Aulus, a young Tuscan standard-bearer, trod on a dipsas, which turned its head and bit him in the foot. The bite was not painful and the wound seemed harmless enough, but the hidden venom began to boil and a devouring flame spread through the marrow of his bones, drying up the moisture which surrounded his vital organs, and the saliva which kept his tongue wet, and the sweat in his pores, and the very tears in his eyes. Aulus was on fire and neither legionary pride nor Cato's urgent orders could restrain him from rushing madly about in quest of the water for which his poisoned heart craved. Cato was greatly grieved to watch these antics: for though the poor fellow had plunged into the Don, the Rhône, or the Po, or drank the Nile in flood, their streams would never have quenched the flame. Yet the dipsas did not deserve the entire credit for this hideous feat; the Libyan climate assisted it considerably. Aulus scrabbled at the sand, digging deeper and deeper in search for moisture, then fled to the Gulf and gulped the salt water, which relieved but did not satisfy his insane thirst. Still unaware that he had been poisoned, he opened his swollen veins with a sword and drank the blood that poured out.

Cato at once had the Eagle raised again and led the army onward before they realized to what frightful deeds thirst might reduce them. But he could not prevent them from watching an even more appalling death. An unlucky soldier named Sabellus felt the barbed fangs of a tiny seps fixed in his leg. He pulled it off and pinned it to the ground with the point of his javelin. This seps is the most destructive of all snakes, despite its smallness. The skin next to the bite began to break and the flesh to melt away until the white thigh-bone showed; then, as the wound widened farther, the body swam in corruption and slowly disappeared, starting with the calves, knees, and thighs. Black matter dripped from the thighs, the muscles which held the belly in place snapped and the guts slid out. Sabellus, in fact, slowly trickled into the ground, and there was unexpectedly little of him left, because the seps' venom reduces the limbs by a chemical process to a small pool of filth. His anatomy was for awhile revealed with painful clearness: ligaments, sinews, the structure of the lungs, the bones of the chest, and all the inner organs. Gradually the strong shoulders and arms and neck and head liquefied, as it were snow when the warm South Wind blows, or wax exposed to the Sun. It is not much to record that the flesh was eaten away – that happens whenever corpses are cremated – but no pyre reduces bones to nothing as this venom did. They vanished as completely as the intestines. So we must award the palm to the seps as the most destructive snake in Africa: the others all kill, but the seps alone disposes of the corpse.

Nasidius, once a Marsian farmer, died in a very different manner: by expansion, not liquefaction. When a fiery prester struck at him, his face turned red as a glowing coal and began to swell until the features could not be recognized. Then the virus spread and puffed him out to the gigantic proportions of ship's canvas in a storm. The man himself was buried deep inside this bloated mass, and the breastplate flew off like the lid of a fiercely steaming cauldron. Soon Nasidius became a great mountain of flesh in which limbs were indistinguishable from trunk; no vultures or wild beasts could have ventured to feast on him, and even his comrades dared not consign him to a pyre. They fled in horror and, as they glanced back, the body was still swelling in every direction.

But stranger sights than these awaited them. Tullus, a brave soldier with an intense admiration for Cato, was bitten by a savage haemorrhois. The poisoned red blood spouted from all his limbs at once; he resembled one of those metal statues with pipes inside them which, when the saffron-water is turned on to perfume the theatre, spray it out from numerous tiny holes in their bodies. (Saffron grows on Mount Corycus, and is said to be the distilled blood of a Cilician giant buried underneath.) Tullus's tears were blood, and blood gushed from mouth, nostrils, and all the other natural apertures; he even sweated streams of blood, so that his body seemed one great wound.

Then an asp bit one Laevus, and numbed his heart. Laevus felt no pain, but at once lapsed into unconsciousness; and his ghost went down like a sleep-walker to join those of his dead comrades. The wizards of Sais in the Delta, who harvest a deadly plant resembling sticks of Arabian incense and doctor wine-cups with it, cannot kill so swiftly as that.

Next a javelin-snake, coiled on a withered tree some distance away, launched itself at the head of a soldier named Paulus. Though not poisonous, it killed him instantly by passing straight through his temples; those present swore that the flight of the Balearic sling bolt or the Scythian arrow was slow by comparison.

One Murrus used his spear to spit a basilisk, but the poison ran up the shaft into his right hand; the unfortunate man, however, at once drew his sword with the left and lopped off the whole forearm at a stroke, thereby saving his life. He stood watching the disintegration of his own flesh as it lay at his feet.

And who would have thought that the scorpion could kill a man rapidly? Yet the Constellation of that name reminds us that a gigantic scorpion, raising its knotted tail, struck and killed the great hunter Orion. And who would be afraid to tread on a nest of the solpuga-ant? Yet the Fates sometimes allow it to cut short a man's life by the virulence of its sting. In consequence Cato's troops had no rest by day or night. They slept uneasily, because, denied comfortable pallets of leaves or straw, they had to lie on the bare ground where their presence attracted the snakes. Snakes grow so cold at night that their poison glands are put out of action; and they come creeping for warmth to sleeping men.

With the stars alone to guide them, these poor wretches had no idea how far they had marched, or in what direction. Here are some of their grumbling complaints: 'Ah, if we were only back at Pharsalus! When we enlisted, we swore to use the sword, but look at us now, dying like cowards. The dipsas and the cerastes are fighting Caesar's war for him. We would much rather go to the fiery South where the chariot of the Sun blazes aloft, and be killed by the fury of Heaven . . . ' 'Nature is not to blame: she has kept men out of Libya, which breeds nothing but monsters, and made it over to snakes. Realizing that the soil was useless for agriculture, she let it stay untilled, and her intention was to provide no human beings for the snakes to attack . . . ' 'Whatever god it may be who disapproves of international trade has set a deadly no-man's-land between East and West, fenced it off to the south with burning desert, and to the north with the unnavigable Gulf of Sirte; and now he punishes us for trespassing here and allowing civil war to initiate us into his secrets . . . ' 'Next, we are going forward to beat at the gates of the West. Heaven alone knows what tremendous sights will greet us when we arrive – the Sun hissing into the Sea, and the sky leaning on the earth? – but meanwhile King Juba's miserable kingdom is quite far enough off. We know of it only by hearsay, and when we get there may well wish ourselves back in this land of snakes; at any rate, we are still alive here . . . ' 'We do not ask to be home in Italy, or anywhere else in Europe or Asia; but we seem to have already marched out of Africa at some point or other – who knows when? At Cyrene, a few days ago, winter had not yet finished. But a short march seems to have turned the year upside down. Have we crossed the Equator and left the old world behind us, so that the South Wind is blowing at our backs, not in our faces? Perhaps we have reached the

Antipodes, with Rome lying directly beneath our feet! All we ask is
that Caesar comes in pursuit of us, and suffers as much as ourselves . . . '

But though they grumbled, they endured these hardships with a
patience inspired by the example of Cato who, defying destiny, kept
watch every night as he lay on the bare sand. Whenever a man was
bitten, Cato was invariably present at the death agony; he would hear
his name called, and hurrying to the scene confer on the victim a greater
gift than that of life: the courage to die nobly. With Cato's eye upon
him no soldier dared utter a groan. No evil could daunt him: he
triumphed over disaster in the hearts of others and his mere presence
was a proof that the worst pain cannot break the human spirit.

Fortune at last wearied of exposing them to so many dangers, and
smiled for a change. Of all the races on earth, one only is proof against
snake-bite: namely the Psyllians of Marmarica. They have voices of
medicinal virtue, and even without the use of charms their own blood
resists every variety of venom. Having chosen to live in a land full of
poisonous snakes they at least gain the advantage of being immune to
them. So great is their reliance on this inherited trait that, when a
Psyllian child is born, they fetch an asp to make sure that the mother
has not contaminated the race by taking a foreign lover. It is as when
the she-eagle, after hatching her eggs, turns the still unfledged eaglets
to face the rising sun; those that pass the test of being able to look at its
fiery disk without blinking, she rears for the service of Juppiter, to
whom they are sacred – those that flinch she leaves to starve. The
Psyllians similarly believe that if a baby plays with the asp, he must be
of the true breed. Nor are they merely content to enjoy this immunity
themselves; but willingly protect strangers against the attacks of
snakes. Psyllians now marched beside the Roman forces and, whenever
Cato encamped for the night, cleared the area within the ramparts
with spells and charms, and lighted fumigatory fires, all around, of
elder-wood; adding Syrian galbanum, tamarisk with its small leaves,
the aromatic Eastern costus, powerful all-heal, Thessalian centaury,
fennel and thapsus (which takes its name from a city in Sicily); not to
mention branches of larch, and southernwood – snakes cannot abide
the smoke – and the horns of stags, though no stags bred anywhere in
Libya. The troops thus slept soundly at night, and if any man were
attacked in daylight the Psyllians would display their extraordinary
powers by rescuing him from the jaws of death. Their battle against

the poison began by rubbing the affected part with spittle, which had the effect of limiting the inflammation; then they would foam at the mouth as they ceaselessly muttered charm after charm, the rapidity with which the bite would otherwise have taken effect did not allow them even to pause for breath. Incantation by itself often proved enough to expel the venom from the blackened flesh; but if it resisted the order to emerge, the Psyllian would lean forward and lick the pale wound, biting a hole in the skin and sucking the poisoned blood until he had dragged the deadly principle from the victim's body and spat it out on the sand. Any Psyllian can easily tell by the taste of the venom what kind of snake has produced it.

Thus the Psyllians at last relieved the Roman troops, who went stumbling on across the barren plains. The moon had waned and twice grown full again during this march, before Cato felt the soil grow firmer under his feet, and saw distant glimpses of trees and rude grass huts. You may be sure that the troops cheered to find themselves confronted only with grim lions, rather than snakes! Leptis was the nearest city, and provided them with safe winter quarters, untroubled by either storms or heat.[1]

*

When Caesar had gloated long enough on the battlefield of Pharsalus, he made Pompey's pursuit his first consideration, and tracked him north to the point where he had embarked. Then, taking ship himself, he sailed along the Thracian coast, until the Hellespont was sighted: a strait named after Helle daughter of Nephele, who was drowned there when she fell from the back of the legendary golden ram. Its banks are famous also for the unhappy loves of Hero and Leander; Hero's tower could be seen from Caesar's ship. This is where Asia and Europe come closest together, although the Bosphorus, which separates Byzantium from the oyster-beds of Calchedon and carries the water of the Black Sea into the Sea of Marmara, is almost equally narrow.[2]

Caesar's interest in the glories of the past had led him to visit the

1. According to Plutarch, Cato marched for seven days; according to Strabo, thirty. But Plutarch was probably thinking of the seven worst days. Lucan's two months may represent the time that Cato took in his march from Berenice to Numidia, where he joined forces with Scipio.

2. The Bosphorus is a good deal narrower than the Dardanelles.

Sigean Promontory with its memories of Achilles, and Rhoeteum where Ajax lay buried, and the river Simois, celebrated by Homer, where so many heroes died. He walked around what had once been Troy, now only a name, and looked for traces of the great wall which the God Apollo had built. But he found the hill clothed with thorny scrub and decaying trees, whose aged roots were embedded in the foundations of King Assaracus's palace and of ancient temples; even the ruins had been destroyed. The natives showed him the rock to which Hesione had been bound when Hercules rescued her from the sea-monster; and the clearing in the wood where his own ancestor Anchises had married Venus; and the cave where Paris sat when he judged the charms of the three rival goddesses; and the spot from which the eagle carried Ganymede off to Olympus; and the peak on which Oenone lamented her desertion by Paris. Every stone thereabouts had its legend. As Caesar crossed a rivulet trickling through the sand, someone remarked: 'This is the famous river Xanthus.' Then, as he walked through a patch of grass, someone else cried: 'That is where they buried Hector. Be careful not to offend his ghost!' And at a pile of loose stones they plucked him by the sleeve with: 'That was the altar of Hercaean Juppiter.' It is remarkable how the sacred labours of poets serve to keep events from oblivion, and bestow immortality on those who participate in them! Yet Caesar need not have felt jealous of the heroes commemorated by Homer, because if Latin poetry has any future at all, this poem of mine will be remembered as long as Homer's: posterity will read these verses about Caesar's deeds in the Civil War and we shall become immortal together, he and I.

When Caesar had done enough sight-seeing, he hastily built a turf altar, and burned incense upon it, uttering prayers and vows to the spirits of the dead. 'Phantoms,' he prayed, 'who haunt these ruins; and you, household-gods of my ancestor Aeneas, whom he rescued from the flames and brought safely to Lavinium and Alba Longa – where the fire fetched from Troy still blazes in our shrines; and you, image of Pallas, notable pledge of Rome's security, now lodged in a recess of Vesta's Temple at Rome, which no eye of man may look upon without being blinded: listen to me! I have come, the most famous descendant of the Julian family, to burn incense upon your altars and solemnly invoke you, here in your ancient home. If you grant me prosperity so long as I live, I undertake to show the gratitude of our Italian people by rebuilding the walls of your city and restoring its inhabitants: the new Troy will be a Roman one.'

Then he returned to his ship, and the fleet sailed off with a favouring wind. So anxious was he to regain the time lost at Troy that he coasted past the wealthy cities of Asia, and even the isle of Rhodes, ploughing on through the rough seas. The same North-west Wind continued to blow until, on the seventh night, he picked up the Pharos light and knew that Egypt was near. But the beacon fire had paled with dawn before he reached the harbour of Alexandria. The confused shouting and argument that rose from the shore decided him against landing; he knew that Egypt was a treacherous kingdom. Presently a courtier came out by boat carrying the King's dreadful gift wrapped in an Egyptian mantle; but did not present it until he had made the following abominable speech to justify the crime:

'Greatest of all Romans, world conqueror, let me be the first to bring you the news that you no longer have a rival to fear; your son-in-law is dead. My master, King Ptolemy, has ended the Civil War in your absence and saved you vexatious journeys over land and sea by supplying the one thing which your victory in Thessaly lacked. When Pompey disembarked here in an attempt to reorganize his defeated forces, King Ptolemy put him to the sword; his death is the heavy fee we offer for your friendship – his blood will seal the treaty between you and us. Egypt is now yours without a fight, from the mouth of the Nile to its source. The King waives whatever reward you may have set on Pompey's head, and begs to be accepted as a valuable ally if only because Fortune has favoured him with the power to destroy your former relative. Nor must you think that this service has cost us nothing; on the contrary, it went greatly against the grain to assassinate an old friend of the Ptolemies: Pompey had, after all, restored the present king's exiled father to the throne.

'I have now delivered my message, and you must either express your satisfaction with our splendid deed, or else admit how much applause it has won throughout the world. If, in your view, a crime has been committed, then your debt to the King is larger still, because you are yourself wholly guiltless.'[1]

With this, the envoy unwrapped the head. Caesar did not turn away

1. The speaker was a Samian rhetorician named Theodatus; five years later he was crucified by order of Cassius, one of Caesar's assassins.

or reject the gift, but closely scrutinized the well-known features which had shrunk since death, until he could be satisfied that they were indeed Pompey's. When no doubt remained and he thought it safe at last to play the loving father-in-law, he forced out tears and groans – his readiest means of disguising too obvious a joy. Caesar was, of course, pretending sorrow that a relative's corpse had been mutilated, so as to make an excuse for withholding gratitude from the King who sent him this disgusting present. And though he had shown no hesitation in trampling on senatorial corpses after Pharsalus and gazing dry-eyed at the battlefield, he could not deny Pompey the tears that his death deserved. What an irony of Fortune! Caesar came wickedly hunting for a man but had to weep over his poor relics, remembering too late whose daughter he had married and whose grandchild he had fathered. No, no! He trusted that in countries where Pompey's name was still beloved this display of grief would serve him in good stead. Or else he wept tears of vexation and jealousy, because Ptolemy had robbed him of the proud vengeance which he had promised himself after winning the victory. Whatever the reason for his tears, we may be certain that they did not spring from true affection. So, if the reason for Caesar's hurried pursuit had been a fear that his son-in-law might get killed somewhere or other, perhaps after all it was a good thing that this fear proved well-founded. Caesar the traitor had failed to pass his intended sentence, and thus stain the honour of Rome with an ineradicable blot: by sparing Pompey's life!

However, he had the impudence to make the following speech which he hoped would support the fiction of grief offered by his tears:

'Horrible, horrible! Remove it from my sight and tell your master the King that his crime has harmed me far more than Pompey: he has denied me the one privilege that civil war confers on a general – that of granting the defeated their lives. If King Ptolemy did not hate his sister, I might have shown my deep disgust with this gift, by revengefully cutting off her head and sending it to him. What right had he to interfere in a purely Roman dispute? Was Pharsalus fought to win King Ptolemy the privilege of behaving exactly as he pleases? Did he think that because Rome proved too small to hold both Pompey and me, he could take Pompey's place? No: the civil war which I have brought on the world will have been fought in vain if a single country remains whose king considers himself my equal. I might have avoided

sailing here, but I had too high a regard for my good name to let anyone suppose that I feared, rather than condemned, this bloody land of
Egypt. I am not deceived; the case is clear as daylight. Had I been
beaten in Thessaly, you Egyptians would have given me the identical
reception that you gave Pompey: my head, not his, would have been
wrapped in a mantle. The risks we ran at Pharsalus were greater than
either of us guessed. I dreaded only exile, and my son-in-law's angry
threats, and public opinion at Rome; yet all the time the penalty for
defeat was to fall into King Ptolemy's power!

'If I agree to spare the boy's life, this is the most he can hope from
me. Let him now bury the head of our noble commander, and "bury"
does not mean merely to conceal his guilt by hiding it in the earth.
He must ask forgiveness of the ghost, he must cremate the head on a
decent pyre, using plenty of incense, and then collect the ashes and
mix them in a single urn with those from the earlier pyre. I want the
dead man to know that he has a relative here, who mourns him sincerely, and the more bitterly because the dead man would have done
anything rather than come to terms with me – he even trusted his life
to an Egyptian lacquey! Because of this obstinacy, the world is denied
the happy day which would have witnessed our reconciliation. I had
prayed Heaven that I might be privileged first to crush Pompey, and
then to embrace him – pleading for a renewal of our old friendship,
with him and me ruling on equal terms. That would have been sufficient fee for my sufferings at his hands; and then, when peace and
loving-kindness had been restored between us, I should have helped
him to pardon Heaven for permitting his defeat, and he would have
helped Rome to pardon my victory. Yet, alas, the Gods turned deaf
ears to this prayer.'

Caesar's speech met with no answering tears in the audience, who
did not believe that he meant a word of it. In fact, their behaviour was
the precise reverse of his: for they hid grief under a mask of joy.
Caesar pretended to mourn; while they were graciously allowed to
smile at the horrid crime that had been committed.

BOOK TEN

WHEN Caesar disembarked on those fatal sands, it remained doubtful whether his fortune would hold and allow him to conquer Egypt, or whether Ptolemy's sword would remove his head as well as Pompey's. But Pompey's ghost defended him, and thus kept the Roman people from thinking any better of that wicked country; as they might have done if not only the vanquished, but the victor, too, had lost his life there.

Caesar proceeded without anxiety to Alexandria, the capital of Egypt, believing that its citizens were now attached to his cause by a sense of guilt inspired by the assassination. But they showed such resentment at the threat to national sovereignty offered by the appearance of his Consular rods and axes, that he at once summed up the situation: Pompey's death had not benefited him in the least, and allegiance to the King was wavering. Yet he hid his apprehensions behind a mask of bravado, as he visited the temples of the Olympian gods, and of early deities – monuments to the splendour of the Macedonian Empire. Caesar had no eyes for costly specimens of religious art, or even for the city walls, but paid a hurried visit to the rock-hewn tomb which housed the body of that mad if glorious adventurer, Alexander the Great; whom Death had cut off in his prime, thus avenging a defeated world. Alexander's limbs should really have been scattered over the whole earth, yet here they were, all together, housed in a consecrated shrine; Fortune had protected the kingdom for him and spared his body from mutilation. Even if mankind had regained its freedom, the body would surely have been preserved as a dreadful example of wickedness – for Alexander had been born to teach humanity how to cringe before a single conqueror. He had spurned the noble city of Athens defeated by his father, and marched out of his own obscure kingdom of Macedonia: impelled by Destiny to batter a passage through Asia, hewing down entire populations as he went. There was no nation into whose breast he did not plunge the sword, and many were the rivers, from the Euphrates to the Ganges, which he stained with Persian or Indian blood. Alexander was a plague, a universal thunderbolt, a disastrous comet. At the time of his death he was preparing to send a fleet to India by way of the Ocean Stream which flows around Africa. Nothing ever barred his advance: neither heat, nor the wide seas, nor the inhospitable Libyan desert stretching between Egypt and the oasis of Ammon. He would have marched over the curve of the world to the extreme West, drunk from the source of the Nile, and passed beyond both poles; but his last day dawned, and Nature called a halt for his restless feet. Then, with characteristic greed, he bore away with him the universal Empire that he had won; and for want of an heir, allowed his generals to make a partition of all his conquests. Yet it was in conquered Babylon that he died, a terror to the Parthians. How shameful to think that they then respected the long spears of the Macedonian phalanx more than they fear the javelins of our Roman legions to-day! Though our Empire extends to the North and extreme West, and though we have imposed our rule on the interior of Africa, we must still yield precedence in the East to the Arsacid dynasty: because of the disaster suffered a century ago by Crassus and his son in Parthia – an empire which this same Alexander reduced to a tranquil Macedonian province.

Young King Ptolemy arrived at Alexandria from Mount Casius, and quieted the discontent of his unwarlike subjects. Caesar now had a royal hostage and considered himself safe at Court. But suddenly Cleopatra, the shame of Egypt, the lascivious fury who was to become the bane of Rome, bribed her brother's guards to unchain the boom across the harbour which she entered in a small bireme, unknown to Caesar. Cleopatra resembled Helen of Sparta, whose dangerous beauty ruined Mycenae and laid Troy in ashes; at all events, the passions she aroused did no less damage to our country. You may say, incredible though it sounds, that the noise of her brazen rattle maddened the Capitol of Rome; that she used the spells of cowardly Egypt to destroy Roman armies, that she nearly headed an Egyptian triumph and led Augustus Caesar a chained captive behind her. Until Actium had been fought it seemed possible that the world would be ruled by a woman, and not a Roman woman, either. Her insolence began on the night when she first gave herself to Caesar; it is easy to pardon Mark Antony's later infatuation when one remembers that she fired a heart so flinty

as Caesar's. Despite his rage and madness, despite his bloody memories
of Pharsalus, he consented in that palace haunted by Pompey's ghost
to let an adulterous love affair complicate his military anxieties; and
even begot a bastard son on the girl. What a disgrace to forget his
daughter Julia, the dead man's wife, and posthumously present her
with a half-brother, child of that abominable Ptolemaic princess! He
even allowed his defeated enemies to rally in far-off Libya, while he
wasted time on a sordid intrigue; and quietly deeded Egypt to Cleopatra instead of conquering it for himself.

She approached him in the manner of a suppliant, with a sorrowful
face, but no resort to weeping, confident in her beauty. Though she
had pretended to tear her hair in grief, it was not sufficiently disarranged
to lose its attraction. 'Great Caesar,' she said, 'birth may count for
little, yet I am still the Princess Cleopatra, a lineal descendant of King
Lagus of Egypt. I have been driven from the throne, and shall never
regain it without your help; which is why I, a queen, herewith stoop
to kiss your feet. Oh, please, become the bright star that blesses
Egypt! If you grant my request, I shall not be the first woman to rule
the Nile valley; we have no law against female sovereignty – as is
proved by my father's testament, in which I am married to Ptolemy
and appointed co-heir to the throne. Were Ptolemy only his own
master, he would show that he loves me; but Pothinus dominates him.
I am not pleading to inherit my father's monarchy; I simply want you
to rescue our royal house from a shameful tutelage, and let Ptolemy
be a real king by breaking Pothinus's ruthless hold on him. That pre-
sumptuous menial, who boasts of having beheaded Pompey, is now
threatening your life as well – I pray the Gods that he will fail!
It is pretty disgraceful for you, Caesar, and for all mankind too, when
a fellow like Pothinus gains the credit of having killed Pompey the
Great!'

Cleopatra would have stood no chance at all with stern-hearted
Caesar, but for the evil beauty of her face and person; she bribed her
judge and wickedly spent the whole night with him. The purchase of
Caesar's favour at so high a price had, of course, to be celebrated with a
banquet, and a tremendous bustle arose when she appeared in her full
magnificence – this being before Roman society had adopted degenerate Eastern fashions. Her banqueting hall was as large as a temple, and
more luxurious than even our present corrupt age could easily imitate.

Its fretted ceilings were encrusted with precious stones, and its rafters heavily plated with gold. The walls were marble, not merely marble-faced; pillars of sheer agate and porphyry supported the roof; and the entire palace had an onyx pavement. Similarly, the great door-posts were solid ebony, not common timber with an ebony veneer; these costly materials, in effect, served a functional, not merely a decorative, purpose. The entrance hall was panelled in ivory, and its doors inlaid with tinted tortoise-shell, the dark patches concealed by emeralds. There were jewel-studded couches, rows of yellow jasper wine-cups on the tables, bright coverlets spread over the sofas – mostly Tyrian purple repeatedly dyed, and either embroidered in gold, or shot with fiery threads of cochineal in Egyptian style. As for the courtiers and the palace staff, what an assemblage they made: old, and young, and of such various pigmentation! Some had black Numidian hair, some hair so blond that Caesar swore he had never seen the like even in the Rhineland; others were Negroes, notable for dusky skins, receding foreheads and kinky curls. One group consisted of unfortunate boys, lately castrated; and opposite them stood a somewhat elder generation of eunuchs, almost as beardless as they.

In this royal banqueting hall Caesar reclined, a power above all kings, and Cleopatra beside him. Neither her sceptre nor her marriage now contented her, and she had added the finishing touches to an already fatal beauty by putting on so many wreaths and necklaces of Red Sea pearls, that she positively panted under their weight. Her white breasts showed through the Chinese silk which, though closely woven when imported, had been teased out by some Egyptian mercer until it became diaphanous. The tables were rounds of citrus-wood, supported on gleaming elephant tusks – Caesar never saw anything so fine even after his conquest of King Juba. What madness to parade this wealth before a guest and thus excite his avarice, especially when the guest was a Civil War general greedily intent on enriching himself with the spoils of all mankind. And imagine what the effect would have been on Romans of an earlier and more frugal age – Fabricius, say, or stern Curius, or Cincinnatus who was ploughing his field when the Senate's messenger saluted him as Dictator and summoned him, grimy-handed as he was, to command the Roman army! If any one of these had been in Caesar's place, he would surely have prayed for the opportunity to win a triumph over Egypt!

Every variety of flesh, fowl, sea-fish or river-fish, every delicacy that extravagance, prompted not by hunger but by a mad love of ostentation, could rout out from the ends of the earth, came served on golden dishes. Cleopatra went so far as to offer Caesar birds and beasts which the Egyptians held sacred; and provided Nile water in ewers of rock crystal for washing his hands. The wine in those huge jewelled goblets was of no local vintage, but a Falernian fetched from Italy, which though a little rough when first casked, becomes nobly mellowed after a few years of careful cellarage at Meroë in Upper Egypt. Each guest had received wreaths of flowering spikenard and perpetual roses, and the fresh oil of cinnamon which they poured on their hair had lost none of its fragrance in transit from the East; and to this they added oil of cardamum recently imported from no great distance. Here Caesar learned how to squander the wealth of the world he had despoiled and, feeling ashamed that his most recent opponent had been Pompey, a comparatively poor man, longed for a pretext to make war on Egypt.

When they had eaten and drunk to repletion, Caesar addressed friendly questions to Acoreus, the High Priest of Isis, who wore a linen robe and occupied the couch of honour.

These were his words:

'Sir, since you are a servant of the Gods and, to judge from your hale old age, must always have earned their good opinion, I should be much obliged if you would discourse on the origins of Egypt, its geographical features, popular customs and cults, and the characteristics of its gods. Perhaps you could also explain the meaning of your ancient temple inscriptions and favour me with whatever other religious information can decently be divulged? Your ancestors consented to teach Plato religious philosophy, but I doubt whether you ever had any guest worthier than myself to receive similar instruction, or more capable of grasping universal secrets. I own that the immediate object of my visit was to search for my son-in-law Pompey; but your fame had also impressed me, and even on campaign I have always found time to study astronomy. Indeed, you will agree, when I institute the Julian calendar, that it compares very favourably with your Eudoxian one. Yet despite my strong interest in science, nothing would satisfy my intellectual curiosity more fully than to be told what makes the Nile rise. If you can enable me to visit its source, which has been a mystery for so many ages, I promise to abandon this civil war.'

The venerable priest answered: 'It is my belief, Caesar, that the Gods intend mankind as a whole to know what laws regulate nature, and that I am therefore at liberty to disclose those secrets of our great ancestors which have been piously concealed from the common people. Well, to begin with: at the first Creation, different powers were assigned to the planets, as opposed to the fixed stars. The Sun, for instance, has always divided time into days and nights, and his rays have restrained the planets in their progress, keeping them stationary now and then. The Moon's phases control the tides. Saturn rules the freezing North, with its eternal snows; Mars, the storm-clouds, which may appear at any season; Jupiter, temperate weather and clear skies; Venus, the seeds of all existence; Mercury, the element of water. Now, as soon as Mercury reaches the point of contact between Lion and Crab, where the Dog-star blazes and where the colure of the solstices embraces both Capricorn and Cancer, he has the secret sources of the Nile immediately below him; when he shines vertically down on them, the water rises up, just as the Ocean does under a waxing moon, and there you have the Nile.[1]

'The ancient belief that the melting of mountain snow in Ethiopia causes the Nile floods is clearly foolish, since the North-star does not shine there, nor does the North Wind blow; you need only look at the sun-burned skins of the Ethiopians, and feel the scorching winds which afflict them, to appreciate the force of this argument. Moreover, all rivers which owe their floods to the thawing of snow begin to rise in early Spring, whereas the Nile is quiescent before the coming of the Dog-star, whereupon the floods continue until the autumnal equinox, when the Scales hold the balance between day and night. Thus the Nile is demonstrably not governed by the laws that affect other rivers: instead of rising in winter when the Sun is far away and the waters are of no material advantage to mankind, he comes in midsummer to mitigate the onset of heat. He then rescues a world which would other-wise melt under the Lion's fiery breath – especially Syene which cries out for help when the masterful Crab is consuming her – and lingers in the fields which he has flooded until the Sun no longer stands quite so high in the heavens, and the pillar at Meroë casts a distinct shadow at

1. For detailed explanation of Lucan's bungled astronomical speculations see Housman's *Lucan*, pp. 334-337.

noon. Who can explain the reason for all this? It is enough to observe that Mother Nature ordained the Nile floods, and that the world needs them.

'The ancient explanation, that they are caused by the steady blowing of the Etesian winds from the north-west, is no more tenable than the other: these winds were assumed to drive storm-clouds towards the south-east and thus force them back against the Ethiopian mountains where they broke in the form of rain; and also to exert a steady pressure on the sea outside the Delta, thus barring the free flow of the Nile and making it flood the fields. According to other theorists, great veins and tunnels lie far beneath the surface of the earth, along which water travels invisibly, being attracted from the cold North to the Equator whenever the Sun stands directly over Meroë and parches the soil. They argue that, though the Nile carries off a great quantity of the underground water, he cannot cope with all of it, so that the Ganges and Po are forced to emerge elsewhere. Others believe that the Nile originates in a distant reach of the Ocean Stream which flows around the world, and that his waters start salty but grow gradually fresher as they advance northward. Still others believe that when the Sun enters the fiery house of the Crab, he sucks up the Ocean and raises more water than the sky can contain, and that at dark this falls on the mountains as rain, which feeds the Nile.

'My own view, for what it may be worth, is that although certain earthquakes released a great deal of subterranean water in the form of rivers, long after the creation of the world, this was no part of any divine plan; but that certain other rivers, among them the Nile, are coeval with the universe and obliged by the Creator to obey laws of their own.

'Your desire, Caesar, to discover the source of the Nile has been anticipated by many rulers of Egypt, Persia, and Macedonia. Each succeeding generation has wished to benefit after ages with the truth of the matter; but hitherto all have failed, the secret being too well kept by Nature. Alexander the Great was vexed that the Nile, who was worshipped as a god by the people of Memphis, should defy him, and sent a party of explorers up through the southernmost regions of Ethiopia. But when the blazing tropical sky made the Nile water boil, they desisted from further progress. Pharaoh Sesostris is said to have visited the Far West and driven his chariots over the necks of kings;

nevertheless, he found it easier to drink the waters of Rhône and Po than the headwaters of the Nile.[1]

'King Cambyses the Mad reached the land of the long-lived Ethiopians, but when famine drove his army to cannibalism, he turned back, and the source of the Nile remained a mystery still. No liar dares claim to have visited this enigmatic spot, and though all visitors question us on the subject, the boast of having won the Nile's secret has so far been withheld from every nation on earth. I will, however, divulge as much geographical information as the Gods have allowed me to collect. Know, then, that the Nile rises at the South Pole, in defiance of the scorching Crab, and flows due north; yet with frequent twists and turns towards Arabia in the East, or Libya in the West. He first visits the Serians of Southern Africa, but even they disclaim precise knowledge of his origin; as do the Ethiopians whom he next approaches. Nature, I repeat, has not disclosed the secret to a living soul: no man has ever seen the river as a mere brook.

'It is the Nile's privilege to rise exactly at the summer solstice and to enjoy a wintry flood when winter is far past; he alone is allowed to roam between the two Poles; but in the North no one knows whence he comes, and in the South no one knows whither he goes. The river divides at Meroë, where Negro farmers enjoy a rich harvest under the gay foliage of numerous ebony-trees, though indeed these throw little shade because of their proximity to the Equator. From Meroë the Nile runs through a sun-scorched wilderness, without loss of water, sometimes in a single stream, sometimes overflowing its soft banks. At Philae, the key to Upper Egypt, he reassembles his scattered forces; here is the frontier between Egypt and the nomads of the South. He then continues gently through the desert, running parallel to the Isthmus of Suez up which merchantmen sail from the Red Sea towards the Mediterranean. It is difficult to realize that so tranquil a stream can express such anger because its course has been broken; yet when the Nile reaches the abrupt cataracts and finds that rocks are challenging his elsewhere uninterrupted flow, he dashes his spray to the stars, lets out an enormous roar that echoes from the cliffs, and foams white with indignation.

'Next comes a sacred islet called "The Inaccessible Isle", against

1. Sesostris is said to have conquered only Thrace; not to have visited Gaul or Italy.

which the raging stream first strikes; beside it lie the crags commonly known as "The Springs of the Nile", since they provide the earliest indication of our seasonal flood. Here Nature has confined the Nile between mountains, the more westerly of which deny Libya the benefit of his waters, and for awhile he flows in dignified silence through a deep valley. Not until he reaches Memphis is he given an opportunity to flood fields and open country; after which he no longer respects any banks.'

Their conversation went on far into the night, as calmly as if the banqueters were enjoying all the security of peace; but Pothinus was mad enough to plan further crimes; it was as though, having once dyed his hands in Pompey's noble blood, no other action of his could be considered wicked by comparison. Pompey's ghost, you might say, had entered his heart and the Furies incited him to fresh enormities.

Fortune almost allowed this vile slave to forestall the noble Roman senators who would later take Caesar's life and so avenge their defeats in the Civil War. Luckily, however, the Fates prevented this blow from being struck by anyone except Brutus – because the example which he set us Romans of how to deal with tyrants would have been lost had the Egyptians taken the initiative. Pothinus showed audacity both in making plans that Destiny had not sanctioned, and trying to overcome the invincible Caesar by simple fighting, rather than a resort to stratagem. So great was the confidence roused in him by his former exploit that he actually ordered Caesar's head to be struck off, just as Pompey's had been, and sent a trusty messenger to notify his partner in crime, Achillas, of this decision. Achillas had been appointed commander-in-chief by Ptolemy, with authority to make war at his own discretion – which meant that the foolish boy was as likely as anyone else to be attacked by him.

Pothinus's message ran as follows:

'Is this a time for sound sleep in a soft bed? Cleopatra has seized the Palace and not merely betrayed Egypt to Caesar but had it given back to her. Why are you not here to act as bride-man at Cleopatra's wedding? The slut is now about to marry her brother after an informal marriage with this Roman general. In her hasty progress from one husband to another, she has won the throne of Egypt by prostituting herself to Rome – she seduced the old fellow by using love-philtres. If you put your trust in that boy Ptolemy, I pity you. Once he submits to her incestuous embraces and responds to them warmly, as if in deference to their father's wishes, but really because of her beauty, then she has only to ask for your head and mine, at the price perhaps of one kiss apiece, and he will grant them both: sentencing us to die on the cross, or at the stake. There is no escape. We are caught between two fires: between the King her husband, and Caesar her lover. Let us face facts: Cleopatra is a severe judge and we are guilty in her eyes – like every other man who has not slept with her.

'We two must sink or swim together on account of the crime we have committed; and, since Caesar is ungrateful to us, I beseech you in the name of our friendship, sealed by Pompey's blood, to help me make a sudden assault on the Palace. Before the night has passed I propose to kill our savage mistress in her marriage-bed, and whichever husband happens to be sharing it with her. The lucky star that has raised Caesar to the sovereignty of the world need not daunt us; you may call us no less distinguished, because it was we who finally dealt with Pompey. Take a look at the shore; it should encourage you in this bold attempt. The bloodstained sea acknowledges our power, and so does Pompey's grave – a mound of sand heaped over the ashes of his mutilated body. Why fear Caesar? He is no greater than Pompey. And what if we be less nobly born, or control less resources than he? Fortune, by placing famous men at our mercy, has given us wonderful opportunities of violence. Caesar is an even nobler victim than Pompey, and we can make peace with the Romans by his assassination – for which they will feel grateful enough to pardon our former crime. No: I can see no reason to fear Caesar; now that he has come without his army, he is no better than a common soldier. To-night the Civil War will end: we shall placate a whole world of ghosts by offering them the head of the man who made them so. Let the native Egyptian army launch a resolute attack on Caesar in defence of their King, and let the Roman mercenaries play for their own hands. No time must be lost, Achillas: you will find Caesar gorged with food and drink, and ripe for sexual debauch. Be bold, and Heaven will grant you the fortune which men like Cato and Brutus have so often implored in vain.'

Achillas at once answered Pothinus's appeal. He assembled his troops under arms and marched off quietly without the usual sound of trumpets. Most of them were Romans but, by living abroad, had so far forgotten their national pride that they now consented to obey a mere slave, one of King Ptolemy's court-officials, though it would have been disgraceful enough to take orders from the King himself. Professional soldiers are notoriously disloyal; they turn mercenaries and treat whoever offers them the highest pay as the leader with the most righteous cause. Their attack on Caesar was prompted by no personal animosity. What a world! Civil war spreading everywhere and soldiers who had not fought at Pharsalus catching the Roman madness on the banks of the Nile! Why, the Ptolemaic court could hardly have shown more courage had it been harbouring Pompey. The fact is that the Gods drew everyone into the fight, especially Romans: they had decided to dismember the state, and the quarrel here was no longer one between Pompey and Caesar, but between an officious Egyptian courtier pretending to be a Roman, and Caesar – who had never been in greater danger of losing his life.

Pothinus and Achillas soon met, and found the Palace staff so busy with the banquet that any treachery would have been possible; they might easily have cut off Caesar's head while he reclined there at table, and sent it rolling among the royal drinking-cups. But they feared that in the haste and confusion of a night-attack King Ptolemy himself might also be accidentally killed; and such was their confidence that they resolved to do nothing in a hurry. The execution of their grand design seemed so pitifully simple, it might well be postponed until dawn; Pothinus and his fellow-slaves therefore called off their men and granted Caesar a night's respite.

When the Sun peeped over Mount Casius and the Land of Egypt began to warm up, Caesar saw an army marching on the city. These were no armed mobsmen, but disciplined campaigners, prepared to engage any troops on equal terms and face the hazards of close combat. Caesar could not risk a stand on the city walls; instead, he shut the Palace gates and, since only a part of this somewhat inglorious refuge was clear of the enemy, concentrated his forces in one wing. His resolution was weakened by fear of the imminent attack; yet he felt angry with himself for entertaining fear. He behaved like a trapped beast that roars and bites at the bars of its narrow cage until its teeth are broken; rage seethed in his breast, as the volcanic fires would seethe in the crater of Etna, were some giant hand to clap a lid on top.

It had not been long since, camped below the Haemus Range in

Thessaly, Caesar boldly defied the leading men of Rome, and the Senatorial armies under the command of Pompey himself. Though with no right to expect that the Gods would favour his disloyal cause, he had felt sure of victory. But now a pack of evil-minded slaves had forced him to take refuge in a house for fear of being pelted by them! Though the Alan, Scythian, and Moorish archers, who grin as they pick off individual enemies, had failed against him at Pharsalus, and though his new Imperial ambitions extended beyond Cadiz in the West, and India in the East, yet here he stood, like any defenceless woman or child when a city has been stormed, and found nothing better than a barred door to keep out the enemy. He hurried uncertainly from room to room, taking King Ptolemy everywhere with him. His one consolation was that if he must die himself, the King would die too; and if the supply of javelins and fire-brands failed he could, in the last resort, hurl the royal head at the attacking force – as when Medea, in the legend, afraid that her father King Aeëtes of Colchis would punish her for stealing the Golden Fleece and eloping with Jason, waited for him with a sword in one hand and the head of her brother Apsyrtus in the other.

Caesar's desperate situation obliged him to demand a parley. A courtier went forward in King Ptolemy's name to rebuke the turbulent slaves and ask who had authorized them to fight. Yet no respect for international law or the courtesy with which ambassadors are universally treated, could save Ptolemy's herald from being butchered; Egypt, however, is so notorious for its crimes that this particular atrocity is perhaps hardly worth mentioning. Neither witch-ridden Thessaly, nor King Juba's barren kingdom, nor Pontus where Pharnaces had revolted against his father Mithridates, nor the cruel land of Spain where the cold Ebro flows, nor the savage Libyan coastland – no country on earth ever ventured on crimes so black as that abode of luxury, Egypt!

Caesar was surrounded and missiles came crashing into the Palace. However, the Egyptian soldiers possessed no siege engines, not even a ram to smash in the gates with a single swing, and were chary of burning the place down. Instead of concentrating their forces at one point, they split up into parties which aimlessly surrounded the vast building. Lack of a plan doomed their attempt to failure; because Fortune protected Caesar like a wall. Egyptian ships attacked a wing of the palace which thrust boldly out into the harbour; but Caesar, with sword or fire, beat off every attempt to gain a lodgement and showed such courage that he appeared to be the besieger rather than the besieged. He made his men hurl resin-dipped torches at the sails of the ships which came crowding in to the assault. Fire soon caught the tow-ropes and well-waxed decks, until both the rowers' benches below and the yards above were fairly ablaze. The burning ships began to sink, and the Egyptian soldiers had to swim for their lives. Next, the flames spread to the houses on the sea-front, and a sudden wind, which sprang up, sent them coursing across the city – as a meteor streaks through the sky, needing no fuel but air to keep it alight.

This disaster temporarily relieved enemy pressure against the Palace: the soldiers dispersed to fight the blaze and by the following night were still engaged in saving Alexandria from destruction. Caesar did not retire to bed, but took advantage of the fresh respite to make a sortie, climb aboard a ship which had escaped being burned, and with his habitual use of surprise, to seize Pharos, now a promontory forming part of the harbour – in the time of the prophetic Proteus it had been an island standing at some distance from the shore, but had since been linked with Alexandria by a causeway. This move helped Caesar doubly: it prevented the enemy from escaping to sea, and allowed him to send for reinforcements. He had no hesitation in putting Pothinus to the death he had so richly deserved; but rather than fit the punish-ment to the crime by sentencing him to the gallows, the stake, or wild beasts in the arena, had him beheaded – like Pompey.

Next, Cleopatra's younger sister Arsinoë was spirited away by a trick of her chamberlain Ganymede and handed over to Caesar's enemies. There, as a princess of the royal house, she took command of the Egyptian army, calling herself King Ptolemy's lieutenant, and very properly ordered Achillas's execution; which supplied Pompey's ghost with a second propitiatory victim. Fortune was determined to let the process of destruction continue; she ruled that it would not be enough to sacrifice Ptolemy and all the remaining members of the dynasty – Caesar himself must be stabbed to the heart, by his own countrymen, before Pompey could be decently avenged.

Moreover, the madness with which Pothinus had infected the Egyptians did not end at his death. There was another rush to arms under Ganymede, who won some successes. Indeed, Caesar faced such danger that any one of the following days might have changed the course of history. His soldiers had formed up behind him on the narrow causeway while he prepared to launch his ships. Suddenly the attack developed: infantry charged along the causeway, the Egyptian fleet in close order made a frontal assault on the quay. No retreat offered and though he showed consummate courage Caesar could hardly hope even to die honourably. To conquer him, at this moment, Ganymede had no need to slaughter an army and force its remnants to flight.

For awhile, Caesar stood irresolute, aghast at his desperate plight, wondering whether to fear death or whether to pray for it. But he was granted a vision of Scaeva, the centurion who had won immortal fame at Dyrrhachium; for when the wall was breached and Pompey's army began to swarm over the ruins, Scaeva had kept them out single-handed . . .

*

Here Lucan paused, partly it seems because he had come to the end of Caesar's own Commentary on the Civil War, which he had been manipulating, partly because his plot against Nero engrossed him. The poem was never finished. The rest of the book would probably have concerned the war in Egypt.

Briefly, Caesar beat off Ganymede's attack, and let King Ptolemy rejoin his fellow-countrymen on the promise of reducing them to good behaviour; but Ptolemy immediately put himself at their head. King Mithridates of Pergamus then marched through Syria to Caesar's relief, and Ptolemy held the eastern branch of the Nile against him. Caesar suddenly sailed from Pharos and attacked Ptolemy's rear; Ptolemy attempted to escape, but drowned in the Nile. This book may have ended with Caesar's 'I came, I saw, I conquered' defeat of King Pharnaces of Pontus at Zela on 2 August, 47 B.C.

Book XI would doubtless have concerned Caesar's return to Rome and his subsequent campaign in Mauretania. The Pompeians there wished Cato to command them; he magnanimously refused, however, because Scipio was of higher rank. Caesar, though greatly outnumbered, crushed Scipio on 6 April, 46 B.C. King Juba, who had brought three regular legions, thirty elephants, eight hundred cavalry and swarms of irregulars to Scipio's help, made himself unpopular with the Romans by his haughtiness and fled from the battlefield when Caesar began to gain the advantage. After Thapsus, Cato tried to hold Utica against Caesar, but the townsfolk would not agree, so he committed

[Probable End of this Epic]

suicide; and on hearing the news King Juba followed his example. At least two hundred lines of this book would have been eulogy of Cato.

Book XII is likely to have opened with sneers at Caesar's fivefold triumph over Gaul, Egypt, Spain, Pontus and King Juba, omitting all mention of Caesar's remarkable mercy towards his defeated enemies; then to have condemned his appropriation of Pompey's estates and followed the adventures of his two sons. The narrative (as promised in Book IV) must have included the appearance of Pompey's ghost to Sextus in Sicily. Lucan doubtless continued by lamenting Caesar's hard-won victory over Gnaeus and Sextus at Munda in Spain; then praised the Roman people for refusing to make Caesar a king as he wished; and ended by glorifying his assassination in the Senate House on 15 March, 44 B.C. More than sixty Pompeians, whose hostility he had pardoned and whose property he had declined to confiscate, took part in the plot.

Lucan has failed to mention that, at Pharsalus, Caesar ordered Brutus's life to be spared, that Brutus, having fled, not only appealed to Caesar's clemency but betrayed Pompey's flight to Egypt. Brutus made no attempt to join Cato in Africa; accepted the command of Cisalpine Gaul from Caesar, and paid him homage until won over to the conspiracy by Cassius. Yet Lucan hated Nero so blindly that, however ungrateful and treacherous Brutus and his fellow-murderers may have been, they appeared godlike heroes to him, because they had rid Rome of a Caesar.